Brief Analytic Geometry

THIRD EDITION

By THOMAS E. MASON

and CLIFTON T. HAZARD

Purdue University

BLAISDELL PUBLISHING COMPANY

A Division of Ginn and Company
New York · Toronto · London

Third Edition, 1957

Sixth Printing, 1965

Preface to the Third Edition

In this edition of *Brief Analytic Geometry* those features which have contributed to the success of former editions have been retained. No major changes in subject matter or methods of presentation have been made. Changes have been made in the numerical data of many of the exercises. Several new exercises have been added. A few of the illustrative examples have been changed where it was felt such changes would be helpful to the student. As in former editions the exercises are numerous and varied, providing not only ample material for drill but also having sufficient difficulty to stimulate the better students, the latter quality being found especially in the miscellaneous exercises at the end of each chapter.

The same sequence of chapters has been kept. In Chapter III, however, opportunity has been taken to change the sequence of some of the topics. The sections on "Functions and their graphs" and "Graphing by composition of ordinates" have been moved to an earlier position in the chapter. The chief reason for these changes, particularly that of "Functions and their graphs," is to place more emphasis on the concept of a function and on the functional notation. The discussion on "function" and "functional notation" has been slightly amplified.

Appreciation is expressed to the members of the Department of Mathematics of Purdue University and to users of the book elsewhere for their helpful suggestions.

PURDUE UNIVERSITY   C. T. H.

Preface to the Third Edition

In this edition of this *Analytic Geometry* a few features which have contributed to the success of former editions have been retained. No major changes in subject-matter or method of presentation have been made. Changes have been made in the numerical detail of many of the examples, and new exercises have been added. A few of the illustrative examples have been changed where it was felt some change would be helpful to the student. As in former editions the exercises are numerous and varied, providing not only ample material to drill but also having sufficient difficulty to stimulate the better students, the latter quality being found especially in the miscellaneous exercises at the end of each chapter.

The same sequence of chapters has been kept. In Chapter III, however, opportunity has been taken to change the sequence of some of the topics. The section on "Functions" and their graphs" and "Composition by composition of ordinates" have been moved to an earlier position in the chapter. The other reason for these changes, particularly that of "Functions and their graphs," is to make more emphasis on the concept of a function and of the functional notation. The discussion on "function," and "functional notation," has been slightly amplified.

Appreciation is expressed to the members of the Department of Mathematics of Purdue University and to users of the book elsewhere for their helpful suggestions.

                                        C. O. O.

Purdue University

Contents

PLANE ANALYTIC GEOMETRY

CHAPTER I. THE POINT

CHAPTER II. THE STRAIGHT LINE

CHAPTER III. EQUATION AND LOCUS

CHAPTER IV. THE CIRCLE

CHAPTER V. OTHER SECOND DEGREE CURVES

THE PARABOLA

THE ELLIPSE

CHAPTER VII. PARAMETRIC EQUATIONS

CHAPTER VIII. POLAR EQUATIONS

SOLID ANALYTIC GEOMETRY

CHAPTER IX. POINTS, PLANES, AND LINES

CHAPTER X. SURFACES AND CURVES

Brief Analytic Geometry

THIRD EDITION

Plane Analytic Geometry

CHAPTER I

THE POINT

1. Definition. Analytic geometry is a branch of mathematics in which one studies geometry by means of algebra. A correspondence is set up between a geometric locus and one or more equations, and properties of the locus are determined from the equations. In order to connect algebra and geometry use is made of a coördinate system which furnishes a means for locating points in a plane or in space.

2. Rectangular coördinates. In the coördinate system employed most frequently two straight lines intersecting at right angles* are used as lines of reference. A point is located in the plane of these lines by giving its perpendicular distance and direction from each of them. The distances with signs indicating directions are called the **coördinates** of the point. The lines from which distances are measured are called the **axes** of coördinates, or briefly

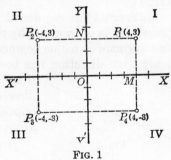

FIG. 1

axes. The point of intersection of the axes is called the **origin** of coördinates, or the **origin.** In Fig. 1 the line XOX' is

*Two lines not at right angles may be used, but the resulting algebra is, in general, more complicated than in the case of lines at right angles. Any system of coördinates using two intersecting lines as axes is called Cartesian after René Descartes (1596–1650), a French mathematician.

called the *x*-axis, and the line YOY' is called the **y-axis**. Distances measured to the right of the y-axis are usually called positive and those measured to the left negative. Distances measured upward from the x-axis are usually called positive and those measured downward negative. The choice of positive direction is a matter of convenience and may change from problem to problem.

That coördinate which indicates the distance of a point to the right or to the left of the y-axis is called the **abscissa**, or *x*-**coördinate** of the point; and that coördinate which indicates the distance above or below the x-axis is called the **ordinate**, or the **y-coördinate** of the point. The position of a point is indicated by writing its coördinates in a parenthesis, thus: (abscissa, ordinate). For example, the point P_1 in Fig. 1 is (NP_1, MP_1), or $(4, 3)$; the point P_2 is $(-4, 3)$; etc. Locating a point when its coördinates are given is called **plotting** the point. It is convenient to plot a point, say P_1, by laying off $OM = x$ and then $MP_1 = y$.

The coördinate axes divide the plane into four parts called **quadrants**, numbered as indicated in Fig. 1—I, II, III, IV.

3. Directed line segments. A line **segment** is that part of a line which is terminated by two given points on it. A **directed line segment** is a line segment to which either a positive or a negative direction has been assigned. If a positive direction is assigned to the line segment directed from A to B (read AB), the opposite direction, from B to A, is negative, and vice versa. In either case

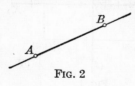

FIG. 2

$$BA = -AB \quad \text{or} \quad AB = -BA.$$

In Fig. 1, for example, NP_1 and MP_1 are line segments. It should be noticed that the abscissa of P_1 is the measure of the line segment directed from N to P_1, not from P_1 to N; while the ordinate of P_1 is the measure of the line segment directed from M to P_1, not from P_1 to M. Is the abscissa of P_2 the measure of NP_2 or P_2N?

4. Length of a line segment parallel to a coördinate axis.
Let P_1P_2 be a line segment parallel to the x-axis and consider
three cases as shown in the accompanying figures. Let M_1
and M_2 be points on the x-axis whose abscissas are the same
as those of P_1 and P_2, respectively. In each of the three
figures
$$P_1P_2 = M_1M_2.$$

In Fig. 3, a, $M_1M_2 = OM_2 - OM_1 = x_2 - x_1$.
In Fig. 3, b, $M_1M_2 = M_1O + OM_2 = OM_2 - OM_1 = x_2 - x_1$.
In Fig. 3, c, $M_1M_2 = M_1O - M_2O = OM_2 - OM_1 = x_2 - x_1$.

Thus in each of the three cases we can say that the length
of P_1P_2 is equal to the abscissa x_2 of the terminal point P_2
minus the abscissa x_1 of the initial point P_1.

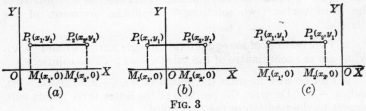

FIG. 3

In a similar manner it can be shown that the length of a line
segment Q_1Q_2 parallel to the y-axis is equal to the ordinate of
the terminal point Q_2 minus the ordinate of the initial point Q_1.

What is the change in temperature if the height of the mercury column in a thermometer changes from the 12° mark
to the 20° mark? from $-12°$ to 20°? from $-12°$ to $-8°$?
from 8° to $-20°$?

EXERCISES

1. Plot the two points and find the length of the line segment
directed from the first point to the second point in each of the
following:

(a) $(1, 0)$ and $(7, 0)$.   (d) $(-4, 7)$ and $(-4, 5)$.
(b) $(0, -6)$ and $(0, 3)$.   (e) $(3, -2)$ and $(3, -9)$.
(c) $(5, 3)$ and $(-2, 3)$.   (f) $(-10, 5)$ and $(2, 5)$.

2. Plot the points $(-2, 9)$, $(-2, 1)$, $(6, 1)$, and $(6, 9)$ and show
that they are the vertices of a square. Find its area.

3. Plot the points $(-3, 4)$, $(-3, -2)$, $(5, -2)$, and $(5, 4)$ and show that they are the vertices of a rectangle. Find the length of its diagonals.

4. Show that the points $(3, 0)$, $(12, 0)$, $(9, 4)$, and $(0, 4)$ are the vertices of a parallelogram. Find its area. What are the coördinates of the midpoint of each of its diagonals?

5. Find the area of the triangle whose vertices are

(a) $(3, 1)$, $(10, 1)$, and $(5, 9)$.   (c) $(-4, -3)$, $(5, -3)$, and $(8, 7)$.

(b) $(7, 4)$, $(-3, 6)$, and $(-3, -3)$.   (d) $(7, 6)$, $(-5, -6)$, and $(7, -5)$.

6. Find the area of the trapezoid whose vertices are $(6, 6)$, $(-2, 6)$, $(-5, -4)$, and $(11, -4)$.

7. The ends of the base of an isosceles triangle are $(-2, 1)$ and $(8, 1)$. The altitude is 12 units. What are the coördinates of the third vertex (two solutions)? Find the perimeter of the triangle.

8. Two vertices of an equilateral triangle are $(0, 0)$ and $(6, 0)$. What are the coördinates of the third vertex? (Two solutions.)

9. Plot on one diagram the points (a, b), $(-a, b)$, $(-a, -b)$, and $(a, -b)$. Describe the position of the latter three points with respect to the position of the first point.

10. In what quadrants do those points lie whose abscissas and ordinates have like signs? unlike signs?

11. Describe the position of all points (a) whose abscissas have the same value; (b) whose ordinates have the same value.

12. Describe the position of all points (a) whose abscissas are zero; (b) whose ordinates are zero.

13. Describe the position of all points whose abscissas and ordinates are (a) equal; (b) numerically equal but opposite in sign.

14. Plot (on the same diagram) at least five points each having the sum of its coördinates equal to 8.

15. Plot at least five points each having its ordinate twice its abscissa.

16. Plot several points each having the product of its coördinates equal to 12.

17. Plot several points each having its ordinate equal to one half the square of its abscissa.

18. Plot all the points (with integral coördinates) each having the sum of the squares of its coördinates equal to 25.

19. Describe the position of all points whose coördinates satisfy the equation (*a*) $x = 3$; (*b*) $y = -2$; (*c*) $x - y = 0$; (*d*) $x + y = 0$.

5. Distance between any two points. Let $P_1(x_1, y_1)$ and $P_2(x_2, y_2)$ be any two points in the plane (Fig. 4). Join P_1 and P_2 by a straight line. Through P_1 draw a line parallel to the *x*-axis and through P_2 draw a line parallel to the *y*-axis. These lines intersect in $M(x_2, y_1)$. The triangle P_1MP_2 is a right triangle. Hence

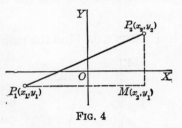

Fig. 4

$$\overline{P_1P_2}^2 = \overline{P_1M}^2 + \overline{MP_2}^2 = (x_2 - x_1)^2 + (y_2 - y_1)^2,$$

and
$$P_1P_2 = \sqrt{(x_2 - x_1)^2 + (y_2 - y_1)^2}. \tag{1}$$

EXAMPLE 1. Find the distance between $(-3, -6)$ and $(5, -2)$.

Choosing $(-3, -6)$ for (x_2, y_2) and using equation (1), we have distance

$$d = \sqrt{[-3 - 5]^2 + [-6 - (-2)]^2} = \sqrt{64 + 16} = \sqrt{80} = 4\sqrt{5}.$$

The positive sign is used before the radical since we are seeking the numerical measure of the distance between the points without regard to the direction in which it is measured. It is also to be noted that $(x_2 - x_1)^2 = (x_1 - x_2)^2$ and $(y_2 - y_1)^2 = (y_1 - y_2)^2$, and hence either point could have been chosen for (x_2, y_2).

If the line segment joining the given points is parallel to an axis, it is recommended that the distance be found directly as explained in Sec. 4.

B2

EXAMPLE 2. Show that the triangle whose vertices are $A(-1, -3)$, $B(5, -1)$, and $C(0, 4)$ is isosceles but not equilateral.

$AC = \sqrt{(-1-0)^2 + (-3-4)^2} = \sqrt{1+49} = \sqrt{50} = 5\sqrt{2}$.
$BC = \sqrt{25+25} = \sqrt{50} = 5\sqrt{2}$
and
$AB = \sqrt{36+4} = \sqrt{40} = 2\sqrt{10}$.

Since $AC = BC \neq AB$ the triangle is isosceles but not equilateral.

EXAMPLE 3. Find the points on the x-axis twice as far from $A(5, 10)$ as from $B(2, 1)$.

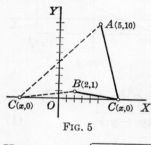

FIG. 5

Locating the points A and B, we see that the required points may be in either position $C(x, 0)$ (located approximately, Fig. 5). For either point C, we must have $AC = 2\,BC$.

But $AC = \sqrt{(x-5)^2 + 10^2}$
and $BC = \sqrt{(x-2)^2 + 1^2}$.

Hence $\sqrt{(x-5)^2 + 10^2} = 2\sqrt{(x-2)^2 + 1^2}$.

Rationalizing and simplifying, we have the *quadratic* equation $x^2 - 2x - 35 = 0$, whose roots are $x = 7$ and $x = -5$. Hence the two points $C(7, 0)$ and $C(-5, 0)$ satisfy the conditions of the problem. (The student should check the answers in the original problem.)

EXERCISES

1. Find the distance between

(a) $(-3, 2)$ and $(5, 8)$.

(b) $(1, 7)$ and $(6, -5)$.

(c) $(-9, 3)$ and $(10, 3)$.

(d) $(0, 0)$ and $(8, 4)$.

(e) $(\sqrt{2}, 1)$ and $(\sqrt{3}, -\sqrt{6})$.

(f) (a, b) and (b, a).

2. Establish the generality of formula (1) (that is, show that it is true no matter in which quadrants the points P_1 and P_2 lie) by applying the argument of Sec. 4.

3. The ends of a diameter of a circle are $(-3, -7)$ and $(9, 1)$. What is the length of the diameter?

4. Find the perimeter of the triangle whose vertices are $(12, -2)$, $(6, 6)$, and $(-9, -2)$.

5. Show that $(7, 4)$, $(-2, 1)$, and $(10, -5)$ are the vertices of an isosceles triangle.

6. Show that $(0, 6)$, $(-3, 0)$, and $(9, -6)$ are the vertices of a right triangle.

7. Show that $(13, 1)$, $(-3, 9)$, and $(0, -12)$ lie on a circle whose center is $(2, -1)$.

8. Show that $(6, 3)$, $(-3, 0)$, $(-5, -4)$, and $(4, -1)$ are the vertices of a parallelogram.

9. Show that $(0, 0)$, $(-4, 4)$, and $(2\sqrt{3} - 2, 2\sqrt{3} + 2)$ are the vertices of an equilateral triangle.

10. Show that $(-6, 3)$, $(3, 6)$, and $(9, 8)$ lie in a straight line.

11. Find x if the distance between $(1, 2)$ and $(x, 8)$ is 10 units.

12. Find the point equidistant from $(1, 7)$ and $(9, 3)$ which lies on the (a) x-axis; (b) y-axis.

13. Find the point whose ordinate equals its abscissa and which is equidistant from $(0, 4)$ and $(8, 0)$.

14. Find the points on the y-axis twice as far from $(6, -1)$ as from $(-3, 5)$.

15. Find the point equidistant from $(1, 8)$, $(7, 2)$, and $(5, -4)$.

16. Two vertices of an equilateral triangle are $(0, 0)$ and $(6, 6)$. Find the third vertex.

17. One end of a chord of a circle with center $(3, 0)$ is $(5, 4)$. Find the other end of the chord if its length is $2\sqrt{10}$ units.

18. Tangents drawn to a circle at the points $(0, 2)$ and $(8, -4)$ on the circle intersect at $(10, 7)$. Find the center of the circle.

19. A right triangle having its legs 8 units and 6 units, respectively, is inscribed in a circle with center at the origin. Find the coördinates of the vertex of the right angle if the hypotenuse lies on the x-axis.

20. Write an equation which is satisfied by the coördinates of all points (x, y) equidistant from $(8, 5)$ and $(2, -1)$.

21. Write an equation which is satisfied by the coördinates of all points (x, y) at a constant distance of 5 units from $(3, 4)$.

22. Write an equation which is satisfied by the coördinates of all points (x, y) equidistant from the y-axis and $(4, 0)$.

6. Point of division. The coördinates of a point P on the line segment P_1P_2 (Fig. 6) such that $P_1P/PP_2 = r_1/r_2$ can be found by the following method. Through P_1, P, and P_2, respectively, draw P_1M_1, PM, and P_2M_2 perpendicular to the x-axis. We have

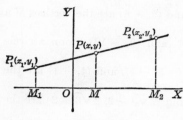

$$\frac{P_1P}{PP_2} = \frac{M_1M}{MM_2} = \frac{x - x_1}{x_2 - x}.$$

But $P_1P/PP_2 = r_1/r_2$. Hence

$$\frac{x - x_1}{x_2 - x} = \frac{r_1}{r_2}.$$

Solving for x, we have

FIG. 6

$$x = \frac{r_1x_2 + r_2x_1}{r_1 + r_2}. \tag{2}$$

Similarly, by drawing lines through P_1, P, and P_2 perpendicular to the y-axis, we can show that

$$y = \frac{r_1y_2 + r_2y_1}{r_1 + r_2}. \tag{3}$$

In case the ratio r_1/r_2 is negative, the line segments P_1P and PP_2 must be opposite in sign, that is, must be measured in opposite directions. In this case P is not between P_1 and P_2. If the ratio r_1/r_2 is numerically greater than 1, the segment P_1P is numerically greater than PP_2 and P lies beyond P_2 on P_1P_2 produced. If the ratio is numerically less than 1, then P lies beyond P_1 on P_2P_1 produced. In either case it can be shown that the coördinates (x, y) of the point of division are given by the equations (2) and (3).

An important particular case of finding the point of division occurs if P is the **midpoint** of P_1P_2. In this case $r_1 = r_2$ and the above equations (2) and (3) become

$$x = \frac{x_1 + x_2}{2}, \quad y = \frac{y_1 + y_2}{2}. \tag{4}$$

For example, the center of a circle having a diameter whose ends are $(-6. 8)$ and $(10, 2)$ is $(2, 5)$.

EXAMPLE. Find the points which divide the line segment joining $(-3, 5)$ and $(7, -2)$ into three equal parts.

Call P_1 the point $(-3, 5)$ and P_2 the point $(7, -2)$. Then for the point of division nearest P_1 we shall have P_1P equal to one third and PP_2 equal to two thirds of the segment. Hence $r_1/r_2 = \frac{1}{2}$. Using equations (2) and (3),

$$x = \frac{1 \cdot 7 + 2 \cdot (-3)}{1 + 2} = \frac{1}{3}, \quad y = \frac{1 \cdot (-2) + 2 \cdot 5}{1 + 2} = 2\tfrac{2}{3}.$$

For the other point of division $r_1/r_2 = 2/1$. Hence

$$x = \frac{2 \cdot 7 + 1 \cdot (-3)}{1 + 2} = 3\tfrac{2}{3}, \quad y = \frac{2 \cdot (-2) + 1 \cdot 5}{1 + 2} = \frac{1}{3}.$$

Therefore the points of trisection of the given line segment are $(\tfrac{1}{3}, 2\tfrac{2}{3})$ and $(3\tfrac{2}{3}, \tfrac{1}{3})$.

EXERCISES

1. Derive formulas (4) directly from a figure.

2. Find the midpoint of the line segment whose ends are
(a) $(-3, 1)$ and $(7, 9)$.
(b) $(-6, 4)$ and $(10, -4)$.
(c) $(1, -2)$ and $(4, 5)$.
(d) (a, c) and (b, d).

3. One end of a diameter of a circle with center $(-3, 2)$ is $(2, -1)$. Find the other end.

4. Find the three points which divide into four equal parts the line segment joining $(-8, 2)$ and $(12, -1)$.

5. Find the lengths of the medians of the triangle whose vertices are $(5, 7)$, $(-5, 1)$, and $(3, -5)$.

6. The ends of the base of an isosceles triangle are $(-5, -4)$ and $(7, 2)$. The vertex opposite the base is $(-3, 7)$. Find the area by using the formula $A = \frac{1}{2} bh$.

7. Show that the line segments which join the midpoints of the opposite sides of the quadrilateral whose vertices are $(8, 7)$, $(-2, 5)$, $(-4, -1)$, and $(6, -7)$ bisect each other.

8. Find the point C on the line through $A(-5, 1)$ and $B(10, 11)$ such that (a) $\dfrac{AC}{CB} = \dfrac{2}{3}$; (b) $\dfrac{AC}{CB} = -\dfrac{2}{3}$; (c) $\dfrac{AC}{CB} = -\dfrac{3}{2}$.

9. Find the two points on the line through $(-7, -2)$ and $(5, -1)$ each of which is twice as far from the first point as from the second point.

10. The line segment directed from $(-3, 1)$ to $(1, 3)$ is extended 10 units. Find the terminal point.

11. A line is drawn across the triangle $A(-4, -3)$, $B(8, 0)$, and $C(6, 12)$ parallel to the base AB, and crossing the side AC at $(0, 3)$. Find the point where it crosses BC.

12. The vertices of a triangle are $(8, 11)$, $(-8, 1)$, and $(12, -3)$. Find the point on each median which is at a distance from the vertex equal to two thirds of the length of the median.

13. The vertices of a triangle are (x_1, y_1), (x_2, y_2), and (x_3, y_3). Show that the point on each median which is at a distance from the vertex equal to two thirds of the length of the median is $\left(\dfrac{x_1 + x_2 + x_3}{3}, \dfrac{y_1 + y_2 + y_3}{3}\right)$. (This point is called the **centroid of the triangle.**)

14. Find the centroid (see Exercise 13) of the triangle whose vertices are $(9, 1)$, $(-2, 6)$, and $(5, -7)$.

15. The midpoints of the sides of a triangle are $(3, 2)$, $(-1, -2)$, and $(5, -4)$. Find the vertices.

16. Three vertices of a parallelogram are $(-1, 6)$, $(2, 1)$, and $(4, 4)$. Find the fourth vertex. (Three solutions.)

17. The ends of a chord of a circle whose radius is $5\sqrt{2}$ are $(3, -4)$ and $(5, 2)$. Find the center of the circle.

18. The base of an isosceles triangle joins the points $(0, 0)$ and $(8, -6)$. The altitude is 5 units. Find the coördinates of the vertex.

7. Angle of inclination. Slope of a line. If a line intersects the x-axis, its angle of inclination is the angle θ (Fig. 7, a and b), $0° < \theta < 180°$, measured from the positive direction of the x-axis to the line. If a line is parallel to the x-axis, its angle of inclination is defined to be $0°$. The slope of a line is the tangent of its angle of inclination. The slope is usually denoted by m.

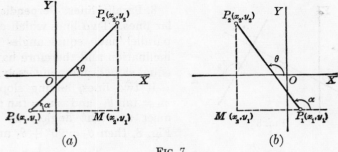

FIG. 7

The slope of the line segment P_1P_2 in Fig. 7 (*a* and *b*) is easily expressed in terms of the coördinates of P_1 and P_2 by drawing the triangle P_1MP_2. In either figure the slope m of the line is given by

$$m = \tan \theta = \tan \alpha = \frac{MP_2}{P_1M},$$

or

$$m = \frac{y_2 - y_1}{x_2 - x_1}. \tag{5}$$

If $x_1 = x_2$, the line is parallel to the y-axis, and the angle of inclination, θ, is 90°. But tan 90° is not a definite number and hence the slope of such a line is not defined. If $y_1 = y_2$, the line is parallel to the x-axis and its slope is zero. In particular the slope of the x-axis is zero and the slope of the y-axis is not defined.

Since

$$\frac{y_2 - y_1}{x_2 - x_1} = \frac{y_1 - y_2}{x_1 - x_2},$$

it is evident that the slope of a line may be interpreted as the ratio of the change in vertical distance to the change in horizontal distance as a point moves along the line in either direction.

EXAMPLE. Find the slope of the line through (2, 3) and (5, − 4).

Using equation (5), we have

$$m = \frac{-4 - 3}{5 - 2} = -\frac{7}{3}.$$

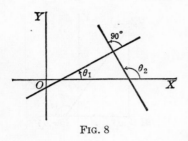

FIG. 8

8. Parallel lines. Perpendicular lines. Two lines which are parallel have equal angles of inclination and therefore have equal slopes, and conversely.

If two lines, having slopes $m_1 = \tan \theta_1$ and $m_2 = \tan \theta_2$, meet at right angles, as in Fig. 8, then $\theta_2 = 90° + \theta_1$ and

$$m_2 = \tan \theta_2 = \tan (90° + \theta_1) = - \cot \theta_1 = - \frac{1}{\tan \theta_1},$$

or
$$m_2 = - \frac{1}{m_1}.$$

Hence two lines which are perpendicular have slopes which are negative reciprocals each of the other, and conversely.

EXAMPLE. Find the slope of a line perpendicular to the line segment joining the points $(2, 3)$ and $(5, -4)$.

The slope of the line segment joining the given points was found in the example at the end of the last section to be $-\frac{7}{3}$. The negative reciprocal of this number is $\frac{3}{7}$. Hence any line with slope $\frac{3}{7}$ will be perpendicular to the line through $(2, 3)$ and $(5, -4)$.

9. Angle of intersection of two lines. Let $m_1 = \tan \theta_1$ and $m_2 = \tan \theta_2$ be the slopes of lines l_1 and l_2 (Fig. 9), respectively.

Let θ be the angle measured from line l_1 to line l_2. Then $\theta = \theta_2 - \theta_1$ and

$$\tan \theta = \tan (\theta_2 - \theta_1)$$
$$= \frac{\tan \theta_2 - \tan \theta_1}{1 + \tan \theta_1 \tan \theta_2},$$

or $\quad \tan \theta = \dfrac{m_2 - m_1}{1 + m_1 m_2}.$

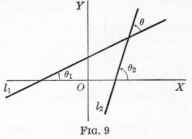

FIG. 9

It will be observed that the expression for $\tan \theta$ gives the tangent of that angle θ which has the line with slope m_1 for its initial *side and the line with slope m_2 for its terminal side, if θ is measured in the counter-clockwise direction.*

EXAMPLE. Given a line through $A(1, 5)$ and $B(4, 1)$, and a line through $C(2, 6)$ and $D(3, -1)$, intersecting at E, find the tangent of the angle DEB.

Plotting the points, it is seen that DE is the initial side. Hence

$$m_1 = \frac{6 - (-1)}{2 - 3} = -7 \quad \text{and} \quad m_2 = \frac{5 - 1}{1 - 4} = -\frac{4}{3},$$

and
$$\tan \angle DEB = \frac{-\frac{4}{3} - (-7)}{1 + \frac{28}{3}} = \frac{17}{31}.$$

We note that $\angle DEB$ is acute since its tangent is positive.

EXERCISES

1. Find the slope of a line whose angle of inclination is (a) $45°$; (b) $60°$; (c) $90°$; (d) $135°$.

2. What is the sign of the slope of a line whose direction is (a) to the right and upward? (b) to the left and upward?

3. A line parallel to the x-axis approaches by rotation a position parallel to the y-axis. Describe the variation of its slope if the rotation is (a) counter-clockwise; (b) clockwise.

4. Find the slope of the line through
   (a) $(-2, 1)$ and $(3, 6)$.
   (b) $(-3, 5)$ and $(7, -1)$.
   (c) $(-3, 2)$ and $(7, 2)$.
   (d) $(4, -5)$ and $(4, 9)$.

5. Draw the line through
   (a) $(3, 0)$ with slope $\frac{1}{2}$.
   (b) $(3, 0)$ with slope $-\frac{1}{2}$.
   (c) $(0, 0)$ with slope $\frac{1}{4}$.
   (d) $(0, 0)$ with slope 4.
   (e) $(0, 1)$ with slope $\frac{2}{3}$.
   (f) $(0, 1)$ with slope $-\frac{3}{2}$.

6. Show that the line through $(3, 5)$ and $(7, -1)$ is
   (a) parallel to the line through $(-4, 4)$ and $(0, -2)$;
   (b) perpendicular to the line through $(0, 0)$ and $(12, 8)$.

7. The vertices of a triangle are $(11, 0)$, $(-5, 4)$, and $(3, 4)$. Find the slopes of its (a) sides; (b) altitudes; (c) medians.

32

8. Show that

(a) $(5, 7)$, $(8, -5)$, and $(0, -7)$ are the vertices of a right triangle.

(b) $(4, 0)$, $(7, 8)$, $(0, 10)$, and $(-3, 2)$ are the vertices of a parallelogram.

(c) $(8, 0)$, $(6, 6)$, $(-3, 3)$, and $(-1, -3)$ are the vertices of a rectangle.

(d) $(10, 8)$, $(-3, 9)$, $(-4, -4)$, and $(9, -5)$ are the vertices of a square.

9. Show that the points $(-3, -7)$, $(0, -2)$, and $(6, 8)$ are collinear (that is, lie on the same straight line).

10. Determine x so that the points $(x, -3)$, $(1, 1)$, and $(-4, 3)$ shall be collinear.

11. Determine y so that the line through $(-3, -2)$ and $(9, y)$ shall be perpendicular to the line through $(5, -3)$ and $(4, y)$.

12. Find to the nearest degree the acute angle of intersection of a line with slope $-\frac{3}{2}$ and the line through $(1, -3)$ and $(7, 9)$.

13. Find to the nearest degree the acute angle between the y-axis and the line through $(-1, 1)$ and $(1, 9)$.

14. The points $P_1(9, 0)$ and $P_2(-3, 4)$ lie on a circle with center $(2, -1)$. Find the acute angle of intersection of the lines tangent to the circle at P_1 and P_2.

15. Find the acute angle of intersection of the diagonals of the quadrilateral whose vertices are $(6, 2)$, $(3, 5)$, $(-2, -2)$, and $(0, -4)$.

16. Find to the nearest minute the angles of the triangle whose vertices are

(a) $(1, 2)$, $(-1, -1)$, and $(9, 1)$.
(b) $(3, 3)$, $(-2, 2)$, and $(1, -1)$.

17. Show that $(-1, -3)$, $(8, 3)$, $(3, 4)$, and $(0, 2)$ are the vertices of an isosceles trapezoid.

18. The angle between two lines is $45°$. The slope of one of the lines is $\frac{3}{2}$. What is the slope of the other line?

19. The slope of the hypotenuse of an isosceles right triangle is -3. What are the slopes of the two legs?

20. Two vertices of an equilateral triangle are $(0, 0)$ and (a, a). Find the slopes of the three sides.

21. Show that if two lines have slopes m and $\dfrac{m-1}{m+1}$, respectively, they include an angle of 45°.

22. Write an equation which is satisfied by the coördinates of all points (x, y) collinear with $(1, 4)$ and $(5, 0)$.

10. Areas of triangles and polygons. If one side of a triangle is parallel to an axis, that side may be considered the base and the altitude drawn to it is parallel to an axis. Their lengths may be calculated and the area computed as one half the base times the altitude. If the vertices are so located that no side is parallel to an axis, auxiliary lines may be drawn in such a way that the required area may be computed by combining the areas of trapezoids and triangles with sides and altitudes parallel to the axes. Or the triangle may be inclosed in a rectangle with sides parallel to the axes and the required area found by subtracting the areas of right triangles from the area of the rectangle. The following example illustrates the use of a trapezoid and triangles.

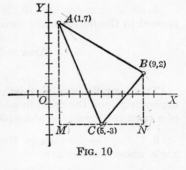

Fig. 10

EXAMPLE. Find the area of the triangle whose vertices are $A(1, 7)$, $B(9, 2)$, and $C(5, -3)$.

Draw through the vertices of the triangle the auxiliary lines MN, AM, and BN, as shown in the figure, and observe that the coördinates of the points M and N are $(1, -3)$ and $(9, -3)$, respectively. Then

area $\triangle ABC$ = area trapezoid $AMNB$

$$- \text{ area } \triangle AMC - \text{ area } \triangle BNC$$

$$= \frac{MA + NB}{2} \cdot MN - \frac{MA \cdot MC}{2} - \frac{CN \cdot NB}{2}$$

$$= \frac{10 + 5}{2} \cdot 8 - \frac{10 \cdot 4}{2} - \frac{4 \cdot 5}{2} = 30.$$

The area of any polygon may be found in a similar manner.

EXERCISES

1. Find the area of the triangle whose vertices are

(a) (1, 2), (5, 1), and (3, 6).
(b) (2, 5), (− 4, 1), and (7, − 2).
(c) (6, − 5), (4, 2), and (− 8, 7).

2. Find the area of the quadrilateral whose vertices are (0, 0), (8, − 2), (10, 5), and (2, 3).

3. Find the area of the polygon whose vertices are (5, 0), (7, 3), (3, 8), (− 2, 2), and (1, − 2).

4. By generalizing the method illustrated in the example of Sec. 10 show that the area of a triangle whose vertices are (x_1, y_1), (x_2, y_2), and (x_3, y_3) is the absolute value of

$$\tfrac{1}{2}(x_1y_2 - x_2y_1 + x_2y_3 - x_3y_2 + x_3y_1 - x_1y_3).$$

5. Show that the area of the triangle in Exercise 4 can be expressed in the determinant form

$$\text{Area} = \tfrac{1}{2} \begin{vmatrix} x_1 & y_1 & 1 \\ x_2 & y_2 & 1 \\ x_3 & y_3 & 1 \end{vmatrix}.$$

(This formula may give either a positive or a negative result depending upon the order in which the vertices are taken. In case of a negative result the absolute value is taken.)

6. Using the formula in Exercise 5, find the area of the triangle whose vertices are

(a) (8, 6), (− 1, 3), and (5, − 1).
(b) (10, 8), (7, − 3), and (− 2, − 6).
(c) (0, 0), (a, b), and (b, a).

7. By combining the areas of triangles find the area of the polygon whose vertices are

(a) (6, 10), (− 1, 6), (− 4, − 2), and (8, − 3).
(b) (0, 0), (9, 2), (7, 6), (− 2, 8), and (− 4, 4).

8. The area of a triangle whose vertices are (1, 6), (5, − 2), and (x, 4) is 20 square units. Find x. (Two solutions.)

9. The vertices of a triangle are A $(-2, 5)$, B $(10, 1)$, and C $(4, 13)$. Find the length of the altitude perpendicular to the side AB.

10. Assuming that $(1, -2)$, $(3, 2)$, and $(6, 8)$ are the vertices of a triangle, show that the area is zero, and hence establish the collinearity of the three given points.

11. Find x if $(-3, 5)$, $(3, 1)$, and $(x, -3)$ are collinear.

12. Write an equation which is satisfied by the coördinates of all points (x, y) collinear with $(-2, 1)$ and $(4, 3)$.

13. The vertices of a triangle are (x, y), $(-2, 1)$, and $(4, 3)$. Write an equation which the coördinates of the vertex (x, y) satisfy if the area is 10 square units. (Two solutions.)

11. Applications to elementary geometry. Choice of axes. The methods of analytic geometry will be found more powerful in the attack upon many of the problems of geometry than the methods which the student has thus far employed. Analytic geometry not only simplifies the proofs of many of the propositions with which we are familiar, but enables us to attack successfully problems which we could handle in elementary geometry only with great difficulty, or not at all. That the tools already developed—the formulas for distance, point of division, and slope—will aid in solving problems of geometry is illustrated by the exercises at the end of this section.

The properties of a geometric figure depend upon the relations of the parts and not upon the particular position in which the figure is drawn. Hence the properties of any geometric figure are independent of the way in which the axes are chosen. In the proof of geometric properties of figures it will, in general, be possible to choose the axes in more than one way. The axes should be chosen in the way which gives the simplest algebra. If we have a vertex of the figure at the origin and some line of the figure for an axis we shall usually have the best choice of axes. Problems differ, however, and no general rule is without exception. Much must be left to the ingenuity of the student.

EXAMPLE. The line joining the midpoints of the nonparallel sides of a trapezoid is equal to one half of the sum of the parallel sides and is parallel to them.

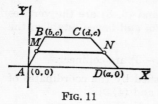

FIG. 11

Choose a base of the trapezoid for the x-axis and one end of that base for the origin, as in the figure. The coördinates of the four vertices may be taken as indicated. The midpoint of AB is $(b/2, c/2)$ and of CD is $((a + d)/2, c/2)$. The slope of MN is found to be zero, and MN is therefore parallel to the x-axis and hence is parallel to AD and BC. Since MN is parallel to the x-axis, its length is

$$MN = \frac{a + d}{2} - \frac{b}{2} = \frac{a + d - b}{2}.$$

But $AD = a$ and $BC = d - b$. Hence

$$MN = \tfrac{1}{2}(AD + BC).$$

EXERCISES

Prove analytically:

1. The diagonals of a rectangle are equal.

2. The diagonals of a square are perpendicular to each other.

3. The diagonals of a rhombus are perpendicular to each other.

4. The diagonals of a parallelogram bisect each other.

5. The line segment drawn from the vertex of the right angle of a right triangle to the midpoint of the hypotenuse is equal to one half of the hypotenuse.

6. The line segment joining the midpoints of two sides of a triangle is equal to one half of the third side and is parallel to it.

7. If two medians of a triangle are equal, the triangle is isosceles.

8. The diagonals of an isosceles trapezoid are equal.

9. If the diagonals of a trapezoid are equal, the trapezoid is isosceles.

10. If the diagonals of a parallelogram are equal, the parallelogram is a rectangle.

11. The line segments which join the midpoints of the sides of a quadrilateral taken in order form a parallelogram.

12. The line segments which join the midpoints of the opposite sides of a quadrilateral bisect each other.

13. The line segment joining the midpoints of the diagonals of a trapezoid is equal to one half the difference of the parallel sides and is parallel to them.

14. The midpoints of two opposite sides of a quadrilateral and the midpoints of its diagonals are the vertices of a parallelogram.

15. The sum of the squares of the sides of a parallelogram is equal to the sum of the squares of its diagonals.

16. If a median is drawn from a vertex to the opposite side of a triangle, the sum of the squares of the other two sides is equal to twice the square of one half of the first side plus twice the square of the median.

17. The sum of the squares of the four sides of a quadrilateral is equal to the sum of the squares of the diagonals plus four times the square of the line segment which joins the midpoints of the diagonals.

18. In any triangle four times the sum of the squares of the medians is equal to three times the sum of the squares of the sides.

19. Two line segments l_1 and l_2 drawn from a vertex of a parallelogram to the midpoints of the opposite sides, respectively, intersect a diagonal of the parallelogram in points each of which is a mutual point of trisection of the diagonal and l_1 and l_2, respectively.

20. The line segments joining the centroid of a triangle to the vertices divide the triangle into parts of equal area. (See Exercise 13, page 12.)

CHAPTER II

THE STRAIGHT LINE

12. Correspondence between geometric figure and equation.
The coördinate system described in Chapter I can be used
to set up a correspondence between equations and certain
geometric figures. In this chapter is discussed the correspondence between straight lines and first degree equations
in two variables. Two problems present themselves:

1. *Given the line, to find the corresponding equation.*
2. *Given the equation, to locate the corresponding line.*

The nature of these two problems will be illustrated by
examples.

EXAMPLE 1. Find the equation which expresses the relation between the abscissa and the ordinate of any (every)
point on the line through the point (3, 1) and with the slope $\frac{1}{2}$.

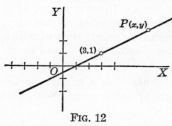

FIG. 12

Let $P(x, y)$ be any point on the
given line. The slope of the line
segment joining P to (3, 1) is $\frac{1}{2}$.
The slope of this line segment
is also $(y - 1)/(x - 3)$. Hence

$$\frac{y - 1}{x - 3} = \frac{1}{2},$$

or $x - 2y = 1,$

is the equation expressing the relation between the abscissa
and the ordinate of any point on the line. It is called the
equation of the line. The equation is of the first degree. It
will be shown in Sec. 20 that to every straight line corresponds
an equation of the first degree in rectangular coördinates,
and conversely.

22

From the foregoing example we see that the coördinates x and y of every point (x, y) on the given line satisfy the equation corresponding to the line. This suggests the method of attack on problem 2, namely, that of locating a line when its equation is given. Pairs of numbers which satisfy an equation of the first degree in two variables are taken as abscissas and ordinates of points. These points when plotted lie on a straight line which corresponds to the given equation. This straight line is called the **graph** of the equation. *It is the line which passes through all the points, and only the points, whose coördinates satisfy the equation.*

EXAMPLE 2. Graph the line represented by the equation $2x - y = 6$.

The following pairs of numbers will be found to be solutions of the given equation:

$x =$	-2	-1	0	1	2	3	4	5	6
$y =$	-10	-8	-6	-4	-2	0	2	4	6

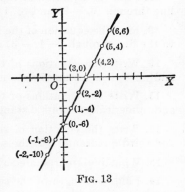

Each pair of numbers represents a point on the required line. It is obviously impossible to write down all the number pairs which are solutions of the equation. If the points represented by these number pairs are plotted, they show the position of the line corresponding to the equation. Since the graph is a straight line, it is necessary to plot but two points, for example, the points $(0, -6)$ and $(3, 0)$.

FIG. 13

The foregoing examples illustrate the correspondence between a straight line and its equation. The line is said to represent the equation *geometrically*; and the equation is said to represent the line algebraically or *analytically*.

EXERCISES

1. Plot at least five points which lie on the line whose equation is given. Draw the line in each case.

(a) $x + y = 5$. (c) $5x + 3y + 10 = 0$.
(b) $3x - 2y = 6$. (d) $x - 2y = 0$.

2. Find the points where each of the following lines crosses the axes and draw the line in each case:

(a) $x - y + 3 = 0$. (c) $2x + y = 0$.
(b) $3x + 4y + 12 = 0$. (d) $y - 4 = 0$.

3. Draw the triangle whose sides lie on the lines $x - 4y = 4$, $3x - 2y = 0$, and $x = 6$.

4. Which of the lines in Exercises 1, 2, and 3 (a) go through the origin? (b) are parallel to an axis?

5. Which of the following points lie on the line $3x + 4y - 10 = 0$? (a) $(1, 2)$; (b) $(-2, 4)$; (c) $(10, -5)$; (d) $(-25, 21)$; (e) $(0, 0)$.

6. Find the equation of the line through $(-1, 2)$ with slope 2.

7. Find the equation of the line through $(2, 5)$ and $(6, -3)$.

8. Find the equation of the line through $(4, 3)$ parallel to the line through $(0, -3)$ and $(6, 1)$.

9. Find the equation of the line through $(3, -2)$ perpendicular to the line through $(-1, -3)$ and $(3, 7)$.

10. Write the equations of the two lines parallel to the x-axis and numerically 5 units distant from it.

11. Write the equations of the two lines parallel to the y-axis and numerically 3 units distant from it.

12. Write the equation of the line which bisects (a) the first and third quadrants; (b) the second and fourth quadrants.

13. What line is represented by the equation (a) $x = 0$? (b) $y = 0$?

14. Find the length of the segment of the line $5x + 12y = 30$ which is included between the axes.

15. Find the length of the segment of the line $3x - 4y = 7$ terminated by the points $(x, -4)$ and $(9, y)$.

16. Find in two ways the equation of the locus of points equidistant from $(-3, 5)$ and $(9, -1)$.

13. Forms of equations of lines. The method of deriving the equation of a straight line depends upon the given geometric conditions which describe the line. A line is usually located by giving one point on it and its direction or slope, by giving two points on it, or by some other way which is essentially equivalent to one of these. Five typical forms of the equation of a straight line will be discussed. These forms are related and can be transformed from one into the other.

14. Equation of a line through a given point and with a given slope. Let $P_1(x_1, y_1)$ be the given point, and let m be the slope of a line through P_1. If $P(x, y)$ is any other point on the line, the slope of the line segment P_1P is m. The slope of the line segment P_1P is $(y - y_1)/(x - x_1)$. Hence the equation of the line through P_1 with slope m is

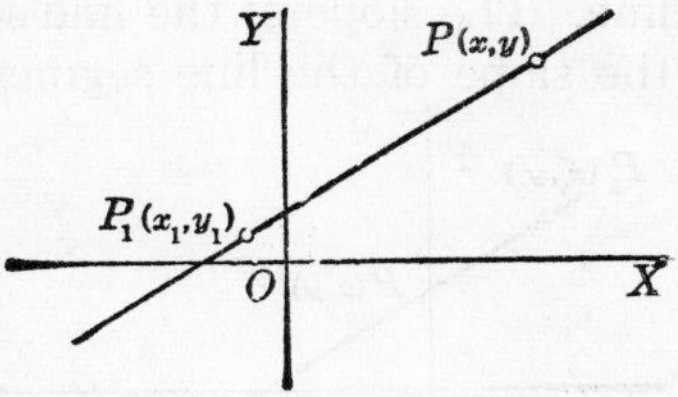

$$\frac{y - y_1}{x - x_1} = m,$$

or $\quad y - y_1 = m(x - x_1).$ (1)

FIG. 14

If the point (x_1, y_1) is the origin $(0, 0)$, the equation becomes

$$y = mx.$$

In case the line is parallel to the x-axis, the slope $m = 0$, and the equation becomes

$$y = y_1.$$

In case the line is parallel to the y-axis, the angle of inclination is $90°$. But $\tan 90°$ is not a definite number and the slope form of the equation cannot be used. A line parallel to the y-axis is at a constant distance from it and hence, for such a line through P_1, $\quad x = x_1.$

Similarly we could have written directly the equation of the line through P_1 parallel to the x-axis without using (1). For example, the equations of the two lines through $(-2, 6)$ parallel to the x- and y-axes, respectively, are $y = 6$ and $x = -2$.

EXAMPLE. Write the equation of the line through $(1, -2)$ perpendicular to the line through $(1, -2)$ and $(4, 3)$.

The slope of the segment joining $(1, -2)$ and $(4, 3)$ is $\frac{5}{3}$. The slope of the required line is therefore $-\frac{3}{5}$. Hence

$$y + 2 = -\tfrac{3}{5}(x - 1), \quad \text{or} \quad 3x + 5y + 7 = 0,$$

is the equation desired. (As a partial check the student should show that the coördinates of the point $(1, -2)$ satisfy the equation. Why is this not a complete check?)

15. Equation of a line through two given points. Let $P_1(x_1, y_1)$ and $P_2(x_2, y_2)$ be two given points on a line whose equation is required, and let $P(x, y)$ be any other point on the line. The slope of the line segment PP_1 must be the same as the slope of the line segment P_1P_2. Hence the equation of the line is

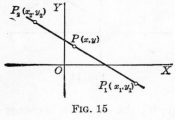

FIG. 15

$$\frac{y - y_1}{x - x_1} = \frac{y_2 - y_1}{x_2 - x_1},$$

or $y - y_1 = \dfrac{y_2 - y_1}{x_2 - x_1}(x - x_1).$ (2)

This is essentially the same as the case of a line through a point and with a given slope, since $(y_2 - y_1)/(x_2 - x_1)$ is the slope of the line joining (x_1, y_1) and (x_2, y_2). If $x_1 = x_2$ the line is parallel to the y-axis and the foregoing equation is not valid (see Sec. 14).

EXAMPLE. Write the equation of the line passing through $(-1, -4)$ and $(5, 5)$.

The slope is $\frac{3}{2}$. The equation of the line through the point $(-1, -4)$ (the other point could be used) and with slope $\frac{3}{2}$ is

$$y + 4 = \tfrac{3}{2}(x + 1), \quad \text{or} \quad 3x - 2y - 5 = 0.$$

(As a check the student should show that the coördinates of both points satisfy the equation.)

16. Definition of intercepts. The intercepts of a line on the axes are the directed distances from the origin to the points where the line crosses the axes. To find the y-intercept let x equal zero in the equation of the line and solve for y; and to find the x-intercept let y equal zero and solve for x. For example, the x- and y-intercepts of the line $3x - 2y - 5 = 0$ are $\frac{5}{3}$ and $-\frac{5}{2}$, respectively.

17. Point of intersection of two straight lines. The coördinates of the point of intersection of two straight lines must satisfy the equation of each line. Hence the point of intersection of two non-parallel straight lines can be found by solving their equations simultaneously.

EXERCISES

1. Find the equation of the line through the given point having the given slope. Find the x- and y-intercepts and draw the line.

   (a) $(2, -3)$, $m = \frac{3}{4}$.   (c) $(7, 0)$, $m = \frac{1}{2}$.   (e) $(0, 5)$, $m = -\frac{2}{3}$.

   (b) $(-\frac{1}{2}, 4)$, $m = -2$.   (d) $(0, 0)$, $m = \frac{2}{5}$.   (f) $(3, 7)$, $m = 0$.

2. Write the equation of the line through $(4, -2)$ with angle of inclination (a) $0°$; (b) $45°$; (c) $90°$; (d) $135°$.

3. Find the equation of the line through the given points in each of the following:

   (a) $(2, -1)$ and $(7, 2)$.   (d) $(3\frac{1}{3}, 0)$ and $(0, 2\frac{1}{2})$.

   (b) $(0, 0)$ and $(6, 3)$.   (e) $(-7, 4)$ and $(8, 4)$.

   (c) $(-3, \frac{3}{2})$ and $(2, \frac{2}{3})$.   (f) $(3, -2)$ and $(3, 5)$.

4. Find the equations of the sides of the triangle whose vertices are $(-2, 7)$, $(5, 0)$, and $(3, -3)$.

5. Find the equations of the medians of the triangle whose vertices are $(5, 3)$, $(1, 11)$, and $(-3, -5)$.

6. Write the equations of the four sides and the two diagonals of the parallelogram whose vertices are $(0, 0)$, $(8, 0)$, $(10, 4)$, and $(2, 4)$.

7. The midpoints of the sides of a triangle are $(6, 0)$, $(-2, 2)$, and $(2, -4)$. Find the equations of its sides.

8. The ends of the hypotenuse of an isosceles right triangle lying in the first quadrant are $(0, 0)$ and $(0, 10)$. Write the equations of its sides.

9. Two vertices of an equilateral triangle lying in the first quadrant are $(0, 0)$ and $(a, 0)$. Write the equations of its sides.

10. Write the equation of the line through the origin which bisects the segment of the line $3x + 5y = 30$ which is included between the axes.

11. Write the equations of the two diagonals of the square two of whose opposite vertices are $(1, -6)$ and $(7, 6)$.

12. Write the equations of the two diagonals of the rectangle three of whose vertices are $(-4, 5)$, $(6, -5)$, and $(12, 1)$.

13. Find the area of the right triangle formed by the coördinate axes and the line through $(1, 3.6)$ and $(7.5, 1)$.

14. Find the point in which the line through $(1, 7)$ and $(6, -3)$ intersects the line $x - 3y = 1$.

15. Find the foot of the perpendicular dropped from $(1, 5)$ upon the line through $(0, -2)$ and $(9, 1)$.

16. Find the shortest distance from $(8, 9)$ to the line through $(-2, 4)$ and $(10, -5)$.

17. The vertices of a trapezoid are $(1, 3)$, $(-1, -1)$, $(11, -5)$, and $(7, 1)$. How far must each of its nonparallel sides be extended to intersect?

18. Find the point on the line $3x - 2y = 19$ equidistant from $(-4, 1)$ and $(8, 7)$.

19. A diameter of a circle lies on the line $7x + 4y = 22$ and has for one end the point whose ordinate is 9. Find the other end if the circle passes through $(10, 3)$.

20. The points $A(1, 6)$ and $B(7, -6)$ lie on a circle with center $(2, -1)$. Find the distance from the center to the point of intersection of the two lines tangent to the circle at A and B.

21. Show that the points $(0, 7)$, $(3, -1)$, and $(6, -9)$ are collinear.

22. Show that the lines $3x - y - 1 = 0$, $x + 2y - 12 = 0$, and $4x - 3y + 7 = 0$ are concurrent (intersect in a common point).

18. Equation of a line in terms of its slope and y-intercept. A line whose y-intercept is b passes through the point $(0, b)$. Hence the equation of a line with slope m and y-intercept b can be obtained by using equation (1). The equation is, therefore,

$$y - b = m(x - 0), \quad \text{or} \quad y = mx + b. \tag{3}$$

The latter equation puts in evidence the slope m and the y-intercept b. (It is not valid for a line parallel to the y-axis.)

19. Equation of a line in terms of its intercepts on both axes.
If the x-intercept is a and the y-intercept is b, the line passes through the two points $(a, 0)$ and $(0, b)$. Hence its equation is

$$y - b = -\frac{b}{a}(x - 0), \quad \text{or} \quad bx + ay = ab.$$

Dividing by ab, we have

$$\frac{x}{a} + \frac{y}{b} = 1. \tag{4}$$

This equation puts in evidence the intercepts a and b. For what lines is the equation not valid?

20. Theorem. *Every straight line can be represented by a first degree equation in two variables in rectangular coördinates; and conversely, every first degree equation in two variables in rectangular coördinates represents a straight line.*

A line is determined by a point on it and by its direction through the point. If the line is parallel to the y-axis, it can be represented by an equation of the form $x = a$, which is of the first degree. If the line is not parallel to the y-axis, a point on it and its direction are sufficient to enable us to find its equation by the method of Sec. 14. We have seen that the equation so derived is of the first degree. Hence the first part of the theorem is proved.

The general equation of the first degree in two variables is

$$Ax + By + C = 0,$$

where A, B, and C are constants. If $B \neq 0$ the equation can be written in the form

$$y = mx + b,$$

where $m = -A/B$ and $b = -C/B$. Transposing b and dividing by x, we have

$$\frac{y - b}{x} = m. \tag{5}$$

From the figure we see that equation (5) expresses the fact that the line joining the point (x, y) to the point $(0, b)$ has the constant slope m. This is true when, and only when, the point (x, y) lies on a straight line through $(0, b)$ with slope m.

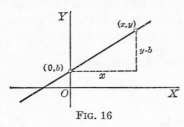

Fig. 16

If $B = 0$ the equation becomes

$$x = k,$$

where $k = -C/A$, and this is true when, and only when, the point (x, y) lies on a line parallel to the y-axis and distant k units from it. Hence every first degree equation in two variables represents a straight line. Since the equation $Ax + By + C = 0$ represents a straight line, it is called a **linear equation**.

21. Reduction of the general equation to the slope and y-intercept form, and to the intercept form. It is often desirable to reduce an equation of the form $Ax + By + C = 0$ to the form $y = mx + b$, because this latter form readily shows the slope m and the y-intercept b of the line. Thus the equation

$$2x + 5y - 15 = 0$$

when solved for y becomes

$$y = -\tfrac{2}{5}x + 3.$$

This equation represents a line with slope $-\tfrac{2}{5}$ and with y-intercept 3.

To reduce an equation of the form $Ax + By + C = 0$ to the intercept form, solve for the intercepts directly from the equation and substitute in the intercept form

$$\frac{x}{a} + \frac{y}{b} = 1.$$

Thus the line whose equation is

$$2x + 5y - 15 = 0$$

has x-intercept $a = \frac{15}{2}$ and y-intercept $b = 3$. The intercept form of the equation is, therefore,

$$\frac{x}{\frac{15}{2}} + \frac{y}{3} = 1.$$

EXERCISES

1. Reduce each of the following equations to the slope and y-intercept form. Determine the slope and y-intercept and draw each line.

    (a) $3x + 4y = 12$.   (c) $2y + 3x + 2 = 0$.
    (b) $5x - y = 10$.   (d) $x - 3y = 0$.

2. Reduce equations (a), (b), and (c) in Exercise 1 to the intercept form. Why cannot (d) be reduced to the intercept form?

3. Show that the line $3x + 4y - 2 = 0$ is

    (a) parallel to the line $9x + 12y + 7 = 0$;
    (b) perpendicular to the line $8x - 6y + 5 = 0$;
    (c) coincident with the line $15x + 20y - 10 = 0$.

4. Show that the lines $\begin{cases} A_1x + B_1y + C_1 = 0, \\ A_2x + B_2y + C_2 = 0 \end{cases}$ are (a) parallel and distinct if $A_2 = kA_1$, $B_2 = kB_1$, $C_2 \neq kC_1$; $k = $ a constant $\neq 0$; (b) coincident if $A_2 = kA_1$, $B_2 = kB_1$, $C_2 = kC_1$; (c) perpendicular if $A_1A_2 + B_1B_2 = 0$.

5. Show that the following lines form the sides of a parallelogram: $2x - 3y + 5 = 0$, $6x + 10y + 15 = 0$, $6x - 9y - 20 = 0$, and $3x + 5y - 20 = 0$.

6. Show that the following lines form the sides of a rectangle: $x - 3y + 2 = 0$, $12x + 4y + 31 = 0$, $2x - 6y - 7 = 0$, and $9x + 3y - 40 = 0$.

7. Show that the equations of the lines through (x_1, y_1) parallel and perpendicular to the line $ax + by = c$ are respectively

        $ax + by = c'$ where $c' = ax_1 + by_1$
and $bx - ay = c'$ where $c' = bx_1 - ay_1$.

8. Find in two ways the equation of each of the two lines through $(3, -1)$ parallel and perpendicular respectively to the line $2x - 7y + 8 = 0$. (*Hint.* See Exercise 7 for one of the ways.)

9. Find the equation of the line on which lie the centers of circles which touch the line $x + 3y + 6 = 0$ at the point where it crosses the y-axis.

10. The line $2x + 3y = 27$ is tangent to a circle with center $(2, -1)$. Find the point of contact.

11. Find the equation of the tangent to the circle in Exercise 10 parallel to the given tangent.

12. Find the shortest distance from the line $x + 7y = 20$ to $(7, 9)$

13. Find to the nearest minute the angles of the triangle formed by the lines $x + 8y = 17$, $3x - 2y + 1 = 0$, and $x - 5y = 4$.

14. Show that the lines $2x - y + 3 = 0$, $x + 7y + 9 = 0$, and $11x + 2y - 51 = 0$ form the sides of an isosceles triangle.

15. The hypotenuse of an isosceles right triangle lies on the line $2x + 3y = 18$. The vertex of the right angle is the origin. Find the equations of the two equal sides.

16. Show analytically that the locus of points equidistant from (x_1, y_1) and (x_2, y_2) is the perpendicular bisector of the segment joining the given points.

22. Normal equation of a line. The normal equation of a line is the equation in terms of the perpendicular distance to the line from the origin, and

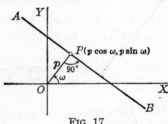

Fɪɢ. 17

the line from the origin, and the positive angle which that perpendicular makes with the positive end of the x-axis. The distance measured from the origin to the line is considered positive. In Fig. 17 let $p = OP$ be the perpendicular distance from the origin to the line, and let ω be the angle which OP makes with the positive end of the x-axis. The coördinates of the point of intersection P of OP with the line AB are $(p \cos \omega, p \sin \omega)$. Since AB is perpendicular to OP its slope is $m = -1/\tan \omega = -\cot \omega$. The equation of the line AB is (see Sec. 14)

$$y - p \sin \omega = -\cot \omega(x - p \cos \omega).$$

Replacing $\cot \omega$ by $\cos \omega/\sin \omega$, we can reduce the equation to

$$x \cos \omega + y \sin \omega = p(\sin^2 \omega + \cos^2 \omega) = p,$$

or $$x \cos \omega + y \sin \omega - p = 0. \qquad (6)$$

This equation is called the **normal** equation of a straight line and is valid for any line.

In case the line crosses a quadrant other than the first, a similar argument leads to an equation of the same form.

EXAMPLE. Write the normal equations of the two lines each of which is distant 5 units from the origin and has an inclination angle of 45°.

Since the inclination angle of each line is 45°, the lines are parallel, and for the line AB, ω is 135°, and for the line CD, ω is 315°. The equations are

$$[AB]\ x \cos 135° + y \sin 135° - 5 = 0$$

and

$$[CD]\ x \cos 315° + y \sin 315° - 5 = 0,$$

or

$$[AB]\ -\frac{\sqrt{2}}{2}x + \frac{\sqrt{2}}{2}y - 5 = 0$$

and

$$[CD]\ \frac{\sqrt{2}}{2}x - \frac{\sqrt{2}}{2}y - 5 = 0.$$

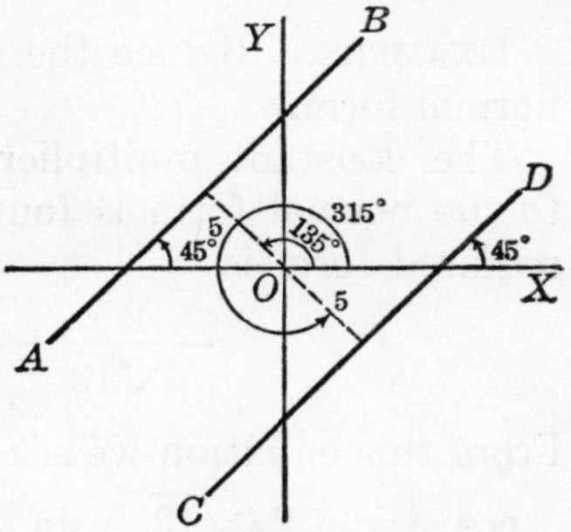

FIG. 18

23. Reduction of the general first degree equation to the normal form. If the general equation of a line,

$$Ax + By + C = 0,$$

and the normal equation,

$$x \cos \omega + y \sin \omega - p = 0,$$

represent the same line, it is possible to multiply one equation by a constant such that the two equations become identical (see Exercise 4 b, page 31). Let us multiply the first equation by k, where k is chosen so that

$$kA = \cos \omega, \quad kB = \sin \omega, \quad \text{and} \quad kC = -p.$$

Squaring the first two of these equations and adding, we have

$$k^2(A^2 + B^2) = \cos^2 \omega + \sin^2 \omega = 1.$$

Hence

$$k = \frac{1}{\pm \sqrt{A^2 + B^2}}.$$

Multiplying the general equation by this value of k, we obtain the normal equation

$$\frac{Ax}{\pm \sqrt{A^2 + B^2}} + \frac{By}{\pm \sqrt{A^2 + B^2}} + \frac{C}{\pm \sqrt{A^2 + B^2}} = 0,$$

where the sign before the radical must be chosen opposite to the sign of C in order to agree with the normal form. If $C = 0$, the line goes through the origin. In this case ω is chosen less than 180°. Hence sin ω is positive and the sign of the radical is chosen the same as the sign of B.

EXAMPLE. Reduce the equation $2x - 3y + 6 = 0$ to the normal form.

The constant multiplier which will reduce the equation to the normal form is found to be $1/(-\sqrt{13})$. Hence the required form is

$$-\frac{2x}{\sqrt{13}} + \frac{3y}{\sqrt{13}} - \frac{6}{\sqrt{13}} = 0.$$

From this equation we see that for the given line

$$\cos \omega = -2/\sqrt{13}, \quad \sin \omega = 3/\sqrt{13}, \quad \text{and} \quad p = 6/\sqrt{13}.$$

24. Distance from a line to a point. The distance from the line AB (Fig. 19) to the point (x_1, y_1) can be found in the following manner. The normal equation of the line AB is

$$x \cos \omega + y \sin \omega - p = 0.$$

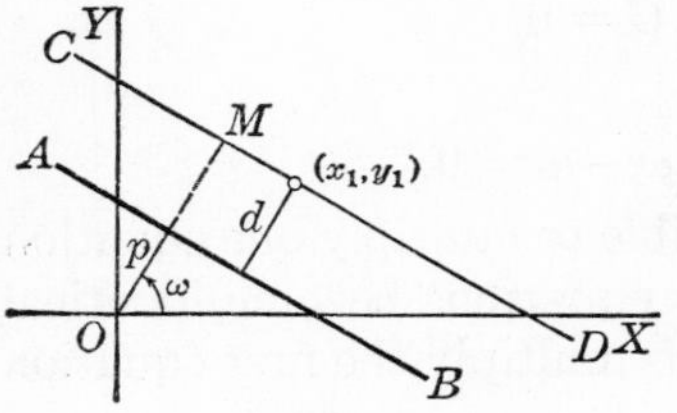

If a line CD is drawn through the point (x_1, y_1) parallel to AB, its equation will evidently be

$$x \cos \omega + y \sin \omega - p_1 = 0,$$

FIG. 19

where $p_1 = OM$. But $OM = p + d$, where d is the distance from the line AB to the point (x_1, y_1). Since the point (x_1, y_1) is on the line CD,

$$x_1 \cos \omega + y_1 \sin \omega - (p + d) = 0,$$

or $\qquad\qquad d = x_1 \cos \omega + y_1 \sin \omega - p. \qquad\qquad (7)$

Therefore, the distance from a line to a point can be found by writing the equation of the line in normal form and substituting in the left member of the equation the coördinates of the point. The result is the distance from the line to the point, and is zero only if the point is on the line. If the point (x_1, y_1) lies on the opposite side of the line AB from the origin, the distance d is positive (note positive sense of direction adopted in Sec. 22), and if the point lies on the same side of the line as the origin, the distance d is negative.

EXAMPLE. Find the distance from the line $7x + y - 10 = 0$ to the point $(3, 4)$.

Reducing the equation to the normal form, we have

$$\frac{7x + y - 10}{5\sqrt{2}} = 0.$$

Substituting in the left member the coördinates of the given point, we have

$$d = \frac{7 \cdot 3 + 1 \cdot 4 - 10}{5\sqrt{2}} = \frac{15}{5\sqrt{2}} = \frac{3\sqrt{2}}{2},$$

the required distance. Since the distance is positive, the given point $(3, 4)$ is on the opposite side of the line from the origin.

25. Equation of the bisector of an angle. EXAMPLE. Find the equations of the bisectors of the angles formed by the lines $3x + 4y + 10 = 0$ and $5x - 12y - 12 = 0$.

We make use of the fact that the bisector of an angle is the locus of points equidistant from the sides of the angle. From the figure we have

$$FP = EP$$

and $\qquad MP' = -NP',$

where FP and EP have the same signs and MP' and NP'

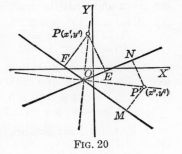

FIG. 20

have opposite signs, since P is on the same side of each line as the origin and P' is not. But

$$FP = \frac{3\,x' + 4\,y' + 10}{--5},$$

$$EP = \frac{5\,x' - 12\,y' - 12}{13},$$

$$MP' = \frac{3\,x'' + 4\,y'' + 10}{-5}, \quad \text{and} \quad NP' = \frac{5\,x'' - 12\,y'' - 12}{13}.$$

Hence the locus of P is

$$\frac{3\,x' + 4\,y' + 10}{-5} = \frac{5\,x' - 12\,y' - 12}{13},$$

and the locus of P' is

$$\frac{3\,x'' + 4\,y'' + 10}{-5} = -\frac{5\,x'' - 12\,y'' - 12}{13}.$$

Clearing of fractions, reducing, and omitting prime marks, we have as the equations of the two bisectors

$$32\,x - 4\,y + 35 = 0 \quad \text{and} \quad 7\,x + 56\,y + 95 = 0.$$

It will be observed that these lines have slopes which are negative reciprocals, and the lines are, therefore, perpendicular. This was proved in elementary geometry and gives a check on our work.

EXERCISES

1. Draw each of the lines for which the following conditions are given and write its equation in normal form:

(a) $\omega = 45°$, $p = 2$.   (d) $\omega = 5\,\pi/4$, $p = 1$.
(b) $\omega = 120°$, $p = 3$.   (e) $\omega = \pi/6$, $p = 0$.
(c) $\omega = 180°$, $p = 5$.   (f) $\omega = \pi/2$, $p = 10$.

2. Reduce each of the following equations to the normal form, determine ω and p, and draw each line:

(a) $3\,x + 4\,y - 10 = 0$.   (c) $x + y + 8 = 0$.
(b) $5\,x - 12\,y + 39 = 0$.   (d) $\sqrt{3}\,x - y = 0$.

3. How far from the origin is the line through $(-3, 5)$ and $(13, -7)$?

4. Which of the lines $4x + 2y - 15 = 0$ and $7x - y + 24 = 0$ is nearer the origin?

5. Show that the distance d from the line $Ax + By + C = 0$ to the point (x_1, y_1) is $d = \dfrac{Ax_1 + By_1 + C}{\pm \sqrt{A^2 + B^2}}$.

6. Find the distance from the given line to the given point in each of the following:

(a) $4x + 3y - 13 = 0$, $(2, 5)$.   (c) $7x + 24y + 27 = 0$, $(7, 1)$.
(b) $12x - 5y - 30 = 0$, $(1, -1)$.   (d) $9x - 7y - 8 = 0$, $(-3, -5)$.

7. Find the distance from the line

(a) $3x + 4y = 0$ to $(2, 1)$.   (b) $3x - 4y = 0$ to $(2, 1)$.

8. The line $8x + 15y - 8 = 0$ is tangent to a circle whose center is $(6, 3)$. Find the length of the radius.

9. Find the length of each of the three altitudes of the triangle whose vertices are $(2, 5)$, $(2, -5)$, and $(10, 1)$.

10. Show that $(1, 1)$ and $(11, 3)$ lie on opposite sides of the line $2x - 11y + 10 = 0$.

11. Find the distance between the parallel lines

(a) $y = 10 - 2x$ and $y = 15 - 2x$.
(b) $x - 3y + 20 = 0$ and $x - 3y - 10 = 0$.

12. The base of a triangle is 10 units in length and lies along the line $9x + 40y - 36 = 0$. Find its area if the vertex opposite the base lies on the line $9x + 40y - 200 = 0$.

13. Find the equation of the locus of points numerically equidistant from the parallel lines in each set of Exercise 11.

14. The distance between two parallel lines is 6. The line $12x + 5y - 39 = 0$ is parallel to them and midway between them. Write the equations of the two lines.

15. The ends of the base of a triangle are $(-5, 3)$ and $(7, -1)$. Find the locus of the vertex opposite the base if the area is constant and equal to 20 square units. (Two solutions.)

16. Find the points equidistant from $(0, 10)$ and $(8, 6)$ and at the distances ± 4 from the line $4x + 3y - 10 = 0$.

17. Derive the normal form from the intercept form of the equation of the straight line.

18. Find the equations of the bisectors of the angles between the lines $x + 3y - 6 = 0$ and $6x + 2y - 3 = 0$.

19. Find the equations of the bisectors of the angles of the triangle formed by the lines $3x - 4y - 10 = 0$, $5x + 12y - 54 = 0$, and $15x + 8y + 62 = 0$, and show that the bisectors are concurrent.

20. Find the radius of the inscribed circle of the triangle formed by the lines $x + 2y - 4 = 0$, $x - 2y + 2 = 0$, and $2x - y - 8 = 0$.

26. Constants in the equation of a straight line. The general equation

$$Ax + By + C = 0$$

has but two essential constants, since if any one of the constants A, B, or C, say A, is different from zero we may divide by it, thus reducing the equation to

$$x + dy + e = 0,$$

where $d = B/A$ and $e = C/A$. The constants we have used are five in number, the slope m, the intercepts a and b on the axes, the perpendicular distance p from the origin, and the direction angle ω of the perpendicular.

The two essential constants in the equation of a line permit two geometric conditions to be imposed on the line. For example, if we want the line $y = mx + b$ to pass through the point $(3, 2)$, we have

$$2 = 3m + b,$$

since the coördinates of a point on a line satisfy the equation of the line. *Thus to the geometric condition that the point is on the line corresponds the algebraic condition* $2 = 3m + b$, *showing a relation between the constants.* A second geometric condition will give a second algebraic equation corresponding to that condition. From our study of simultaneous equations in algebra we recall that two independent equations are sufficient to determine two unknowns. *Hence we may put as many independent geometric conditions on a line as there are undetermined essential constants in the equation of a line, namely, two.*

27. Families of lines. When we consider the equation
$y = 2x + b$, we see that it represents a line with slope 2 for
each value of b. Giving particular values to b, we have
parallel lines with different y-intercepts. The figure is drawn
for $b = -2, -1, 0, 1$, and 2. Such a system of lines, depending upon an arbitrary constant, is
called a **family of lines**. The arbitrary constant is frequently called
a **parameter**. If we want the line of
this family which passes through
some given point, for example (3, 10),
we determine the parameter b so that
the coördinates (3, 10) satisfy the
equation. Substituting these coördinates in the equation $y = 2x + b$, we
find $b = 4$. Hence the desired equation is $y = 2x + 4$.

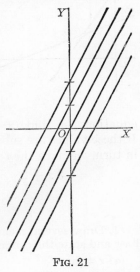

Fig. 21

Each of the type forms of the equation of the straight line represents a
family of lines depending upon the
parameters in it. When the parameters are given definite values, a particular member is selected from the
family of lines represented by the equation with parameters.
A line can be made to satisfy as many conditions as there are
parameters in the type equation.

EXAMPLE 1. From the family of lines represented by the
equation $y = mx + b$ select the one passing through (3, 3)
and $(-1, -5)$.

Since these points are on the line, the coördinates of each
must satisfy the equation, and we have

$$3 = 3m + b \quad \text{and} \quad -5 = -m + b.$$

Solving simultaneously, we obtain $m = 2$ and $b = -3$. Hence
$y = 2x - 3$ is the line of the family $y = mx + b$ which passes
through the given points.

B2

EXAMPLE 2. Write the equations of all lines through (4, 3) each of which has the product of the intercepts on the axes equal to 54.

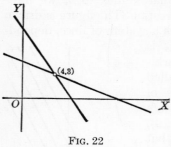

(4,3)

FIG. 22

Since we need the intercepts on the axes we use the equation

$$x/a + y/b = 1.$$

The point (4, 3) is on the line; hence

$$4/a + 3/b = 1. \qquad (8)$$

From the statement of the problem

$$ab = 54. \qquad (9)$$

The simultaneous solutions of equations (8) and (9) are $a = 6$, $b = 9$ and $a = 12$, $b = 4\frac{1}{2}$. If these values are substituted in the equation $x/a + y/b = 1$ in turn, we have the required equations

$$3x + 2y = 18 \quad \text{and} \quad 3x + 8y = 36.$$

EXERCISES

1. Draw several members of each of the following families of lines and state the common property possessed by each family:

(a) $x = k$.

(b) $y = mx + 3$.

(c) $x/a + y/4 = 1$.

(d) $y - 2 = m(x - 3)$.

(e) $x + y = c$.

(f) $x + cy = c$.

(g) $x \cos \pi/3 + y \sin \pi/3 - p = 0$.

(h) $x \cos \omega + y \sin \omega - 5 = 0$.

2. Write an equation of the family of lines each member of which (a) is parallel to the x-axis; (b) is perpendicular to the line $2x + 5y = 9$; (c) goes through the origin; (d) has the sum of its intercepts on the axes equal to 10. In (a), (b), (c), and (d) select the member which goes through (3, 2).

3. Determine k so that a member of the family of lines $kx + (k + 1)y - 10 = 0$ shall (a) go through $(4, -2)$; (b) have its slope $-\frac{2}{3}$; (c) have the sum of its intercepts on the axes equal to 15; (d) have its distance from the origin equal to 2.

4. Draw several members of the family of lines $y = cx - c^2$ and determine c so that a member of the family shall go through (a) $(2, -3)$; (b) $(2, 1)$; (c) $(2, 2)$.

5. Write the equations of all lines through (5, 1) each of which has the product of its intercepts on the axes equal to 20.

6. Find the equations of all lines through (2, 1) each of which has its x-intercept equal to the square of its y-intercept.

7. Find the equations of all lines through $(- 3, 2)$ each of which has its x-intercept equal to the reciprocal of its y-intercept.

8. Work Example 2, page 40, by selecting the required lines from the family $y - 3 = m(x - 4)$.

9. Write the equation of the line through (2, 4) which forms with the positive axes a right triangle of area (a) 25 square units; (b) 16 square units; (c) 12 square units.

10. Write the equation of the line through $(- 6, 2)$ and (4, 7), using in turn each of the following forms:

(a) $y = mx + b$;   (b) $\dfrac{x}{a} + \dfrac{y}{b} = 1$;   (c) $x \cos \omega + y \sin \omega - p = 0$.

11. Show that the equation $Ax + By + C = 0$, $C \neq 0$, can be written in the form $kx + ly = 1$. Using the latter form find the equation of the line through (a) $(- 2, 1)$ and (7, 4); (b) $(- 2, 6)$ and $(1, - 3)$. Explain the difficulty encountered in (b).

12. Verify that the coördinates of the point of intersection of the lines (1) $x + 2y - 8 = 0$ and (2) $4x - y - 5 = 0$ satisfy the equation (3) $x + 2y - 8 + k(4x - y - 5) = 0$ for all values of the constant k.

28. Lines through the point of intersection of two given lines. The coördinates of the point of intersection of the two lines

$$a_1x + b_1y + c_1 = 0 \quad \text{and} \quad a_2x + b_2y + c_2 = 0$$

satisfy the equation

$$(a_1x + b_1y + c_1) + k(a_2x + b_2y + c_2) = 0 \tag{10}$$

for every value of k, since the substitution of the coördinates of the point of intersection makes each expression in parentheses equal to zero. Equation (10) is of the first degree and, therefore, represents a straight line. Hence equation (10) represents a straight line through the intersection of the first two lines for every value of k. By the proper choice of the parameter k this line can be made to satisfy one more condition.

EXAMPLE. Find the equation of the line through the intersection of the lines $3x - y - 2 = 0$ and $x - 2y + 6 = 0$ and (a) through (6, 1); (b) with slope $\frac{2}{3}$.

(a) The equation of the family of lines through the intersection of the given lines is

$$3x - y - 2 + k(x - 2y + 6) = 0. \tag{11}$$

We now determine k so that a member of the family passes through (6, 1). Letting $x = 6$, $y = 1$ in (11), we find $k = -\frac{3}{2}$. Substituting this value of k in (11) and reducing, we have the required equation

$$3x + 4y - 22 = 0.$$

(b) Writing (11) in the form $Ax + By + C = 0$, we have

$$(3 + k)x - (1 + 2k)y - 2 + 6k = 0, \tag{12}$$

from which we see that the slope of any member of the family is

$$m = -\frac{A}{B} = \frac{3 + k}{1 + 2k}.$$

Since the slope of the line whose equation is desired is $\frac{2}{3}$, we let

$$\frac{3 + k}{1 + 2k} = \frac{2}{3}.$$

This gives $k = 7$. Substituting this value of k in either (11) or (12) and reducing, we have the required equation

$$2x - 3y + 8 = 0.$$

EXERCISES

Work the following exercises without finding the point of intersection of the given lines:

1. Find the equation of the line through the intersection of the given lines in the example of Sec. 28 which

        (a) passes through the origin.

        (b) has its x-intercept equal to 4.

        (c) is distant 2 units from the origin.

2. Find the equation of the line through the intersection of the lines $3x + y - 1 = 0$ and $x - y + 5 = 0$ which is parallel to the (a) x-axis; (b) y-axis.

3. Find the equations of all lines through the intersection of the lines $x - 2y = 2$ and $3x - y = 16$ each of which has (a) numerically equal x- and y-intercepts; (b) the sum of its intercepts 15.

4. Find the equations of all lines through the intersection of the lines $x + y - 5 = 0$ and $x - 2y + 1 = 0$ each of which has its x-intercept equal to the square of its y-intercept.

5. Find the equation of each of the lines through the intersection of the lines $x + 2y - 5 = 0$ and $3x - 5y + 7 = 0$ parallel and perpendicular respectively to the line $5x - y + 7 = 0$.

6. Show that the lines $x - y + 2 = 0$, $x + y - 6 = 0$, and $x - 3y - 6 = 0$ form a right triangle and find the equation of the line through the vertex of the right angle perpendicular to the hypotenuse.

7. Write the equations of all lines through the intersection of the lines $x + y - 8 = 0$ and $2x - y + 2 = 0$ each of which forms with the positive axes a right triangle of area 27 square units.

8. Find the equations of all lines through the intersection of the lines $x - 3y + 1 = 0$ and $2x + 5y - 9 = 0$ and having their distance from the origin (a) 2 units; (b) $\sqrt{5}$ units; (c) 3 units.

9. Show that the lines $2x + y - 1 = 0$, $x - y + 4 = 0$, and $4x + 3y - 5 = 0$ are concurrent by showing that there can be selected from the family of lines through the intersection of any two of the given lines a member which is coincident with the remaining line.

10. Discuss the validity of equation (10), Sec. 28, with respect to its representing a line through the intersection of the lines $a_1x + b_1y + c_1 = 0$ and $a_2x + b_2y + c_2 = 0$ and a second point P in case P lies on either one of the given lines.

MISCELLANEOUS EXERCISES

1. The vertices of a triangle are $(0, 0)$, $(18, 0)$, and $(6, 12)$. Show that

(a) the medians intersect in a common point (centroid).

(b) the perpendicular bisectors of the sides intersect in a common point (circumcenter).

(c) the lines through the vertices perpendicular to the opposite sides intersect in a common point (orthocenter).

(d) the centroid, circumcenter, and orthocenter of (a), (b), and (c), respectively, are collinear.

2. How far must the line segment directed from $(-2, -5)$ to $(1, 1)$ be extended to intersect the line $3x + y = 11$?

3. Find the point on the line $x - 2y = 4$ nearest $(3, 7)$.

4. Find the point on the line $x - 3y + 4 = 0$ equidistant from $(-3, 2)$ and $9, -4)$.

5. Find the point equidistant from $(8, 1)$, $(0, 7)$, and $(-4, -5)$.

6. Find the point of intersection of the two lines l_1 and l_2 parallel and perpendicular, respectively, to the line $2x + 5y = 7$ if l_1 goes through $(-5, 6)$ and l_2 goes through $(3, -3)$.

7. Two vertices of an equilateral triangle lying in the first quadrant are $(a, 0)$ and $(0, a)$. Write the equations of its three sides.

8. A point P moves along the line whose x- and y-intercepts are -9 and 3 respectively. Find the minimum distance between P and $(5, 8)$.

9. The lines $3x + 4y + 18 = 0$ and $3x + 4y - 12 = 0$ are parallel tangents to a certain circle. What is the length of the diameter of the circle?

10. Determine a so that the points $(-10, 5)$, $(-2, 2)$, and $(a, -1)$ shall be collinear.

11. Determine c so that the lines $x - y + 7 = 0$, $2x + y - 1 = 0$, and $3x + 2y + c = 0$ shall be concurrent.

12. The equations of two adjacent sides of a parallelogram are $x + 2y - 4 = 0$ and $3x + y + 3 = 0$. One vertex is $(8, -7)$. Write the equations of the other two sides and the two diagonals.

13. Two sides and one diagonal of a parallelogram are the lines $3x - 8y + 4 = 0$, $3x - 8y - 24 = 0$, and $x + 2y + 6 = 0$, respectively. The other diagonal passes through $(1, 0)$. Find the four vertices.

14. Show that the lines $x - 3y + 13 = 0$, $7x - y + 31 = 0$, $x - 3y - 7 = 0$, and $x + y = 11$ inclose an isosceles trapezoid.

15. The base of an isosceles triangle lies on the line whose equation is $x + 2y + 10 = 0$ and has for one end the point whose abscissa is 8. The vertex opposite the base is $(3, 6)$. Find the equations of the two equal sides.

16. A diagonal of a square lies on the line $3x - 5y = 14$. One vertex is $(0, 4)$. Find the equations of the sides.

17. The diagonals of a rectangle lie on the lines $x - y + 1 = 0$ and $x + 7y - 31 = 0$. One of the sides lies on a line through $(7, 2)$. Find the vertices. (Two solutions.)

18. Find the equations of all lines through $(3, 1)$ each of which is 3 units distant from the origin.

19. Find the equations of all lines through $(4, -3)$ each of which has its x-intercept equal to the cube of its y-intercept.

20. Write the equations of all lines through $(2, 7)$ each of which has the length of its segment included between the axes equal to $5\sqrt{2}$.

21. Write the equation of the line through the intersection of the lines $2x + y + 4 = 0$ and $x - y - 1 = 0$ and through the intersection of the lines $2x - y + 1 = 0$ and $3x - 2y + 3 = 0$ without finding the point of intersection of either pair of lines.

22. A pole 50 ft. long leans away from a vertical pole 60 ft. long. The bases of the poles are 30 ft. apart and the leaning pole makes an angle Arc tan $\frac{24}{7}$ with the ground (horizontal). Find the distance from the base of the vertical pole to the point where the line through the tops of the poles strikes the ground.

23. Show analytically that the perpendicular distance from the vertex of the right angle of a right triangle upon the hypotenuse is equal to the product of the lengths of the two legs divided by the length of the hypotenuse.

24. Show that equation (2), Sec. 15, can be reduced to the form

$$\begin{vmatrix} x & y & 1 \\ x_1 & y_1 & 1 \\ x_2 & y_2 & 1 \end{vmatrix} = 0.$$

25. Work Exercise 1 for the triangle whose vertices are $(0, 0)$, $(2a, 0)$, and $(2b, 2c)$.

CHAPTER III

EQUATION AND LOCUS

29. Graph of an equation. In Chapter II we have seen that every equation of the first degree in two variables has a straight line associated with it, and conversely. We shall now consider equations of higher degree than the first and their corresponding geometric loci. Consider, for example, the equation $4y = x^3$. It is evidently satisfied by infinitely many pairs of values of x and y. Writing the equation in the form $y = x^3/4$ and assigning values to x, we can easily obtain corresponding values for y. A few of these pairs of values are

$x =$	-4	-3	-2	-1	0	1	2	3	4
$y =$	-16	$-6\frac{3}{4}$	-2	$-\frac{1}{4}$	0	$\frac{1}{4}$	2	$6\frac{3}{4}$	16

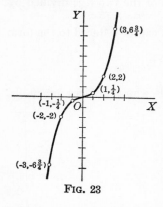

FIG. 23

Using the pairs of values of x and y found above, we can plot the points shown in Fig. 23. We observe that these points do not lie on a straight line but appear to lie on a smooth curve, as shown in the figure. If additional pairs of values of x and y are found and the corresponding points plotted, a more accurate curve can be drawn. It should be observed that the curve recedes indefinitely far from the axes in the first and third quadrants. The curve recedes more rapidly from the x-axis than from the y-axis since the ordinate y varies as the cube of the abscissa x.

46

Definition. *The locus or graph of an equation in two variables is the curve* containing all the points, and only the points, whose coördinates satisfy the equation.*

Assuming that the curve shown in Fig. 23 satisfies the conditions of the definition, we call it the graph of the equation $4y = x^3$.

As a second illustration consider the equation $xy = 1$. Writing the equation in the form $y = 1/x$ and assigning values to x, we find corresponding values of y and tabulate them as follows:

$x =$	1	2	3	4	$\frac{1}{2}$	$\frac{1}{3}$	$\frac{1}{4}$	-1	-2	-3	-4	$-\frac{1}{2}$	$-\frac{1}{3}$	$-\frac{1}{4}$
$y =$	1	$\frac{1}{2}$	$\frac{1}{3}$	$\frac{1}{4}$	2	3	4	-1	$-\frac{1}{2}$	$-\frac{1}{3}$	$-\frac{1}{4}$	-2	-3	-4

Having plotted these points, the student may be puzzled as to how to join them. As in the preceding example the points are confined to the first and third quadrants, but it should be noted that the value $x = 0$ must be excluded, since for the value $x = 0$ there is no corresponding value of y. The curve, therefore, does not cut the y-axis, and hence is composed of two separate branches, as shown in the figure.

Although $x = 0$ is excluded, we observe that as x approaches zero through positive values, y increases without limit and the branch in the first quadrant approaches the positive extension of the y-axis. Also as x

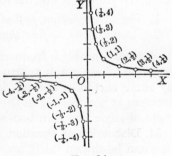

FIG. 24

increases without limit y approaches zero and the curve approaches the positive extension of the x-axis. Similarly we see that the branch in the third quadrant approaches the negative extensions of the x- and y-axes.

---

*The word "curve" used in a general sense includes the straight line.

EXERCISES

Draw the graphs of the following equations:

1. $2\,y = x^2$.
2. $2\,y = x^2 - 4$.
3. $y = x^2 - 3\,x$.
4. $y = 3\,x - x^2$.
5. $y^2 = 4\,x$.
6. $y^2 = -\,4\,x$.

7. $y = \sqrt{x}$.
8. $y = -\,\sqrt{x - 1}$.
9. $y = (x - 2)^2$.
10. $y = (x - 2)^3$.
11. $4\,x = y^3$.
12. $4\,y = -\,x^3$.

13. $y^2 = x^3$.
14. $y^3 = x^2$.
15. $xy = 9$.
16. $xy = -\,9$.
17. $x^2 y = 10$.
18. $xy^2 = -\,10$.

19. $x^2 + y^2 = 25$.
20. $x^2 - y^2 = 25$.
21. $y = x^2 - 2\,x - 3$.

22. $y = x^3 - x$.
23. $y = x^3 - x^2$.
24. $y = x^4 - x^2$.

25. $y = x^3 - 3\,x^2 + 2\,x + 3$.

30. The two fundamental problems of a first course in analytic geometry. In the preceding chapter we studied two types of problems: (1) given the equation of a line, to locate the corresponding line; (2) given the line, to find the corresponding equation. We are now interested in considering the similar problems for equations and loci in general:

1. *Given an equation, to find the corresponding locus or graph.*
2. *Given a locus, to find the corresponding equation.*

This second problem frequently takes the form of finding an equation whose graph approximately fits a set of points given by some sort of observed data. This phase of the second problem is not treated in this book, but is treated under the topic of *curve fitting* in books on "numerical analysis."

31. Discussion of equation. A curve representing an equation can be drawn fairly accurately if a sufficient number of points are plotted. In many cases, however, so many points are required to furnish an accurate conception of the curve that the point method becomes very laborious. Furthermore, the point method in itself furnishes little or no information concerning some of the important properties of the curve. There are certain properties, however, easily detected from the equation, which if discovered and used will enable one to draw the curve with a minimum amount of point plotting. Some of these properties are discussed in the sections following.

32. Intercepts. The **intercepts** of a curve are the directed distances from the origin to the points where the curve crosses or touches the axes. To find the x-intercept, let $y = 0$ in the equation of the curve and solve for x. Similarly, to find the y-intercept, let $x = 0$ and solve for y.

33. Symmetry. Two points are symmetric with respect to a line if that line is the perpendicular bisector of the line joining the two points. Two points are symmetric with respect to a third point if that third point is the midpoint of the line joining the first two points. It follows immediately from these definitions that the

point (x, y) is symmetric to $\begin{cases} (x, -y) \text{ with respect to the} \\ \quad x\text{-axis.} \\ (-x, y) \text{ with respect to the} \\ \quad y\text{-axis.} \\ (-x, -y) \text{ with respect to the} \\ \quad \text{origin.} \end{cases}$

A curve is symmetric with respect to a line or with respect to a point if the symmetric point of each point on the curve is also a point on the curve. The curve will be symmetric with respect to the x-axis if for each point (x, y) on the curve the symmetric point $(x, -y)$ is also on the curve. For example, this is true of the curve whose equation is $x + y^2 = 3$. The equation must be such that the substitution of $-y$ for y does not change its form. This will be true if y occurs in the equation to even powers only.

Similarly, a curve is symmetric with respect to the y-axis if x occurs to even powers only.

A curve is symmetric with respect to the origin if the substitution of $-x$ for x and of $-y$ for y does not change the form of the equation of the curve. Thus the curves of the illustrative examples in Sec. 29 are symmetric with respect to the origin. Symmetry with respect to both axes implies symmetry with respect to the origin, but not conversely.

34. Extent of a curve. Our graphical scheme represents points with real coördinates only. Hence values of x must be excluded for which y is imaginary and values of y must be excluded for which x is imaginary. Such cases will arise if in expressing one variable in terms of the other we have a negative radicand and an even root index. Thus if $y = 2\,ax + \sqrt{9 - x^2}$, we see that x cannot be greater than 3 nor less than -3 if y is to be real. Hence the curve lies between the two lines $x = \pm 3$. And if $x = \sqrt{y - 5}$, it is obvious that y cannot be less than 5 if x is to be real. Hence the curve lies above the line $y = 5$. The student should solve for x and y in turn and see if the curve is limited in extent.

35. Examples of graphing. EXAMPLE 1. Draw the curve $y^2 = 4\,x + 4$.

Since y occurs to an even power only, there is symmetry with respect to the x-axis. There is no symmetry with respect to the y-axis or the origin. The intercepts are ± 2 on the y-axis and -1 on the x-axis. Solving the equation for y, we have

$$y = \pm 2\sqrt{x + 1},$$

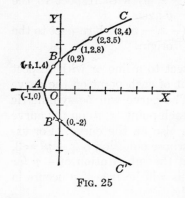

Fig. 25

which shows that values of x less than -1 must be excluded, since corresponding values of y would be imaginary. Also, it is seen that y increases numerically as x increases. Hence the curve will recede from the x-axis as x increases. For $x = -\frac{1}{2}$, $y = \pm 1.4 +$; for $x = 1$, $y = \pm 2.8 +$; for $x = 2$, $y = \pm 3.5 -$; for $x = 3$, $y = \pm 4$; etc. Marking off the intercepts and plotting the points with positive ordinates, we draw a smooth curve ABC (Fig. 25) through them in the order of increasing abscissas. The lower branch $AB'C'$ is next drawn symmetric to the branch ABC with respect to the x-axis.

It should be noticed that the double sign before the radical in the equation $y = \pm 2\sqrt{x + 1}$ also indicates symmetry with respect to the x-axis, since for every value of x there are two values of y numerically equal but opposite in sign.

EXAMPLE 2. Draw the curve $4x^2 + 9y^2 = 36$.

The curve is symmetric with respect to each axis and therefore with respect to the origin. The x-intercepts are ± 3 and the y-intercepts are ± 2. Solving the equation for y, we have

$$y = \pm \tfrac{2}{3}\sqrt{9 - x^2}.$$

This equation shows that x cannot be numerically greater than 3. It also shows that for $x = 0$, y has its largest numerical value, namely 2, and that as x increases toward 3, y de-

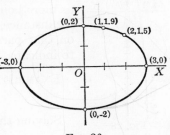

FIG. 26

creases numerically toward zero. For $x = 1$, $y = \pm 1.9 -$; and for $x = 2$, $y = \pm 1.5 -$. Marking off the intercepts and plotting the points which lie in the first quadrant, we draw the entire curve (Fig. 26), keeping in mind the facts of symmetry and the limitations on x and y.

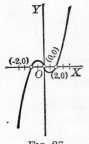

FIG. 27

EXAMPLE 3. Draw the curve $y = x^3 - 4x$.

If we replace x by $-x$ and y by $-y$ the equation becomes

$$-y = -x^3 + 4x \quad \text{or} \quad y = x^3 - 4x.$$

Hence the curve is symmetric with respect to the origin. The x-intercepts are -2, 0, and 2. The y-intercept is 0. Writing the equation in the form

$$y = (x + 2)x(x - 2),$$

we see that for $x < -2$, y is negative since each factor in the right member of the equation is negative; for $-2 < x < 0$,

y is positive; for $0 < x < 2$, y is again negative; **and for $x > 2$, y is positive.** With the information in regard to the change in sign of y, the intercepts, and symmetry with respect to the origin, a rough sketch of the curve can be indicated as in Fig. 27. However, if a few additional points are plotted, such as $(1, -3)$ and $(3, 15)$, a more accurate sketch is obtained (Fig. 28). And even this sketch can be further refined as more points are plotted. We are not sure, for instance, that $(1, -3)$ is the lowest point on that part of the curve, as Fig. 28 seems to indicate.

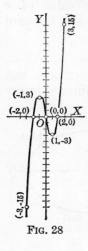

FIG. 28

EXAMPLE 4. Draw the curve
$$x^2 + y^2 - 8x = 0.$$

Solving the equation for x, we have
$$x = 4 \pm \sqrt{16 - y^2}.$$

This equation shows that the curve is symmetric with respect to the line $x = 4$, since for each value of y there are two values of x, one as much less than 4 as the other is greater than 4. The curve is also symmetric with respect to the x-axis. The curve goes through the origin and crosses the x-axis again at $x = 8$. The values of y cannot be greater than 4 nor less than -4, and the corresponding values of x lie in the interval from 0 to 8. The curve is shown in Fig. 29.

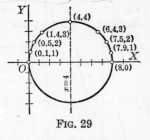

FIG. 29

The foregoing examples illustrate some of the different methods of attack upon problems that will confront the student in drawing the graphs corresponding to given equations. They do not exhaust the devices which may be used but are meant to be suggestive of types of attack to employ.

EXERCISES

Discuss and draw the graphs of the following equations:

1. $x^2 - 3y = 9$.

2. $x + y^2 = 4$.

3. $x - y^2 = 4$.

4. $4x^2 + y^2 = 16$.

5. $4x^2 - y^2 = 16$.

6. $4y^2 - x^2 = 16$.

7. $y = x^3 + 1$.

8. $y^2 = x^3 + 1$.

9. $y^2 = (x + 1)^3$.

10. $y = 4x - x^3$.

11. $2y = x^3 + x$.

12. $y = (x + 1)(x - 2)^2$.

13. $y = (x^2 - 1)(x - 4)$.

14. $y = (x^2 - 1)(x^2 - 4)$.

15. $y = x^5 - 5x^3 + 4x$.

16. $y = (x^2 - 1)^2$.

17. $y = x^2(x - 3)^3$.

18. $y^3 = x + 4y$.

19. $y^2 = x(x - 4)^2$.

20. $y^2 = x^3 - 4x$.

21. $y = x\sqrt{9 - x^2}$.

22. $y = x^2\sqrt{9 - x^2}$.

23. Solve for y in terms of x, determine the line of symmetry, and draw the graph: $y^2 - 4y - x + 3 = 0$.

24. Solve for x in terms of y, determine the line of symmetry, and draw the graph: $x^2 - 6x - y + 5 = 0$.

25. In Example 4, Sec. 35, solve for y in terms of x and draw the graph.

26. If an equation is changed by substituting $-x$ for x, what is the effect on its graph? Illustrate in the case of $y = x^2 - 2x - 3$.

27. If an equation is changed by interchanging x and y, show that the graph of the new equation is symmetric to the graph of the first with respect to the line $y = x$. Illustrate in the case of $y^2 = 4x$.

36. Horizontal and vertical asymptotes. A curve may have the property that a point P can move along it so that the distance OP from the origin to the point increases without limit, as for example, the curves in Figs. 23, 24, 25, and 28. If the distance between the point P and a fixed straight line approaches zero as the distance OP increases without limit the line is called an **asymptote** of the curve. The axes are asymptotes of the curve in Fig. 24.

We shall consider here only horizontal and vertical asymptotes, i.e. those that are parallel to or coincident with the axes.

EXAMPLE 1. Draw the curve $xy + y = x$. Solving the equation for y, we have

$$y = \frac{x}{x + 1}. \tag{1}$$

If $x = -1$, the denominator of the fraction is zero and there is no corresponding value of y. As x approaches -1, y increases numerically without limit. We now draw the line $x = -1$ and note that it is an asymptote of the curve in accordance with the foregoing definition of an asymptote.

For $x < -1$, y is positive since both numerator and denominator of the fraction in (1) are negative. Hence as x approaches -1 from the left y *increases* without limit. For $-1 < x < 0$, y is negative since the numerator is negative and the denominator is positive. Hence as x approaches -1 from the right y *decreases* without limit.

Dividing the numerator and denominator of the fraction in (1) by x, we have

$$y = \frac{1}{1 + \frac{1}{x}}. \tag{2}$$

As x increases numerically without limit the term $\frac{1}{x}$ in (2) approaches zero and y approaches 1.* The line $y = 1$ is, therefore, an asymptote of the curve. For $x < -1$, y is greater than 1. Hence as x decreases without limit y approaches 1 through values greater than 1, or in other words the curve approaches the line $y = 1$ from *above*. For $x > -1$, y is less than 1. Hence as x increases without limit y approaches 1 through values less than 1 and the curve approaches the line $y = 1$ from *below*.

---

*A convenient method of finding the limit of a rational fraction as the variable becomes infinite is to divide numerator and denominator by the highest power of the variable which occurs and then evaluate the limit.

The origin is on the curve. As x passes through zero from left to right y changes sign from negative to positive. Hence as x increases through zero the curve crosses the x-axis at the origin from "below" to "above."

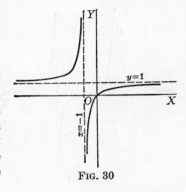

From the preceding discussion we now make a sketch of the curve which can be made more accurate if a few points are plotted. The asymptotes should be drawn as soon as they are determined since they serve as guiding lines in drawing the curve (Fig. 30).

FIG. 30

It is left as an exercise for the student to discuss the graph if the equation is solved for x in terms of y.

EXAMPLE 2. Draw the curve $x^3y - 3x^2y - x + 1 = 0$. Solving the equation for y,* we have

$$y = \frac{x-1}{x^2(x-3)}. \tag{3}$$

The denominator is zero for $x = 0$ and $x = 3$. The lines $x = 0$ and $x = 3$ are vertical asymptotes. As x approaches zero from either the left or the right y increases without limit. As x approaches 3 from the left y decreases without limit; as x approaches 3 from the right y increases without limit.

Dividing the numerator and the denominator of the fraction in (3) by x^3, we have

$$y = \frac{\dfrac{1}{x^2} - \dfrac{1}{x^3}}{1 - \dfrac{3}{x}}. \tag{4}$$

*Note the difficulty encountered in solving for x.

As x increases numerically without limit the terms $\dfrac{3}{x}, \dfrac{1}{x^2}$, and $\dfrac{1}{x^3}$

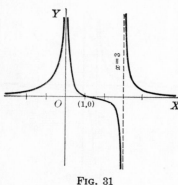

FIG. 31

in (4) approach zero and hence y approaches zero. The x-axis is, therefore, a horizontal asymptote. As x either decreases or increases without limit y approaches zero through values greater than zero.

For $x = 1$, y is zero. As x passes through 1 from left to right y changes sign from positive to negative. The curve is shown in Fig. 31.

EXERCISES

Discuss and draw the graphs of the following equations:

1. $y = \dfrac{2}{x-1}$.

2. $y = \dfrac{2x}{x-1}$.

3. $y = \dfrac{x-1}{x+2}$.

4. $y = \dfrac{x-2}{3-x}$.

5. $y = \dfrac{9}{(x-3)^2}$.

6. $y = \dfrac{8}{(x-2)^3}$.

7. $y = \dfrac{4}{x^2-4}$.

8. $y = \dfrac{4x}{x^2-4}$.

9. $y = \dfrac{2(x-1)}{x^2-x-6}$.

10. $y = \dfrac{x^2-2x}{x^2-2x-3}$.

11. $y(x^2 - 1) = x^2 + 1$.

12. $y(x^2 + 1) = x^2 - 1$.

13. $x^2y + 2y = 6$.

14. $x^2y + 2y = 6x$.

15. $y(x^2 - 1)^2 = 1$.

16. $y(x^2 - 1)^2 = x$.

17. $x^2(y - 1) = y - 2$.

18. $x^2(y - 1) = 4y - x$.

19. $y(x^2 - 1) = x - 2$.

20. $y(x - 1)^2 = x^2 - 2$.

21. $y^2(x + 1) = 4$.

22. $y^2(10 - x) = x^3$.

23. $x^2y^2 = 4 - x^2$.

24. $x^2y^2 = x^2 - 4$.

37. Functions and their graphs. If two variables are related in such a way that one or more values of one are determined when a value is assigned to the other, then the first is said to be a function of the second. Thus the area of a circle is a function of its radius, $A = \pi r^2$; the volume of a cube is a function of its edge, $V = e^3$. To indicate that y is a function of x, the notation $y = f(x)$ is used. Other symbols used are $F(x)$, $g(x)$, $f_1(x)$, $f_2(x)$, $\phi(x)$, etc. The symbol $y(x)$ often is used to signify that y is a function of x. The concept of a function is readily extended to include functions of more than one variable. Thus the volume of a circular cone is a function of the radius of its base and its altitude,

$$V = f(r, h) = \pi r^2 h/3.$$

An equation in x and y may define y as a function of x or it may define x as a function of y. If we solve $y^2 - x + 1 = 0$ for y, we get $y = \pm \sqrt{x-1}$, two distinct functions of x, viz., $y_1 = f_1(x) = \sqrt{x-1}$ and $y_2 = f_2(x) = -\sqrt{x-1}$. If we solve for x, we have $x = g(y) = y^2 + 1$, a single-valued function of y. Certain functions are real-valued only on a limited range of their variable. Thus $f(x) = \sqrt{a^2 - x^2}$ is real-valued on the range $-a \leqq x \leqq a$, while $f(x) = \sqrt{x-1}$ is real-valued for all $x \geqq 1$.

The graph of a function displays the relationship between the value of the function and its variable, as is illustrated in the following examples:

EXAMPLE 1. Show graphically the relation between the time t and the distance s a body would fall in a vacuum.

From physics we have $s = \frac{1}{2} g t^2$, s representing distance in feet and t representing time in seconds. Choosing the horizontal axis for the time axis and the vertical axis for the distance axis with positive s measured downward, we construct the graph as shown in Fig. 32, using $g = 32$. The part of the curve to the right of the s-axis represents the relation in which we are interested. The part of the curve to the left of the s-axis represents the relation that is shown by the equation but does not represent the physical problem.

When graphing a function it may be desirable to choose the unit scale on one of the axes different from the unit scale chosen on the other.

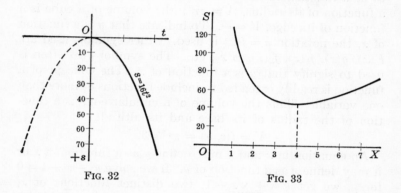

FIG. 32   FIG. 33

EXAMPLE 2. A rectangular box of capacity 32 cu. ft. is to be made with a square base and an open top. Express the number of square feet of material needed as a function of a side x of the base. Draw the graph and from it estimate the value of x for which the amount of material is a minimum.

Let h feet equal the depth of the box. The surface of the box is $S = x^2 + 4 hx$ and the volume is $V = x^2h = 32$. From the latter equation we have $h = 32/x^2$. Hence

$$S = x^2 + \frac{128}{x}.$$

From the graph (Fig. 33) we see that S is a minimum if x is approximately 4 ft.

In calculus the student will learn an elegant and direct method of finding the maximum and minimum values of functions.

The functions used in this section and in the preceding sections belong to a class of functions called *algebraic*. In a later chapter (Ch. VI), the graphs of a class of functions called *transcendental* will be treated.

1. If the graph of $f(x)$ is a straight line, $f(x)$ is called a **linear function.** Show that $f(x) = mx + b$ is a linear function.

2. Graph $f(x) = 2x - 5$. For what values of x is $f(x)$ positive? zero? negative?

3. The equation $F = \frac{9}{5}C + 32$ expresses the relation between the Fahrenheit and centigrade thermometer readings. Draw an accurate graph of this equation and from the graph give the Fahrenheit readings corresponding to the following centigrade readings: $-5°, 0°, 20°, 32°$. Give the centigrade readings corresponding to the following Fahrenheit readings: $-12°, 0°, 15°, 32°$.

4. If a body is thrown upward with an initial velocity v_0, its velocity at the end of t seconds is given by the equation $v = v_0 - gt$, where g is approximately 32 ft./sec.^{2} Graph this equation for $v_0 = 160$ ft./sec. For what values of t is v positive? zero? negative?

5. A sum of money P at simple interest will in n years amount to $A = P + Prn$, where r is the interest rate. Graph this equation for (a) $P = \$100$ and $r = .06$; (b) $P = \$90$ and $r = .08$; (c) $P = \$75$ and $r = .08$. If (a) and (b) are graphed on the same axes explain the significance of the intersection of the graphs.

6. The function $f(x) = ax^2 + bx + c$ is called a **quadratic function.** What are the zeros of this function?

7. Graph $f(x) = 5 + 4x - x^2$. For what values of x is $f(x)$ positive? zero? negative? For what value of x does $f(x)$ have its largest positive value?

8. Illustrate graphically that $f(x) = x^2 - 6x + 10$ is positive for all values of x. What is the smallest value of the function?

9. Illustrate graphically the values of x for which the function $f(x) = (x + 3)(x - 1)(x - 6)$ is positive; zero; negative.

10. Express the volume, total surface, and length of a diagonal of a cube as functions of one of its edges, and draw the graph of each of these functions.

11. Two masses, m_1 and m_2, at a distance of r units apart attract each other with a force F given by the equation $F = m_1 m_2 / r^2$. If $m_1 = 2$ and $m_2 = 5$, draw the graph showing the relation between F and r.

12. According to Boyle's law the pressure and volume of a gas at a constant temperature are connected by the equation $PV = k$. Graph this equation for $k = 20$.

13. If a stone is thrown upward from the earth's surface with an initial velocity of 80 ft./sec., the distance s, measured in feet, from the starting point in t seconds is given by the equation $s = 80\,t - \frac{1}{2}\,gt^2$. Assuming $g = 32$, illustrate graphically the relation between s and t. What is the greatest height reached by the stone?

14. A rectangular plot of ground is to be inclosed by a fence on three of its sides. The fence on the remaining side is a "line fence" already constructed. If there are 40 rods of fencing available for the three sides, express the area to be inclosed as a function of the side x parallel to the constructed fence. Draw the graph and from it determine the maximum area which can be inclosed.

15. The length of one of the equal sides of an isosceles triangle is 6 in. Express the area of the triangle as a function of x (where $x =$ one half the base of the triangle), and draw the graph. Estimate from the graph the value of x for which the area is largest.

16. Equal squares of side x are cut from the corners of a piece of tin 12 in. square and the edges are folded up so as to form a box with an open top. Express the volume of the box as a function of x and draw the graph. Estimate from the graph the value of x for which the volume of the box is largest.

38. Graphing by composition of ordinates. It is sometimes possible to draw more easily the graph of a function by breaking it up into parts, graphing each part separately and combining the graphs. The method is illustrated by graphing the equation $y = x + 1/x$.

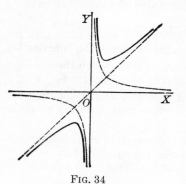

FIG. 34

Let $y_1 = x$ and $y_2 = 1/x$; then $y = y_1 + y_2$. Graph $y_1 = x$ and $y_2 = 1/x$ on the same axes. Then add the ordinates corresponding to the same abscissas and the result will be the ordinate of $y = y_1 + y_2 = x + 1/x$. The curve is shown in Fig. 34. Similarly a difference of two functions can be graphed.

EXERCISES

Sketch the graphs of the following equations:

1. $y = x^2/9 + 3/x$.
2. $y = 9/x^2 + x/3$.

3. $y = x - 1/x$.
4. $y = 1/x^2 + 1/x$.

5. $y = x + 1 + 1/(x - 1)$.
6. $x^2 - 2\,x^2y + 4 = 0$.

7. $2\,y = x^2 + x - 2$.
8. $x^2y = x^3 - x^2 + 1$.

9. $y = x \pm \sqrt{x}$.
10. $y = x \pm \sqrt{16 - x^2}$.

11. $y = x^3/2 + 1/(x^2 + 1)$.
12. $y = x^2/4 + 3\,x/(x^2 + 2)$.

13. Show that the line $y = x$ is an asymptote of the curve $y = x + \dfrac{1}{x}$ (Fig. 34) by showing that the difference between the ordinate of the curve and the ordinate of the line corresponding to the same abscissa approaches zero as x increases numerically without limit.

39. Factorable equations. If the first member of an equation $f(x, y) = 0$ can be factored into two or more factors, as $f(x, y) = f_1(x, y) \cdot f_2(x, y) = 0$, it is evident that only those points (x, y) whose coördinates satsify either $f_1(x, y) = 0$ or $f_2(x, y) = 0$ will lie on the locus of $f(x, y) = 0$. Hence the graph of $f(x, y) = 0$ will be made up of the graphs of $f_1(x, y) = 0$ and $f_2(x, y) = 0$.

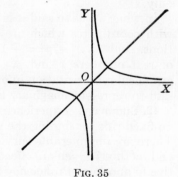

FIG. 35

EXAMPLE. Graph

$$x^2y - xy^2 - x + y = 0.$$

Factoring, we have

$$x^2y - xy^2 - x + y$$
$$= (xy - 1)(x - y) = 0.$$

Hence the required graph is made up of the graphs of the equations $xy - 1 = 0$ and $x - y = 0$. The complete graph is shown in Fig. 35.

40. Operations on equations. The student will recall from his study of algebra that certain operations performed on an equation may produce a non-equivalent equation. Consequently the locus of an equation may be modified by such operations. For example, if each member of the equation $x^2 - xy = 2\,x$ is divided by the variable factor x the locus of $x = 0$ would be lost as a part of the complete locus. Moreover, if we square the two members of the equation $y = x$, the locus of the derived equation $y^2 = x^2$ would consist not only of the locus of $y = x$ but of the locus of $y = -x$ as well.

41. Equation in two variables. In any equation we have graphed by plotting points we have seen that the points tend to lie on a curve rather than to cover an area. It can be proved that any equation in rectangular coördinates, $f(x,\ y) = 0$, represents a curve, isolated points, or no real locus. The proof is beyond the scope of this book.

Some equations are satisfied by the coördinates of only one point, or of a finite number of points, and their graphs are called **point loci.** The equation $x^2 + y^2 = 0$ is satisfied by the coördinates of the point $(0,\ 0)$ only. The equation $(x^2 - 1)^2 + (y^2 - 1)^2 = 0$ is satisfied by the coördinates of the four points $(1,\ 1)$, $(1,\ -1)$, $(-1,\ 1)$, and $(-1,\ -1)$ only.

In what we have said it is understood that we mean points with coördinates which are real numbers. There are equations, such as $x^2 + y^2 = -1$, which are satisfied by no pair of real numbers x and y. Hence such equations have no graphical representation in our system of coördinates and are said to represent **imaginary loci.**

42. Summary. Experience will soon teach the student that no fixed rule for finding the graph of an equation will suffice. There are innumerable curves each with different properties, and methods which are effective in one case may not be effective in another. Proficiency in graphing can be attained only by drawing many curves. The following outline includes the more important items to be considered when analyzing the locus of an equation:

(a) *Intercepts on the axes.* Note particularly if the curve goes through the origin.

(b) *Symmetry.* Investigate for symmetry with respect to one or both axes, or the origin.

(c) *Extent.* Investigate for limitations on the values of the variables.

(d) *Asymptotes.* Investigate for vertical and horizontal asymptotes.

(e) *Factorization.* If the equation is written in the form $f(x, y) = 0$, the left member may be factorable, in which case the graphing of the equation is simplified.

(f) *Point locus; imaginary locus.* The locus may consist of one or more isolated points only, or of a curve of one or more branches and one or more isolated points, or of no real points. In the latter case the locus is imaginary.

EXERCISES

1. What is the locus of $xy = 0$?

2. Draw the graphs of the following equations:

(a) $x^2 - 4 y^2 = 0$.   (d) $x^2 y^2 = 2 xy$.

(b) $y^2 - 3 y - 4 = 0$.   (e) $2 x^2 - 3 xy - 2 y^2 = 0$.

(c) $x^2 + 2 x = 0$.   (f) $x^4 - x^3 y = xy - y^2$.

             (g) $x^2 + y^2 = 1 + x^2 y^2$.

3. Show that the following equations represent either isolated points or no real loci:

(a) $x^2 + y^2 = 0$.   (c) $(x - 1)^2 + (y + 2)^2 + 1 = 0$.

(b) $x^2 + 4 = 0$.   (d) $(x - 1)^2 + (y + 2)^2 = 0$.

4. State how the second equation is derived from the first and compare the loci of the equations in each of the following pairs:

(a) $y = - x$,   (c) $(x^2 + y^2)(x + y - 1) = x^2 + y^2$,

     $y^2 = x^2$. $x + y = 2$.

(b) $y = x$,   (d) $(x^2 + y^2 + 1)(x + y) = 0$,

     $y^2 = xy$. $x + y = 0$.

5. Compare the loci of the equations in each of the following pairs:

(a) $y^2 = x$,
$\quad y = \sqrt{x}$.

(c) $y^2 = x(x - 3)^2$,
$\quad y = (x - 3)\sqrt{x}$.

(b) $y^2 = 4 - x^2$,
$\quad y = -\sqrt{4 - x^2}$.

(d) $x + y = xy$,
$\quad 1/x + 1/y = 1$.

Sketch the graphs of the following equations:

6. $x^2 y = x^2 - 9$.

7. $2\,x^3 y = x^2 - 1$.

8. $y(x - 2)^2 = x$.

9. $y(x - 2)^2 = x^2 - 1$.

10. $y(x^2 - 4) = x^2 - 1$.

11. $x - 2\,y = 2 - xy$.

12. $y(x^2 - 2) = x^2 - x$.

13. $y^2(x - 1)^2 = x$.

14. $x^2 y^2 = 4 + x^2$.

15. $x^4 + x^2 y^2 = y^2$.

16. $y^2(2 - x) = 2 + x$.

17. $y^2(1 - x) = 2 - x$.

18. $y^2(x^2 + 1) = 4\,x$.

19. $y^2(x - 1) = x$.

20. $y^2 = x^2(x - 3)$.

21. $y^2(1 - x^2) = x$.

22. $y^4 = x^2 + y^2$.

23. $x^2 + 2\,xy + y^2 + 1 = 0$.

24. $x^4 y^2 - x^2 y^4 = x^2 - y^2$.

25. $(x^2 + y^2)^2 - x^2 - y^2 = 0$.

43. Intersections of curves. If two curves are drawn on the same set of axes it is evident that the coördinates of the points of intersection of the two curves must satisfy the equation of each curve. Hence, to find the coördinates of the points of intersection of two curves, solve their equations simultaneously.

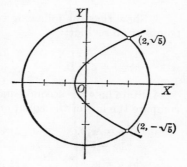

EXAMPLE 1. Find the points of intersection of the curves

$$x^2 + y^2 = 9$$

and $\quad\quad y^2 = 2\,x + 1.$

FIG. 36

Solving the two equations simultaneously, we have

$$x = 2, \; y = \pm \sqrt{5} \quad \text{and} \quad x = -4, \; y = \pm \sqrt{-7}.$$

Thus there are four algebraic solutions, only two of which are real. Hence the curves intersect in but two real points, $(2, \sqrt{5})$ and $(2, -\sqrt{5})$ (Fig. 36).

EXAMPLE 2. Find the points of intersection of $y^2 = x^3$ and $3x - y = 4$.

Eliminating y from the two equations, we have the equation

$$x^3 - 9x^2 + 24x - 16 = 0,$$

whose roots are found to be 1, 4, 4. Hence there are three solutions, $(1, -1)$ and $(4, 8)$ twice. The significance of the repeated solution $(4, 8)$ is shown in Fig. 37. At this point the line is tangent to the curve.*

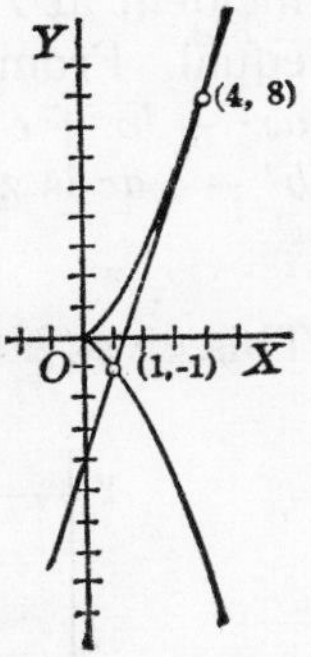

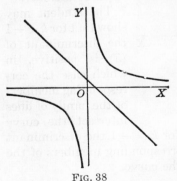

FIG. 37

Two equations when treated simultaneously may have no solution or may have imaginary solutions only. In either case the graphs of the equations do not intersect.

EXAMPLE 3. Find the points of intersection of $xy = 9$ and $x + y = 1$.

Solving for x, we find

$$x = \frac{1 \pm \sqrt{-35}}{2}.$$

Hence the two loci do not intersect in real points (Fig. 38).

FIG. 38

EXAMPLE 4. From the family of lines $y = x + k$ select the member which is tangent to the curve $y^2 = 4x - 8$.

Eliminating y from the two equations, we have

---

*A repeated solution does not always signify tangency. Note exceptions in Exercises 18 and 22, page 67.

$$x^2 + 2(k - 2)x + k^2 + 8 = 0. \tag{5}$$

The real and distinct roots x_1 and x_2 of (5) are the abscissas of the points of intersection of a member, l_1 say, of the family of lines and the curve (Fig. 39). Now let us consider k being changed in such a manner that l_1 is moved into the position of l_2 assumed to be tangent to the curve at P. The points P_1 and P_2 in this process move along the curve and become coincident at P. The abscissas x_1 and x_2 of P_1 and P_2 are now equal. From algebra the two roots of the quadratic equation $ax^2 + bx + c = 0$ are equal if and only if the discriminant $b^2 - 4ac$ is zero. Hence the roots of (5) are equal if

$$[2(k - 2)]^2 - 4(k^2 + 8) = 0.$$

This gives $k = -1$. Substituting this value of k in the equation of the family of lines we have

$$y = x - 1,$$

the equation of the required member.

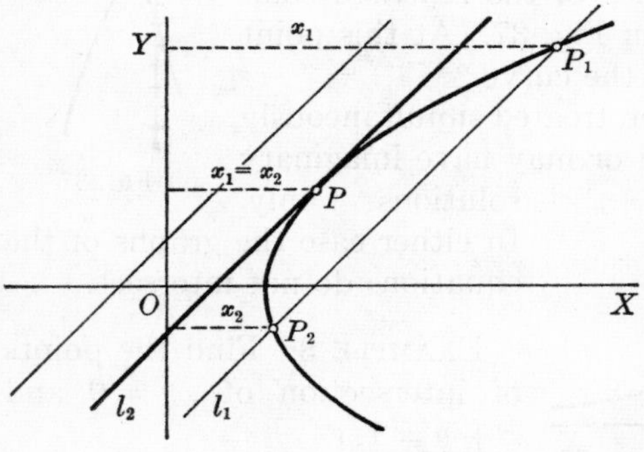

FIG. 39

The student may show that for $k < -1$ the discriminant of (5) is positive, in which case the corresponding members of the family of lines intersect the curve in real and distinct points, and for $k > -1$ the discriminant is negative, in which case the corresponding members of the family of lines do not intersect the curve.

EXERCISES

Find the points of intersection of the graphs of the equations in each of the following pairs and illustrate graphically:

1. $x + y = 4,$
   $x^2 - 2y = 0.$

2. $x - y = 2,$
   $x^2 + y^2 = 20.$

3. $x + 2y = 7,$
   $y^2 + 3x = 12.$

4. $2x + y = 6,$
   $x^2 + y^2 = 9.$

5. $x^2 + y^2 = 4,$
   $x^2 + y^2 = 9.$

6. $y^2 - 2x = 6,$
   $4x^2 - y^2 = 0.$

7. $x + y = 3,$
   $y = \sqrt{5 - x}.$

8. $x^2 + y^2 = 20,$
   $y^2 - 2x = 12.$

9. $x^2 + y^2 = 4,$
   $y^2 - 2x = 5.$

10. $x^2 y - 1 = 0,$
    $y - 2x = 3.$

11. $x^2 + y^2 = 20,$
    $xy - 8 = 0.$

12. $x + 2y = 6,$
    $y(x^2 + 9) = 27.$

13. $y^2 - x = 0,$
    $x^2 - 8y = 0.$

14. $x - 2y + 1 = 0,$
    $y(x^2 + 3) = 4x.$

15. $2x^2 + 3y^2 = 18,$
    $x^2 + y^2 = 7.$

16. $2x - y = 5,$
    $y^2(10 - x) = x^3.$

17. $2x^2 + y^2 = 4,$
    $2y^2 - x^2 = 3.$

18. $x + y = 3,$
    $y^2 = x(x - 3)^2.$

19. $x + y = xy,$
    $x^2 + y^2 = 8.$

20. $y^2 = x^3 + 64,$
    $x^2 + y^2 = 64.$

21. $x^2 - 2y = 0,$
    $x^3 - y = 0.$

22. $y^2 = 10x^2 - x^4,$
    $x - y = 0.$

23. $x - y = 2,$
    $y^2 - x^3 = 0.$

24. $y = (x - 2)(x^2 - 4),$
    $x - y + 2 = 0.$

25. $7x - 3y = 4,$
    $y^2 - x^3 = 0.$

26. $x - y + 1 = 0,$
    $y = x^3 - 3x^2 + 4x.$

27. $y(x^2 + 4) = 8,$
    $x^2 y = 4.$

28. $y(x^2 + 1) = 4 - x^2,$
    $5x + 2y = 8.$

29. $y^2 = 3 - x,$
    $xy = 2.$

30. $y^2 = x - 1,$
    $y^2(3 - x) = x - 1.$

31. From the family of lines $y = mx + 1$ select the members which are tangent to the curve in Example 4, p. 65.

32. From the family of lines $2x + y = c$ select the members which are tangent to the curve $x^2 + y^2 = 20.$

33. Determine b so that the line $y = x + b$ shall be tangent to the curve $y^2 = 4x.$

34. Find m if the line $y = mx + b$ touches the curve $xy = 1.$

44. To find the equation of a given locus. The method of finding the equation corresponding to a given locus will vary from problem to problem. In general, the following steps should be taken in order:

(a) *Choose a suitable set of axes.* If the problem does not fix the axes, any suitable lines may be chosen. Generally some line of the figure suggested by the problem taken as an axis or some fixed point as origin will serve best. The best selection of axes is that which gives the simplest equation.

(b) *Locate all data with respect to these axes.*

(c) *Locate approximately on the graph a point satisfying the conditions of the problem and call its coördinates (x, y).*

(d) *Draw any auxiliary lines suggested by the conditions of the problem.*

(e) *Out of the figure thus constructed obtain an equation involving the coördinates (x, y) of the point whose locus is given.*

Relations of the sides of a right triangle, similar triangles, related slopes, and related distances are some of the possibilities for use in forming the desired equation.

Having found the equation, we may use it to aid in plotting the locus.

A locus is defined by giving some characteristic geometric property of it. From this property we derive an equation connecting the coördinates of any point on the locus. Then every other property of the locus is involved in the equation and may be obtained by an analysis of the equation.

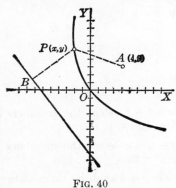

FIG. 40

EXAMPLE 1. Find the equation of the locus of points which are equidistant from the line $4x + 3y + 25 = 0$ and from the point $(4, 3)$.

Draw the line and locate the point on a set of axes. Select

$P(x, y)$ any point on the locus and draw PA and PB. From the problem

$$PA = PB.$$

But $PA = \sqrt{(x-4)^2 + (y-3)^2}$ and $PB = \dfrac{4x + 3y + 25}{5}$. Hence the required equation is

$$\frac{4x + 3y + 25}{5} = \sqrt{(x-4)^2 + (y-3)^2}.$$

Squaring, clearing of fractions, and collecting terms, we have

$$9x^2 - 24xy + 16y^2 - 400x - 300y = 0.$$

EXAMPLE 2. Find the equation of the locus of a point which moves so that it is always three times as far from one end of a line segment as from the other, where the line segment is eight units long.

If we choose the midpoint of the line segment as origin and the line including the segment as the x-axis, the coördinates of the end points are $A(-4, 0)$ and $B(4, 0)$. By the condition of the problem $AP = 3\,BP$ or $BP = 3\,AP$. We shall solve the problem for $AP = 3\,BP$. Let (x, y) be the coördinates of P.

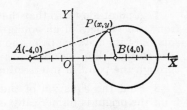

FIG. 41

Then $AP = \sqrt{(x+4)^2 + y^2}$

and $BP = \sqrt{(x-4)^2 + y^2}$.

Hence the equation of the locus of P is

$$\sqrt{(x+4)^2 + y^2} = 3\sqrt{(x-4)^2 + y^2}.$$

Squaring and reducing, we may write the equation in the form

$$x^2 + y^2 - 10x + 16 = 0.$$

The locus may be graphed from this equation. In Sec. 46 the student will learn that the locus is a circle (Fig. 41).

A number of the succeeding chapters further illustrate the problem of finding the equation of a locus.

EXERCISES

1. Write the equation of the locus of points at a distance (a) 5 units from the origin; (b) 4 units from (1, 2).

2. A point moves so that the square of its distance from (0, 3) diminished by the square of its distance from (4, 0) is equal to the square of the distance between the given points. Find the equation of its locus.

3. Work Exercise 2 if the word "diminished" is replaced by the word "increased."

4. A point moves so that the sum of the squares of its distances from the ends of the hypotenuse of a right isosceles triangle is twice the square of its distance from the vertex of the right angle. Find the position of its path relative to the triangle.

5. Find the equation of the locus of points twice as far from (12, 0) as from (3, 0).

6. What is the equation of the locus of the centers of circles tangent to both axes?

7. A point moves so that the sum of the squares of its distances from two vertices of an equilateral triangle is equal to twice the square of its distance from the third vertex. Show that its locus is a straight line parallel to a side of the triangle and passing through the point of intersection of the medians.

8. Find the equation of the locus of a point whose distance from the origin is numerically equal to the slope of the line joining it and the origin.

9. Find the equation of the locus of points equidistant from (a) (3, 0) and the y-axis; (b) (3, 4) and the line $x = 5$.

10. Find the equation of the locus of points equidistant from (a) (0, 3) and the x-axis; (b) (1, 1) and the line $y = 2$.

11. A point moves so that the sum of its numerical distances from (2, 0) and (− 2, 0) is 8. Find the equation of its locus.

12. A point moves so that the difference of its numerical distances from (8, 0) and (− 8, 0) is ± 8. Find the equation of its locus.

13. Find the equation of the locus of points the difference of whose numerical distances from (2, 2) and (− 2, − 2) is ± 4.

14. A point moves so that the slope of the line joining it and $(-1, -3)$ is three times the slope of the line joining it and $(1, 1)$. Find the equation of its locus.

15. Given $A(-1, 0)$, $O(0, 0)$, and $B(1, 0)$. Find the locus of $P(x, y)$ if the product of the slopes of AP and BP equals the slope of OP.

16. Given $A(-1, 0)$ and $B(1, 0)$. Find the locus of $P(x, y)$ if the sum of the slopes of AP and BP equals (a) the abscissa of P; (b) the reciprocal of the abscissa of P.

17. A line segment of variable length has its ends on the coördinate axes and forms with them a triangle of constant area. Find the locus of its midpoint.

18. The triangle ABC has a fixed base $AB = 2a$. Find the locus of the vertex C if $\overline{AC}^2 + \overline{BC}^2 = 4\,\overline{MC}^2$ where M is the midpoint of the base.

45. Change of axes. It sometimes happens that the choice of axes made at the beginning of the solution of a problem does not give the simplest form of the equation. Two types of change of axes are in common use. They are called **translation of axes** and **rotation of axes**; they will be described and illustrated in the next two sections.

46. Translation. Translation of axes is a change from one set of axes to a new set parallel to the old axes. In Fig. 42 we shall express the coördinates (x, y) of the point P in terms of the coördinates (x', y') of the same point referred to the new axes $X'O'Y'$. The coördinates of O' are (h, k). From the figure we have

$$x = OM = ON + NM = h + x'$$

and

$$y = MP = MR + RP = k + y',$$

or $x = x' + h$ and $y = y' + k$.

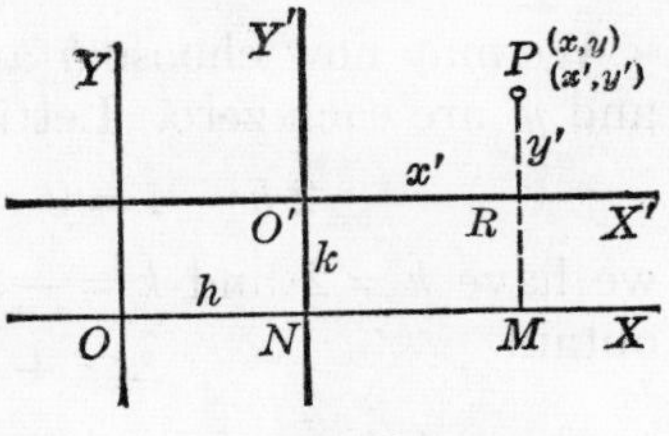

FIG. 42

The necessary substitutions for changing from the new axes back to the old are obtained by solving for x' and y'; they are

$$x' = x - h \quad \text{and} \quad y' = y - k.$$

EXAMPLE 1. In Example 2, Sec. 44, transform the equation $x^2 + y^2 - 10\,x + 16 = 0$ by translating the axes so that the origin is at $(5, 0)$.

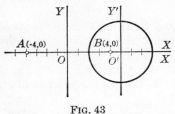

FIG. 43

The equations of translation are

$$x = x' + 5 \quad \text{and} \quad y = y'.$$

Substituting these values, we obtain

$$(x' + 5)^2 + y'^2 - 10(x' + 5) + 16 = 0,$$

or
$$x'^2 + y'^2 = 9,$$

thus changing the form of the equation but not changing the locus. By reference to the expression for the distance between two points, it is seen that the last equation states that the square of the distance from (x', y') to the origin is 9. Hence the point (x', y') lies on a circle of radius 3 with the center at the origin of the new axes, or with the center at the point $(5, 0)$ referred to the original axes.

EXAMPLE 2. Translate the axes to a new set of axes in such a way as to remove the x and y terms from the equation $x^2 + y^2 - 4\,x + 6\,y - 12 = 0$.

First method. Let $x = x' + h$ and $y = y' + k$ and collect terms. The result is

$$x'^2 + y'^2 + (2h-4)x' + (2k+6)y' + h^2 + k^2 - 4\,h + 6\,k - 12 = 0.$$

We may now choose h and k so that the coefficients of x' and y' are each zero. Letting

$$2\,h - 4 = 0 \quad \text{and} \quad 2\,k + 6 = 0,$$

we have $h = 2$ and $k = -3$. Substituting these values, we obtain
$$x'^2 + y'^2 - 25 = 0$$

as the equation of the locus referred to new axes, chosen so that there are no x' or y' terms in the equation. The new origin is at $(2, -3)$. The locus is a circle of radius 5 with the center at the new origin.

Second method. Upon completing squares in the equation $x^2 + y^2 - 4x + 6y - 12 = 0$, we may write

$$(x - 2)^2 + (y + 3)^2 - 25 = 0.$$

If we replace $x - 2$ by x' and $y + 3$ by y', we have

$$x'^2 + y'^2 - 25 = 0.$$

Hence the two methods of determining the translation lead to the same equation.

47. Rotation. Rotation of axes is changing from one set of axes to a new set which can be obtained by rotating the old axes about the origin. The problem is to express the coördinates (x, y) of a point P in terms of the coördinates (x', y') of the same point with respect to the axes $X'OY'$, which make the angle θ with the axes XOY. Drawing such auxiliary lines as are indicated in the figure, we see that

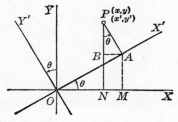

FIG. 44

$$x = ON = OM - NM = OM - BA$$
$$= OA \cos \theta - AP \sin \theta = x' \cos \theta - y' \sin \theta,$$

or
$$x = x' \cos \theta - y' \sin \theta,$$

and
$$y = NP = NB + BP = MA + BP$$
$$= OA \sin \theta + AP \cos \theta$$
$$= x' \sin \theta + y' \cos \theta,$$

or
$$y = x' \sin \theta + y' \cos \theta.$$

The equations of rotation hold for any angle θ; that is, the transformed equation represents the same curve as the original equation no matter what value of θ is used. In many cases a value of θ can be chosen so that the transformed equation is simpler than the original equation. In Chapter V the student will learn how to choose a value of θ so as to remove the xy-term from a second-degree equation.

EXAMPLE. In Example 1, Sec. 44, transform the equation of the locus by rotating the axes through an angle θ such that $\sin \theta = \frac{3}{5}$ and $\cos \theta = \frac{4}{5}$.

The equations of rotation are

$$x = \tfrac{4}{5} x' - \tfrac{3}{5} y' \quad \text{and} \quad y = \tfrac{3}{5} x' + \tfrac{4}{5} y'.$$

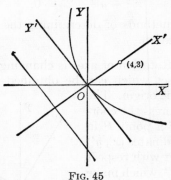

FIG. 45

Making these substitutions in the equation, we have

$$9\left(\frac{4\,x' - 3\,y'}{5}\right)^2 - 24\left(\frac{4\,x' - 3\,y'}{5}\right)\left(\frac{3\,x' + 4\,y'}{5}\right) + 16\left(\frac{3\,x' + 4\,y'}{5}\right)^2$$
$$- 400\left(\frac{4\,x' - 3\,y'}{5}\right) - 300\left(\frac{3\,x' + 4\,y'}{5}\right) = 0.$$

Reducing, we have $y'^2 - 20\,x' = 0$.

EXERCISES

1. Simplify the following equations by translating the origin to the given point and draw their graphs:

(a) $(y - 2)^2 = 4(x - 4)$; $(2, 4)$.
(b) $(x + 2)(y - 1) = 2$; $(-2, 1)$.
(c) $2\,y = x^2 - 6\,x + 5$; $(3, -2)$.
(d) $x^2 + y^2 - 8\,x - 6\,y = 0$; $(4, 3)$.

2. By an appropriate translation of axes simplify the following equations and draw their graphs:

(a) $y = (x - 2)^3$.
(b) $(y - 1)^2 = (x + 3)^3$.
(c) $(y + 1)(x - 3) = 5$.
(d) $y(x + 2)^2 = 4$.
(e) $(x - 6)^2 + (y + 3)^2 = 36$.

3. Remove the first-degree terms from the following equations by translating the axes:

$$(a) \ x^2 + y^2 - 6\,x - 10\,y + 18 = 0.$$
$$(b) \ x^2 + 4\,y^2 + 4\,x - 24\,y + 24 = 0.$$
$$(c) \ 4\,x^2 - 9\,y^2 - 16\,x - 18\,y - 29 = 0.$$

4. Remove the x-term from the equation $x^2 - 4\,x + 4\,y = 0$ by translating the y-axis. Can the y-term be removed by translating the axes?

5. Remove the y-term and the constant term from the equation $y^2 - 8\,y - 2\,x + 18 = 0$ by translating the axes. What are the coördinates of the new origin?

6. To what point must the origin be translated in order to remove the x-term and the constant term from the equation $y = ax^2 + bx + c$?

7. The origin is translated to a point on the curve whose equation is $x^2 - 4\,x - 2\,y + 10 = 0$ so that the new y-axis is a line of symmetry. Write the transformed equation of the curve.

8. The origin is translated to any point $(h,\ k)$ on the line $Ax + By + C = 0$. Write the transformed equation of the line.

9. The origin is translated to the point of intersection of the lines $x + 2\,y - 5 = 0$ and $3\,x - 7\,y - 2 = 0$. Write the transformed equations of the lines.

10. Translate the origin to $(2,\ 3)$ and show that the curve $y = x^3 - 6\,x^2 + 7\,x + 5$ is symmetric with respect to this point. Draw the curve.

11. Simplify the equation $41\,x^2 - 84\,xy + 104\,y^2 = 500$ by rotating the axes through the acute angle Arc tan $\frac{1}{2}$.

12. Transform $9\,x^2 + 24\,xy + 16\,y^2 - 20\,x - 110\,y + 150 = 0$ by rotating the axes through the acute angle Arc tan $\frac{4}{3}$ and simplify the transformed equation by translating the axes.

13. Find the equation of the locus of points the sum of whose numerical distances from $(1,\ 1)$ and $(-1,\ -1)$ is 4. Transform the equation by rotating the axes through $45°$. Draw the locus.

14. Transform the equation $x^2 - y^2 = a^2$ by rotating the axes through $-45°$.

15. Show that the equation $x^2 + y^2 = a^2$ is unchanged by a rotation of the axes.

MISCELLANEOUS EXERCISES

1. Discuss and draw the graphs of the following equations:

    (a) $x^2 + y^2 = x^2 y^2$;   (b) $x^2 - y^2 = x^2 y^2$.

2. Sketch the curves:

    (a) $y(x - 2)^3 = x$;   (b) $y(x - 2)^3 = x^2$.

3. Sketch the curves:

    (a) $y(x - 1)^2 = (x + 2)^2$;   (b) $y^2(4 - x^2) = x^2$;

           (c) $y^2(x - 1)^2 = x - 2$.

4. Draw the graph of $(x^2 - 1)^2 + (y - 1)^2 = 1$.

5. Sketch the curve $xy^4 - 4\,xy^2 - 4 = 0$.

6. Graph the function $F(x) = 2\,x^n/(x^3 + 1)$ for $n = 0, 1, 2, 3$.

7. If $\phi(x) = x^2 - 1$, graph each of the following functions:

    (a) $\phi(x)$.   (b) $1/\phi(x)$.   (c) $\phi(1/x)$.

    (d) $\phi(x + 1)$.   (e) $[\phi(x)]^2$.   (f) $\phi[\phi(x)]$.

8. A closed cylindrical can has a capacity of $16\,\pi$ cu. in. Express the total surface area of the can as a function of r, the radius of its circular ends. Draw the graph and from it estimate the value of r for which the surface is a minimum.

9. Draw several members of each of the following families of curves and in each case select the member of the family which goes through the given point:

    (a) $y = x^2 + c$, $(2, 1)$.   (d) $y^2 = cx^3$, $(-2, 4)$.

    (b) $y^2 = cx$, $(6, 2)$.   (e) $xy = c$, $(3, -2)$.

    (c) $y = x^c$, $(2, 8)$.   (f) $y(x - c) = cx$, $(3, 6)$.

10. Draw the members of the family of loci $x^n + y^n = 2^n$ corresponding to $n = 1, 2, 3, 4$.

11. Draw the locus of each of the following equations:

    (a) $x^4 - y^4 - x^2 + y^2 = 0$;   (b) $x^4 - y^4 + x^2 - y^2 = 0$.

12. Show that the equations $x^2 - 2\,xy + y^2 - x + y - 12 = 0$ and $y^2 - y - 6 = 0$ represent lines which form a parallelogram, and find (a) the lengths of its sides; (b) its area.

13. Find the angle between the two lines represented by the equation $6\,x^2 + xy - y^2 - 2\,x - y = 0$.

14. The vertices of a triangle are $(0, 0)$, $(1, 0)$, and $(1, 2)$. Write an equation of the third degree which represents the lines that form the sides of the triangle.

15. Show that $Ax^2 + Bxy + Cy^2 = 0$ represents (a) two distinct lines intersecting at the origin if $B^2 - 4\,AC > 0$, (b) two coincident lines if $B^2 - 4\,AC = 0$.

16. Discuss the locus which $Ax^2 + Bxy + Cy^2 = 0$ represents if $B^2 - 4\,AC < 0$.

17. What is the condition under which $Ax^2 + Bxy + Cy^2 = 0$ represents two perpendicular lines?

18. Find the intersections of the line $y = b$ with the curve $y = (x^2 - 1)^2$ and discuss the following cases: $(a)\ b < 0$; $(b)\ b = 0$; $(c)\ 0 < b < 1$; $(d)\ b = 1$; $(e)\ b > 1$. Illustrate graphically.

19. Find the intersections of the line $4\,y = 8\,x + 1$ and the curve $4\,y = (4 - x^2)^2$ and illustrate graphically.

20. Find the intersections of the line $x - y = 1$ and the locus of $y^2 = (x - 1)^2(x - 2)$ and illustrate graphically.

21. Show that a branch of the curve $xy(x - 2)^2 = x^3 + 1$ is tangent to the horizontal asymptote of the other two branches.

22. Determine m so that the line $y = mx + 5$ shall be tangent to the curve $y = 4 - x^2$.

23. Find the equations of the two tangents to the curve $y^2 + 2\,x = 0$ which intersect in $(4, 1)$. *(Hint.* Select the required lines from the family $y - 1 = m(x - 4)$.)

24. Show that the curve $x^2 - y^2 = 1$ can have no tangent with slope numerically less than 1. *(Hint.* Assume the line $y = mx + b$ tangent to the curve and find a relation between m and b.)

25. A point moves so that the slope of the line joining it and the origin equals n times the slope of the line joining it and $(a, 0)$. Discuss the position of its locus for $n = -3, -2, -1, 0, \frac{1}{2}, 1, 2, 3$.

26. Show that $f_1(x,\ y) + kf_2(x,\ y) = 0$ represents a family of curves passing through all the points of intersection of the two curves $f_1(x, y) = 0$ and $f_2(x, y) = 0$.

CHAPTER IV

THE CIRCLE

48. Equation of a circle. A circle is the locus of points in a plane which are equidistant from a given point called the center.

Let (h, k) be the center of a circle of radius r. From the definition the distance from any point $P(x, y)$ on the circle to the center (h, k) is r. Hence the equation is

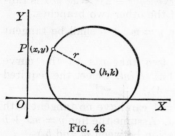

FIG. 46

$$\sqrt{(x-h)^2 + (y-k)^2} = r,$$
or $(x-h)^2 + (y-k)^2 = r^2.$ (1)

This may be written in the form

$$x^2 + y^2 + ax + by + c = 0, \quad (2)$$

where $a = -2h$, $b = -2k$, and $c = h^2 + k^2 - r^2$.

Any circle is determined by its center and radius. Hence any circle can be represented by an equation like (2). For example, the circle whose radius is 5 and center $(-2, 3)$ is represented by the equation $x^2 + y^2 + 4x - 6y - 12 = 0$.

If the center of the circle is at the origin, $h = k = 0$, and equation (1) becomes

$$x^2 + y^2 = r^2.$$

49. Theorem. *The equation*

$$Ax^2 + Ay^2 + Bx + Cy + D = 0, \quad (A \neq 0) \quad (3)$$

in which the coefficients of x^2 and y^2 are equal and in which there is no xy term, represents a circle.

Dividing equation (3) by A, we have an equation of the form

$$x^2 + y^2 + ax + by + c = 0,$$

78

where $a = B/A$, $b = C/A$, and $c = D/A$. Completing the squares in the left member and transposing c, we have

$$x^2 + ax + \frac{a^2}{4} + y^2 + by + \frac{b^2}{4} = \frac{a^2}{4} + \frac{b^2}{4} - c,$$

or $\qquad \left(x + \frac{a}{2}\right)^2 + \left(y + \frac{b}{2}\right)^2 = \frac{a^2}{4} + \frac{b^2}{4} - c.$ $\qquad$ (4)

Equation (4) is the condition that the distance from the point (x, y) to the fixed point $(-a/2, -b/2)$ is a constant. This condition is satisfied by any point (x, y) which lies on the circle whose center is $(-a/2, -b/2)$ and whose radius is $\sqrt{\frac{a^2}{4} + \frac{b^2}{4} - c}$, and by no other point. Hence equation (3) represents a circle.

If $a^2/4 + b^2/4 - c = 0$, equation (4) is satisfied by the coördinates of only one real point, $(-a/2, -b/2)$, and the locus is sometimes called a **point circle**.

If $a^2/4 + b^2/4 - c < 0$, there is no real locus.

EXAMPLE. Find the center and radius of the circle

$$x^2 + y^2 - 8x + 10y - 4 = 0.$$

Completing squares and rearranging, we may write

$$(x - 4)^2 + (y + 5)^2 = 45.$$

Comparing with equation (1), we see that the center of the circle is $(4, -5)$ and the radius is $r = \sqrt{45} = 3\sqrt{5}$. The circle should be drawn with the center and radius just found.

EXERCISES

1. Find the equations of the following circles and draw the circle in each case:

(a) With center at the origin and radius 6.
(b) With center at the origin and passing through $(2, 6)$.
(c) With center at $(2, 6)$ and passing through the origin.
(d) With ends of a diameter at $(-7, 2)$ and $(5, 4)$.
(e) With center at $(r, 0)$ and radius r.
(f) With center at $(0, r)$ and radius r.

B2

2. Reduce each of the following equations to the form of equation (1) (Sec. 48), determine the center and radius, and draw the circle:

(a) $x^2 + y^2 - 6x - 2y - 6 = 0$.　　(d) $x^2 + y^2 - 10x - 11 = 0$.

(b) $x^2 + y^2 + 4x - 5y + 4 = 0$.　　(e) $3x^2 + 3y^2 - 6x + 4y = 1$.

(c) $x^2 + y^2 = 8x + 8y$.　　(f) $4x^2 + 4y^2 + 28y + 13 = 0$.

3. Show that the following equations (a) and (b) represent, respectively, a point circle and an imaginary locus:

(a) $x^2 + y^2 - 4x - 2y + 5 = 0$;　　(b) $x^2 + y^2 - 4x - 2y + 6 = 0$.

4. Write the equations of the two circles with centers at (5, 3), one touching the x-axis and the other touching the y-axis.

5. Write the equation of the circle with center on the line $y = 2x$ and touching the (a) x-axis at (3, 0); (b) y-axis at (0, − 2).

6. Write the equation of the circle which has for a diameter the segment of the line $4x - 5y = 40$ included between the axes.

7. Write the equation of the circle with center at (1, 7) and touching the line $x + 3y = 12$.

8. The ends of a diameter of a circle are the points (− 3, 5) and (9, − 1). Find the length of the chord which the circle cuts from the y-axis.

9. Show that the circle $x^2 + y^2 - 10x - 8y + 16 = 0$ is tangent to the y-axis and intersects the x-axis in two distinct points.

10. Draw the circles $x^2 + y^2 = 8x$ and $x^2 + y^2 = 4y$ on the same axes and find their points of intersection.

11. Verify that $P(-2, 3)$ is on the circle $x^2 + y^2 - 2x + 6y = 35$ and write the equation of the line tangent to the circle at P.

12. Show that the line $2x - y + 2 = 0$ is tangent to the circle $x^2 + y^2 - 10x - 4y + 9 = 0$ and find the point of contact.

13. Write the equation of the line of centers (the straight line containing the centers) of the circles $x^2 + y^2 - 6x + 5 = 0$ and $2x^2 + 2y^2 - 2x + 6y + 3 = 0$.

14. What form does equation (2) (Sec. 48) assume if the circle (a) passes through the origin? (b) has its center on the x-axis? (c) has its center on the y-axis? (d) has its center on the line $y = x$?

15. Write the equations of each of the following families of circles:

(a) With center at the origin.

(b) With center on the x-axis and passing through the origin.

(c) With center on the y-axis and passing through the origin.

(d) With center on the line $y = x$ and passing through the origin.

(e) Touching the lines $y = \pm 6$.

16. If two circles are concentric, how do their equations differ?

17. Write the equation of the circle passing through (4, 2) and concentric with the circle $x^2 + y^2 + 5x - 6y + 6 = 0$.

18. Show that the locus of points twice as far from (0, 3) as from (6, 0) is a circle and show its position relative to the given points.

50. Circle determined by three conditions. It will be observed that the general equation of the circle contains three independent constants. A circle can, therefore, be found that will satisfy three suitable conditions; for example, that will pass through three points not in a straight line. Suppose that (x_1, y_1), (x_2, y_2), and (x_3, y_3) are three points not in the same straight line. The equation of any circle may be written in the form

$$x^2 + y^2 + ax + by + c = 0.$$

If this circle passes through the three given points, the equation must be satisfied by the coördinates of each point. Substituting in turn the coördinates of the three points, we get the equations

$$x_1{}^2 + y_1{}^2 + ax_1 + by_1 + c = 0,$$
$$x_2{}^2 + y_2{}^2 + ax_2 + by_2 + c = 0,$$
$$x_3{}^2 + y_3{}^2 + ax_3 + by_3 + c = 0;$$

these will determine a, b, and c when solved simultaneously.

The equation of the circle may be used in the form

$$(x - h)^2 + (y - k)^2 = r^2,$$

in which case we have

$$(x_1 - h)^2 + (y_1 - k)^2 = r^2,$$
$$(x_2 - h)^2 + (y_2 - k)^2 = r^2,$$
$$(x_3 - h)^2 + (y_3 - k)^2 = r^2.$$

The simultaneous solution of these equations determines h, k, and r.

EXAMPLE 1. Find the equation of the circle through $(-2, -2)$, $(10, -8)$, and $(7, 1)$.

The three equations expressing the condition that the circle $x^2 + y^2 + ax + by + c = 0$ goes through the three points $(-2, -2)$, $(10, -8)$, and $(7, 1)$ are

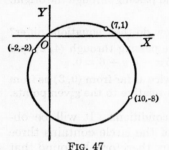

FIG. 47

$$4 + 4 - 2a - 2b + c = 0,$$
$$100 + 64 + 10a - 8b + c = 0,$$
$$49 + 1 + 7a + b + c = 0.$$

Solving simultaneously, we find $a = -8$, $b = 10$, and $c = -4$. This gives the required equation,

$$x^2 + y^2 - 8x + 10y - 4 = 0.$$

EXAMPLE 2. Find the equation of the circle which is tangent to the line $3x - 4y - 20 = 0$, which has its center on the line $y = 2x$, and which passes through the point $(-2, -2)$.

The equation which expresses the condition that the center (h, k) of the circle is on the line $y = 2x$ is

$$k = 2h.$$

Since the circle is tangent to the line $3x - 4y - 20 = 0$, the distance from the line to the center is r. This condition is

$$\frac{3h - 4k - 20}{5} = -r,$$

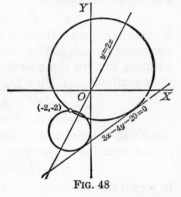

FIG. 48

in which $-r$ is used since the center is on the same side of the line as the origin. The condition that the circle passes through $(-2, -2)$ may be written

$$(-2 - h)^2 + (-2 - k)^2 = r^2.$$

Solving the three equations simultaneously, we find two sets of values for h, k, and r; namely, $h = 1$, $k = 2$, $r = 5$ and $h = -2$, $k = -4$, $r = 2$. Hence there are two circles satisfying the conditions of the problem. The equations of the two circles are

$$(x - 1)^2 + (y - 2)^2 = 25$$

and

$$(x + 2)^2 + (y + 4)^2 = 4.$$

EXERCISES

1. Determine a, b, and c if the circle $x^2 + y^2 + ax + by + c = 0$ goes through $(1, 5)$, $(4, 2)$, and $(-2, -1)$.

2. Find the equation of the circle through the following points:

(a) $(5, 3)$, $(-1, 9)$, and $(3, -3)$.   (c) $(1, 5)$, $(4, 2)$, and $(-1, -1)$.
(b) $(2, 8)$, $(-2, 0)$, and $(5, -1)$.   (d) $(0, 0)$, $(-2, 6)$, and $(8, 1)$.

3. Find the equation of the circle circumscribing the triangle whose vertices are:

(a) $(0, 3)$, $(6, 1)$, and $(3, -3)$; (b) $(3, 11)$, $(-10, -2)$, and $(6, 10)$.

4. Show that $(-1, 3)$, $(1, 0)$, $(4, -2)$, and $(14, 13)$ are concyclic (lie on the same circle).

5. Find the equation of the circle whose y-intercepts are 6 and -2 and whose center is on the line $2y = x$.

6. Find the equation of the circle which touches the x-axis at $(4, 0)$ and goes through $(7, 1)$.

7. Find the equation of the circle which goes through $(1, -3)$ and $(5, 5)$ and whose center is on the line $3x - y + 6 = 0$.

8. Find the equation of the circle passing through $(-2, 5)$ and touching the line $x - 3y = 3$ at $(6, 1)$.

9. Find the equations of the two circles touching both axes and going through $(8, 1)$.

10. Write the equations of the two circles with radii 10 and passing through $(-2, 3)$ and $(6, -1)$.

11. Find the equations of the two circles touching the line $x + y = 4$ with centers on the x-axis and with radii $\sqrt{2}$.

12. Find the equations of the two circles each with center on the line $x + 2y = 6$ and touching both axes.

13. Find the equations of the two circles touching the x-axis and going through $(-3, 10)$ and $(1, 2)$.

14. In each of the following cases find the equations of all the circles which are tangent to the line $3x + y = 3$ and pass through (a) $(3, 4)$ and $(1, 2)$; (b) $(3, 4)$ and $(9, -14)$; (c) $(3, 4)$ and $(12, 7)$.

15. Write the equations of the two circles touching the lines $3x - 4y + 1 = 0$ and $4x + 3y - 7 = 0$ and passing through $(2, 3)$.

16. Find the equation of the circle inscribed in the triangle formed by the lines $x + y - 15 = 0$, $x - 7y - 11 = 0$, and $17x + 7y + 65 = 0$.

51. Circles through the intersections of two circles. The equation

$$(x^2 + y^2 + a_1x + b_1y + c_1) + k(x^2 + y^2 + a_2x + b_2y + c_2) = 0 \quad (5)$$

represents a circle through the points of intersection of the circles

$$x^2 + y^2 + a_1x + b_1y + c_1 = 0 \quad \text{and} \quad x^2 + y^2 + a_2x + b_2y + c_2 = 0$$

for every value of k except for $k = -1$. Equation (5) represents a circle because it can be put in the form of equation (3)

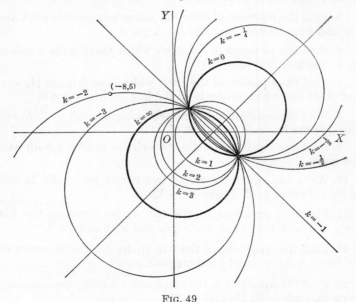

Fig. 49

(Sec. 49). It will pass through the points of intersection of the two circles for every k, since the coördinates of the points of intersection make each expression in parentheses equal to zero. Equation (5) contains the parameter k. By the proper choice of k we can make the circle (5) satisfy one more suitable condition. Equation (5) already satisfies two conditions, since the circle represented by (5) passes through the two points of intersection of two circles.

In case $k = -1$, equation (5) reduces to

$$(a_1 - a_2)x + (b_1 - b_2)y + c_1 - c_2 = 0.$$

This is the equation of the line through the points of intersection of the two circles. This line is called the **radical axis**. The common chord is a segment of this line. If the circles do not intersect, the line does not intersect either circle.

EXAMPLE 1. Write the equation of the circle through the points of intersection of the circles $x^2 + y^2 - 16x - 6y + 37 = 0$ and $x^2 + y^2 - 2x + 8y - 33 = 0$ and through $(-8, 5)$.

The equation of the family of circles through the points of intersection of the two circles is

$$x^2 + y^2 - 16x - 6y + 37 + k(x^2 + y^2 - 2x + 8y - 33) = 0,$$
$$k \neq -1. \quad (6)$$

We now determine k so that a member of the family shall go through $(-8, 5)$. Substituting $x = -8$, $y = 5$ in (6), we find $k = -2$. Using this value of k in (6) and reducing, we get

$$x^2 + y^2 + 12x + 22y - 103 = 0,$$

the equation of the required circle (Fig. 49, $k = -2$).

EXAMPLE 2. Find the equation of the radical axis of the given circles in Example 1.

Letting $k = -1$ in (6) and reducing, we get

$$x + y - 5 = 0,$$

the equation of the radical axis (Fig. 49, $k = -1$).

Other members of the family of curves (6) are drawn in Fig. 49 for $k = -3, -\frac{1}{2}, -\frac{1}{3}, -\frac{1}{4}, 1, 2,$ and 3. The given circles are designated by $k = 0$ and $k = \infty$. Explain.

52. Distance from a point to a circle along a tangent. From a point $P(x', y')$ outside the circle (Fig. 50)

$$(x - h)^2 + (y - k)^2 - r^2 = 0 \qquad (7)$$

draw the tangent PT and the line PC. The triangle CTP has

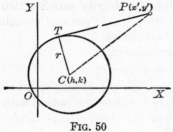

FIG. 50

a right angle at T. Hence

$$\overline{PT}^2 = \overline{PC}^2 - \overline{CT}^2$$
$$= (x' - h)^2 + (y' - k)^2 - r^2.$$

We observe that the expression for $\overline{PT}^2$ can be obtained by substituting x' and y' for x and y, respectively, in the left member of equation (7). There-fore, if the coördinates of a

point outside the circle are substituted in the left member of the equation of the circle in the form (7), that expression is no longer zero, but is the square of the distance from the point to the circle measured along the tangent. The equation
$$x^2 + y^2 + ax + by + c = 0,$$

being a rearrangement of

$$(x - h)^2 + (y - k)^2 - r^2 = 0,$$

may be used instead of the latter form to find this distance.

Assume that (x', y') is a point from which the distances to the two circles

$$x^2 + y^2 + a_1x + b_1y + c_1 = 0,$$
$$x^2 + y^2 + a_2x + b_2y + c_2 = 0$$

measured along the tangents are equal. Then

$$x'^2 + y'^2 + a_1x' + b_1y' + c_1 = x'^2 + y'^2 + a_2x' + b_2y' + c_2,$$

or $\qquad (a_1 - a_2)x' + (b_1 - b_2)y' + c_1 - c_2 = 0.$

But this is the condition that the point (x', y') lies on the radical axis. Hence *the radical axis of two circles is the locus of all points from which tangents of equal length may be drawn to the two circles.*

EXERCISES

Write the equation of the circle through the points of intersection of the following circles:

1. $x^2 + y^2 + 2x - 6y = 15$ and $x^2 + y^2 - 12x - 10y + 45 = 0$ and through the origin.

2. $x^2 + y^2 + 4x - 4y = 17$ and $2x^2 + 2y^2 - 5x + y = 3$ and through $(5, 1)$.

3. $x^2 + y^2 - 8x - 4y = 16$ and $x^2 + y^2 + 2x + 6y - 16 = 0$ and through the center of the first circle.

4. $x^2 + y^2 - x - 5y + 1 = 0$ and $x^2 + y^2 + 7x - y - 3 = 0$ and with its center on (a) the x-axis; (b) the line $x - y = 0$.

5. Write the equations of the radical axes of the given pairs of circles in Exercises 1, 2, 3, and 4.

6. Find the distance from $(5, 10)$ measured along the tangent line to the circle $x^2 + y^2 - 6x + 2y - 15 = 0$.

7. Find the distance measured along the tangent line from $(4, 2)$ to the circle $2x^2 + 2y^2 - x + 3y - 10 = 0$.

8. Show in two different ways that the point $(3, 7)$ is on the radical axis of the two circles $x^2 + y^2 - 3x + 5y - 34 = 0$ and $x^2 + y^2 - 19x - 3y + 70 = 0$.

9. A circle of radius 4 has its center at the origin. The center of a circle of radius 2 moves along the x-axis. Discuss the position of the radical axis of the two circles when the center of the second circle is at (a) $(8, 0)$; (b) $(6, 0)$; (c) $(4, 0)$; (d) $(2, 0)$; (e) $(1, 0)$; (f) $(0, 0)$.

10. Show that the radical axis of $x^2 + y^2 + a_1x + b_1y + c_1 = 0$ and $x^2 + y^2 + a_2x + b_2y + c_2 = 0$ is perpendicular to the line of centers of the two circles.

11. Show that the radical axes of any three circles, the circles being taken in pairs, intersect in a common point (radical center) or are parallel.

12. Find the radical center of the circles $x^2 + y^2 + 6x - 8y = 0$, $x^2 + y^2 - 14x + 40 = 0$, and $x^2 + y^2 - 6x + 16y + 72 = 0$.

MISCELLANEOUS EXERCISES

1. Draw the locus of each of the following equations:
(a) $y = \sqrt{2\,rx - x^2}$; (b) $x = -\sqrt{2\,ry - y^2}$, $r > 0$ in both cases.

2. Find the equation of the circle circumscribing the equilateral triangle whose vertices are $(-a, 0)$, $(a, 0)$, and $(0, a\sqrt{3})$.

3. Find the point on the circle $x^2 + y^2 + 4\,x - 2\,y - 40 = 0$ nearest $(3, 11)$.

4. Find the length of the common chord of the two circles $x^2 + y^2 - 2\,x - 10\,y - 39 = 0$ and $x^2 + y^2 - 10\,x + 6\,y + 9 = 0$.

5. A circle with center $(4, -6)$ cuts a chord of length 6 units from the line $x - 3\,y = 2$. Find the equation of the circle.

6. Find the points on the line $x + 2\,y - 9 = 0$ each at a distance of 5 units from $(2, 1)$.

7. Find the equations of the two circles touching the line $x + 3\,y = 7$ at $(4, 1)$ and having radii $\sqrt{10}$.

8. Two adjacent vertices of a square inscribed in a circle are $(2, 3)$ and $(6, 1)$. Find the equation of the circle. (Two solutions.)

9. Write the equations of the two circles with centers at the origin which touch the circle $x^2 + y^2 - 2\,x - 2\,y - 30 = 0$.

10. Show that the circle $x^2 + y^2 + 6\,x + 12\,y - 45 = 0$ is tangent to the circle $x^2 + y^2 - 18\,x + 4\,y + 75 = 0$ and find the point of contact.

11. Find the point of intersection of the two lines tangent to the circle $x^2 + y^2 - 2\,x + 12\,y - 48 = 0$ at the points $(-1, 3)$ and $(7, 1)$ on the circle.

12. Two tangents to the circle $x^2 + y^2 + 4\,y = 16$ intersect at $(2, 4)$. Find the points where they touch the circle.

13. Show that the equation of the line tangent to the circle $x^2 + y^2 = r^2$ at the point (x_1, y_1) on the circle is $x_1x + y_1y = r^2$.

14. Show that the equations of the two tangents to the circle $x^2 + y^2 = r^2$ with slope m are $y = mx \pm r\sqrt{1 + m^2}$.

15. Write the equations of the two lines with slope 3 which are tangent to the circle $x^2 + y^2 = 40$.

16. Find the equations of the tangents to the circle $x^2 + y^2 = 10$ which intersect at $(5, 5)$.

17. The line $y = mx$ is tangent to a circle with center $(h, 1)$ and radius 1. Find m.

18. Prove analytically that an angle inscribed in a semicircle is a right angle.

19. Prove analytically that all angles inscribed in the same segment of a circle are equal.

20. Show that the perpendicular dropped from any point of a circle upon a diameter is a mean proportional between the segments into which it divides the diameter.

21. A point moves so that the square of its distance from a given point equals its distance from a given line. Show that its locus is a circle.

22. Show that the locus of a point whose distances from two fixed points are in a constant ratio k ($k \neq 1$) is a circle.

23. Show that the locus of a point, the sum of the squares of whose distances from n fixed points is a constant, is a circle. (The locus may be a point circle or imaginary. See Exercise 24.)

24. Find the locus of a point, the sum of the squares of whose distances from $(0, 0)$, $(6, 0)$, and $(0, 3)$ is (a) 45; (b) 30; (c) 15.

25. A point moves so that the sum of the squares of its distances from two vertices of an equilateral triangle equals the square of its distance from the third vertex. Show that the locus is a circle and determine its position relative to the triangle.

26. Find the equation of the locus of a point if lines drawn from it to two fixed points include an angle of 45°.

27. A rod 10 inches long has its ends moving on two perpendicular lines. Find the locus of its midpoint.

28. Show that $(10, 10)$, $(1, 13)$, $(-14, -2)$, and $(13, -11)$ are concyclic. Show that the feet of the perpendiculars drawn from any one of these points to the sides (extended) of the triangle whose vertices are the other three points are collinear.

CHAPTER V

OTHER SECOND DEGREE CURVES

THE PARABOLA

53. Definition and equation of a parabola. *A parabola is the locus of points which are equidistant from a fixed point and a fixed straight line.* The fixed point is called the **focus** and the fixed line is called the **directrix** of the parabola.

In Fig. 51 (*a* and *b*) let *AB* be the directrix, and let *F* be the focus. Draw a line through *F* perpendicular to *AB* and

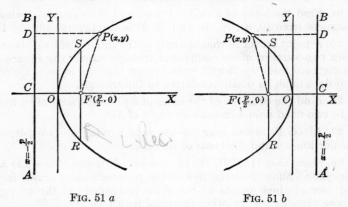

FIG. 51 *a*   FIG. 51 *b*

intersecting it in *C*. By definition, the midpoint *O* of *CF* is a point on the parabola. Choosing *O* as origin and the line through *C* and *F* as the *x*-axis, we denote the coördinates of *F* by (*p*/2, 0), where *p* is the distance from the directrix to the focus and is a positive number in Fig. 51 *a* and a negative number in Fig. 51 *b*. The equation of the directrix in each

90

case is $x = -p/2$. Let $P(x, y)$ be any point on the parabola and draw FP and DP. By definition,

$$FP = DP \text{ in Fig. 51 } a$$

and $$FP = PD = -DP \text{ in Fig. 51 } b.$$

But $FP = \sqrt{\left(x - \frac{p}{2}\right)^2 + y^2}$, and $DP = x + \frac{p}{2}$;

hence $\sqrt{\left(x - \frac{p}{2}\right)^2 + y^2} = x + \frac{p}{2}$ in Fig. 51 a

and $\sqrt{\left(x - \frac{p}{2}\right)^2 + y^2} = -\left(x + \frac{p}{2}\right)$ in Fig. 51 b. $\qquad(1)$

Either form of equation (1) reduces to

$$x^2 - px + \frac{p^2}{4} + y^2 = x^2 + px + \frac{p^2}{4}. \qquad(2)$$

Simplifying, we have

$$y^2 = 2\,px. \qquad(3)$$

The simplicity of this equation is due to the particular way in which the axes have been chosen.

Conversely, the equation $y^2 = 2\,px$ represents a parabola.

Adding $x^2 - px + p^2/4$ to each member of equation (3), we have equation (2). Extracting the square root of each member of equation (2), we obtain the two equations (1). But equations (1) are satisfied by the coördinates of points which are equidistant from a point and a line, and by the coördinates of no other points. Hence equation (3) represents a parabola.

In case the focus of a parabola is the point $(0, p/2)$ and the directrix is the line $y = -p/2$, the equation of the parabola is $\qquad x^2 = 2\,py, \qquad(4)$

where p is positive if the focus is above the directrix and is negative if the focus is below the directrix.

It will be observed that p is the distance from directrix to focus.

54. Discussion of the equation. Solving equation (3) for y, we have

$$y = \pm \sqrt{2\,px}.$$

If p is positive (as shown in Fig. 51 a), x must be positive in order that y may be real. Hence the curve lies to the right of the y-axis. If p is negative, x must be negative, and the curve lies to the left of the y-axis (Fig. 51 b). To each value of x correspond two values of y, numerically equal but opposite in sign; hence the curve is symmetric with respect to the x-axis. As x increases numerically, y increases numerically and the curve extends indefinitely away from both axes. The line of symmetry is called the **axis** of the parabola, and the point of intersection of the parabola and its axis is called the **vertex** of the parabola. The chord RS through the focus perpendicular to the axis is called the **latus rectum.** Its length is $2\,p$. Why?

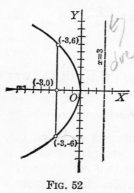

FIG. 52

EXAMPLE. Discuss and graph the parabola $y^2 = -12\,x$. (Fig. 52)

There is symmetry with respect to the x-axis. The parabola lies to the left of the y-axis since x must be negative to give real values for y. The vertex of the parabola is at the origin. The distance from the directrix to the focus is $p = -6$; hence the focus is at $(-3, 0)$ and the equation of the directrix is $x = 3$. The length of the latus rectum is 12.

EXERCISES

1. Find the coördinates of the focus, the length of the latus rectum, and the equation of the directrix of each of the following parabolas and sketch:

(a) $y^2 = 4\,x$; (b) $y^2 = -6\,x$; (c) $x^2 = 16\,y$; (d) $x^2 = -2\,y$.

2. Find the equations of the two parabolas through each of the following points, one with axis along the x-axis and the other with axis along the y-axis, the vertex of each parabola being at the origin: (a) $(3, 1)$; (b) $(5, -3)$; (c) $(-10, 4)$; (d) $(-\frac{1}{2}, -\frac{2}{3})$.

3. Draw on the same set of axes the parabolas $y^2 = 2\,px$ for $p = \frac{1}{2}$, 1, 2, 3, 4. What effect does the changing of the value of p have upon the shape of the parabola?

4. Show that for any parabola the two lines from the vertex to the ends of the latus rectum include a constant angle.

5. Derive the equation of a parabola with focus at $(p, 0)$ and with the y-axis as directrix.

6. By a suitable translation of axes transform the equation derived in Exercise 5 to the form of (3), Sec. 53.

7. Show that the locus of the centers of the circles which are tangent to a given line and pass through a fixed point is a parabola.

8. Find the equation of the circle which has for a diameter the latus rectum of the parabola $y^2 = 2\,px$. Show that the circle touches the directrix.

9. Find the equation of the circle through the vertex and the ends of the latus rectum of the parabola $y^2 = 8\,x$.

10. An isosceles right triangle is inscribed in the parabola $y^2 = 2\,px$ so that the vertex of the right angle is at the origin. Find the length of the hypotenuse.

11. Find the points of intersection of the parabolas $y^2 = 9\,x$ and $3\,x^2 = 8\,y$ and illustrate graphically.

12. The vertex of a parabola with axis on the x-axis is at the origin. Find the length of that chord through the focus which has one end at $(1, 4)$.

13. Using the definition, write the equations of the following parabolas:

    (a) Focus at $(0, 0)$, directrix $x = 4$.

    (b) Focus at $(0, 0)$, directrix $x = -4$.

    (c) Focus at $(1, 3)$, directrix $y = -1$.

14. Find the length of the chord cut from the x-axis by the parabola whose focus is $(2, 1)$ and whose directrix is $y = 3$.

15. The common focus of two parabolas with their axes on the x-axis is $(3, 0)$. Each parabola goes through $(6, 4)$. Find their equations.

16. An arch in the form of an arc of a parabola with its vertex at the center of the arch is 18 ft. across at the base, and its highest point is 8 ft. above the base. What is the length of a beam parallel to the base and 6 ft. above it?

17. The diameter of the circular front of a parabolic reflector is 12 in. and its depth is 4 in. How far from the vertex is the focus?

18. The cable of a suspension bridge hangs in the shape of an arc of a parabola. The supporting towers are 40 ft. high and 300 ft. apart and the lowest point on the cable is 8 ft. above the roadway. Find the length of a supporting rod 75 ft. from the center of the bridge.

19. A variable y varies as the square of a variable x. Write the relationship between x and y in the form of an equation. If $y = 2$ when $x = 4$, find y when $x = 6$. Illustrate graphically.

20. Given the two parabolas (a) $y^2 = k_1 x$ and (b) $y^2 = k_2 x$. A line with slope m is drawn through their common vertex O intersecting (a) and (b) again in P_1 and P_2 respectively. Show that the ratio $\dfrac{OP_1}{OP_2} = \dfrac{k_1}{k_2}$.

55. Vertex not at the origin. It is frequently necessary or convenient to study the parabola when the vertex is not at the origin. We shall obtain the equation when the vertex of the parabola is at (h, k) and the axis of the curve is a line parallel to the x-axis.

Draw through the point (h, k) lines parallel to the x- and y-axes. If these lines are used as x'- and y'- axes, the vertex

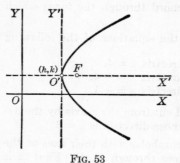

FIG. 53

of the parabola will be at the origin and its equation will be

$$y'^2 = 2\,px'.$$

But $x = x' + h$ and $y = y' + k$, or $x' = x - h$ and $y' = y - k$. Making these substitutions, we obtain

$$(y - k)^2 = 2\,p(x - h). \quad (5)$$

This is, therefore, the equation of a parabola with vertex at (h, k) and with axis parallel to the x-axis. Similarly, for a parabola with vertex at (h, k) and with axis parallel to the y-axis, the equation is

$$(x - h)^2 = 2\,p(y - k). \quad (6)$$

It will be noted that equations (5) and (6) become equations (3) and (4), respectively, for $h = k = 0$.

The translation of axes leaves unchanged the position of the focus and directrix with respect to the parabola.

Any equation of the form (5) or (6) can be put in the form of (3) or (4), respectively, by a translation of axes, and hence such an equation represents a parabola.

56. Theorem. *In general,* the equations*

$$Ay^2 + Bx + Cy + D = 0 \tag{7}$$

and $$A'x^2 + B'x + C'y + D' = 0 \tag{8}$$

represent parabolas.

By completing squares and rearranging terms, the equations (7) and (8) can be put in the form of (5) and (6), respectively, and hence represent parabolas.

EXAMPLE. Discuss and graph $y^2 - 6x - 8y - 2 = 0$. Transposing and completing the square, we may write

$$y^2 - 8y + 16 = 6x + 18,$$

or $$(y - 4)^2 = 6(x + 3).$$

The parabola represented by this equation has its vertex at $(-3, 4)$ and has for axis the line $y = 4$. The distance from directrix to focus is given by $2p = 6$, or $p = 3$. Since p is positive, the parabola opens toward the right. The focus is $\frac{3}{2}$ units to the right of the vertex and hence is $(-\frac{3}{2}, 4)$. The directrix is $x = -\frac{9}{2}$. The graph is shown in Fig. 54.

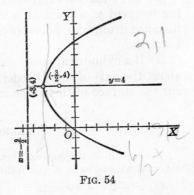

FIG. 54

*Exceptions occur if the constants are such that the equations reduce to the first degree, or if the left members factor into first-degree factors (see Sec. 39).

57. Scientific applications of the parabola. In the following illustrations either an arc of a parabola is used or the variable quantities are related in the same manner as the coördinates of a point on a parabola. The list is meant to be suggestive of the many applications of the parabola.

(a) The cable of a suspension bridge hangs in the form of an arc of a parabola.

(b) Some of the largest steel bridges are built with arches which are arcs of parabolas.

(c) A reflecting surface made by rotating a parabola about its axis will send the light out in parallel rays if the source of light is at the focus.

(d) The large reflector in a reflecting telescope is usually parabolic.

(e) The path of a projectile, if air resistance is neglected, is a parabola.

(f) The equation expressing the relation between the distance a freely falling body traverses and the time required is the equation of a parabola.

(g) The equation expressing the relation between the period and the length of a simple pendulum is the equation of a parabola.

(h) The equation expressing the relation between the bending moment at a point on a uniformly loaded beam and the distance from the point of support is the equation of a parabola.

(i) If a cylindrical vessel partly filled with water is whirled about the axis of the cylinder, a plane through the axis will cut the surface of the water in a parabola.

EXERCISES

1. Determine the vertex, focus, length of latus rectum, directrix, and axis of each of the following parabolas and sketch:

(a) $y^2 - 2y - 8x + 25 = 0$.

(b) $y^2 + 6y + 6x = 0$.

(c) $x^2 - 4x - 2y - 8 = 0$.

(d) $2x^2 - 10x + 5y = 0$.

(e) $3y^2 = 8x - 16$.

(f) $5x^2 + 4y = 12$.

2. Write the equations of the following parabolas and sketch:

    (a) Directrix $x + 2 = 0$, vertex at $(1, 3)$.
    (b) Directrix $y = 3$, vertex at $(-2, 2)$.
    (c) Directrix $y = 0$, focus at $(3, 1)$.
    (d) Directrix $x = 5$, focus at $(-1, 0)$.
    (e) Vertex at $(-\frac{5}{2}, 1)$, focus at $(0, 1)$.

3. Write the equations of the two lines through the vertex and the ends of the latus rectum of the parabola $y^2 - 4y - 6x - 2 = 0$.

4. Find the equation of the parabola with vertex at $(2, 1)$ and passing through $(5, -2)$ with axis (a) parallel to the x-axis; (b) parallel to the y-axis.

5. Write each of equations (7) and (8), Sec. 56, in a form involving three essential constants.

6. Given the equation $y = ax^2 + bx + c$,

    (a) show that it represents a parabola with axis parallel to the y-axis;

    (b) show that the parabola is concave upward if $a > 0$; downward if $a < 0$;

    (c) find the x-intercepts. Under what condition are they real and distinct? real and equal? imaginary?

    (d) show that the axis of the parabola is the line $x = -b/2a$;

    (e) show that the vertex of the parabola is $\left(-\dfrac{b}{2a}, \dfrac{4ac - b^2}{4a}\right)$;

    (f) show that the distance from the vertex to the focus is $\dfrac{1}{4a}$;

    (g) discuss the position of the parabola if $c = 0$; $b = 0$; $b = c = 0$.

7. Find the x- and y-intercepts, the axis, and the vertex of each of the following parabolas and sketch:

    (a) $y = x^2 - 6x + 5$.   (d) $y = 2x^2 - 2x + 1$.
    (b) $y = 3 + 2x - x^2$.   (e) $x = 4y^2 - 16y + 7$.
    (c) $y = 4x^2 - 12x + 9$.   (f) $2x = 5y - y^2$.

8. Determine a, b, and c so that the parabola $y = ax^2 + bx + c$ shall go through $(-2, 7)$, $(1, -8)$, and $(4, -5)$. Find the lowest point on the parabola.

9. Determine a, b, and c so that the parabola $x = ay^2 + by + c$ shall go through $(3, 2)$, $(-2, 1)$, and $(0, -1)$.

10. Find the equation of the parabola through $(1, -2)$, $(2, 1)$, and $(-1, 4)$ with axis parallel to the (a) y-axis; (b) x-axis.

11. Find the points of intersection of the loci in (a) and (b) and illustrate graphically:

(a) $y = 3x - x^2$, (b) $y^2 - 4y - 2x = 0$,
      $2x - y = 2$. $6y = x^2 - 4x + 24$.

12. Find the length of the common chord of the parabolas $y^2 = 2x + 12$ and $y^2 + 2y = 4x$. Draw the figure.

13. A parabola with axis parallel to the x-axis passes through $(3, 3)$, $(6, -3)$, and $(11, 7)$. Find its focus and directrix without finding its equation.

14. Find the equation of the parabola which has for its focus and directrix the origin and the line $x - y + 2 = 0$, respectively. How does the equation differ essentially from equations (7) and (8), Sec. 56?

THE ELLIPSE

58. **Definition and equation of an ellipse.** *An ellipse is the locus of points the sum of whose numerical distances from two fixed*

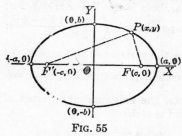

FIG. 55

points is constant. The two fixed points are the **foci** of the ellipse. Let the distance between the fixed points be $2c$, and let the constant sum be $2a$, $(a > c)$. If we choose the line through the foci as the x-axis and the point midway between the foci as origin, the coördinates of the foci are $(c, 0)$ and $(-c, 0)$. By definition

$$F'P + FP = 2a,$$

or $$\sqrt{(x+c)^2 + y^2} + \sqrt{(x-c)^2 + y^2} = 2a.$$

Transposing the second radical, squaring, and reducing, we have

$$cx - a^2 = -a\sqrt{(x-c)^2 + y^2}.$$

Squaring again and reducing, we may write

$$x^2(a^2 - c^2) + a^2 y^2 = a^2(a^2 - c^2).$$

Since $a > c$, let $b^2 = a^2 - c^2$. Making this substitution and dividing by $a^2 b^2$, we obtain

$$\frac{x^2}{a^2} + \frac{y^2}{b^2} = 1. \tag{9}$$

If the foci are the points $(0, c)$ and $(0, -c)$, the equation of the ellipse is

$$\frac{x^2}{b^2} + \frac{y^2}{a^2} = 1. \tag{10}$$

Conversely, any equation of the form (9) *or* (10) *represents an ellipse.* The proof will not be set down here. It consists in showing that the steps used in obtaining equations (9) and (10) can be reversed, as was done in the case of the parabola.

59. Discussion of the equation. Equation (9) shows that the locus is symmetric with respect to both axes and hence is symmetric with respect to the origin. Solving for y, we have

$$y = \pm \frac{b}{a} \sqrt{a^2 - x^2};$$

whence it appears that real values of y exist only when $x^2 \leqq a^2$. Hence the curve lies between the lines $x = a$ and $x = -a$. The largest numerical value is attained by y when $x = 0$; hence the curve lies between the lines $y = b$ and $y = -b$. The x-intercepts are $\pm a$ and the y-intercepts are $\pm b$. The segment of the line of symmetry through the foci, from $(-a, 0)$ to $(a, 0)$, of length $2a$, is called the **major axis** of the ellipse. The segment of the line of symmetry at right angles to the major axis, from $(0, -b)$ to $(0, b)$, of length $2b$, is called the **minor axis**. The lengths a and b are the **semimajor** and **semiminor** axes, respectively. The point of intersection of the major and minor axes is the **center** since the ellipse is symmetric with respect to this point. The ends of the major axis are the **vertices** of the ellipse.

A similar discussion of equation (10) will show that it represents the same curve with major axis along the y-axis.

EXAMPLE. Graph the ellipse $4x^2 + y^2 = 16$ and find its semiaxes and foci.

Dividing by 16, we obtain

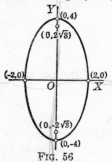

FIG. 56

$$\frac{x^2}{4} + \frac{y^2}{16} = 1.$$

The equation shows that the major axis lies along the y-axis. The semimajor axis is $a = 4$ and the semiminor axis is $b = 2$. The vertices of the ellipse are at $(0, \pm 4)$ and the ends of the minor axis are at $(\pm 2, 0)$. From $b^2 = a^2 - c^2$, we have $c = 2\sqrt{3}$. Hence the foci are at $(0, \pm 2\sqrt{3})$.

What information about the axes of the ellipse could be obtained directly by finding its x- and y-intercepts?

60. Eccentricity. Location of foci. The ratio c/a, denoted by e, is called the **eccentricity** of the ellipse. Since $c^2 = a^2 - b^2$, we may write

$$e = \frac{\sqrt{a^2 - b^2}}{a}.$$

This shows that as b approaches a, the eccentricity e approaches zero. But for $b = a$, the locus is a circle. Hence the circle is sometimes called an ellipse of eccentricity zero.

From the equation connecting a, b, and c, it is seen that a is the hypotenuse of a right triangle with legs b and c. Hence the distance from the end of the minor axis to a focus is a. The foci may, therefore, be located by drawing an arc with an end of the minor axis as center and a radius equal to a. The points in which the arc cuts the major axis are the foci.

EXERCISES

1. Find the semiaxes, vertices, foci, and eccentricity of the following ellipses and sketch:

(a) $9x^2 + 25y^2 = 225$.

(b) $9x^2 + 4y^2 = 144$.

(c) $x^2 + 4y^2 = 100$.

(d) $2x^2 + y^2 = 50$.

(e) $x^2 + 3y^2 = 3$.

(f) $5x^2 + y^2 = 80$.

(g) $24x^2 + 25y^2 = 600$.

(h) $x^2 + 50y^2 = 200$.

2. Derive the equation of the locus of points the sum of whose distances from $(0, \pm 5)$ is 20.

3. Write the equations of the following ellipses and sketch:

    (a) Major axis 8, foci at $(\pm 2, 0)$.
    (b) Minor axis 10, foci at $(0, \pm 3)$.
    (c) Major axis 18, foci at $(0, \pm 3\sqrt{6})$.
    (d) Minor axis $2\sqrt{3}$, foci at $(\pm \sqrt{3}, 0)$.

4. A latus rectum of an ellipse is the chord through either focus perpendicular to the major axis. Show that the length of a latus rectum of the ellipse $x^2/a^2 + y^2/b^2 = 1$, $(a > b)$, is $2 b^2/a$

5. Write the equation of the parabola with vertex at the origin which passes through the ends of the latus rectum through the right focus of the ellipse $x^2 + 5 y^2 = 20$.

6. Find the equation of the ellipse with center at the origin and axes on the coördinate axes which passes through (a) $(1, 3)$ and $(4, 2)$; (b) $(2, 6)$ and $(3, 4)$.

7. Write the equation of the ellipse whose foci are $(\pm 4, 0)$ and which goes through $(3, 2\frac{2}{5})$.

8. Find the locus of the midpoints of the ordinates of the circle $x^2 + y^2 = 36$.

9. The ends of a rod 12 in. long move along two perpendicular lines. Find the loci of its points of trisection.

10. A semielliptic arch is 50 ft. long across the base and 15 ft. high with the major axis horizontal. Find the distance from the level of the top to the point on the arch (a) 15 ft. from the minor axis; (b) 20 ft. from the minor axis.

11. The semiaxes of an ellipse are 3 ft. 4 in. and 2 ft., respectively. Find the lengths of those diameters of the ellipse which make angles of 30° and 60°, respectively, with the major axis.

12. Find the points of intersection of the loci in each of the following pairs and illustrate graphically:

    (a) $4 x^2 + y^2 = 20$,
        $6 x + y = 10$.

    (b) $x^2 + 4 y^2 = 16$,
        $x^2 + y^2 = 4 x$.

    (c) $3 x^2 + y^2 = 52$,
        $y^2 - 3 x = 16$.

    (d) $x^2 + 2 y^2 = 54$,
        $5 x^2 + y^2 = 45$.

13. Find the equation of the locus in each of the following and show that the two loci are identical ellipses.

(a) The locus of a point whose distance from (1, 0) is one half its distance from the line $x - 4 = 0$.

(b) The locus of a point whose distance from (− 1, 0) is one half its distance from the line $x + 4 = 0$.

61. Center not at the origin. Let the center of the ellipse

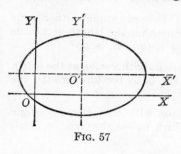

FIG. 57

be at the point (h, k), and let the major axis be parallel to the x-axis. Draw through (h, k) lines parallel to the x- and y-axes and call these lines the x'- and y'-axes. The equation of the ellipse referred to these axes is, by (9) (Sec. 58),

$$\frac{x'^2}{a^2} + \frac{y'^2}{b^2} = 1.$$

But $x = x' + h$ and $y = y' + k$, or $x' = x - h$ and $y' = y - k$; and this gives

$$\frac{(x - h)^2}{a^2} + \frac{(y - k)^2}{b^2} = 1, \qquad (11)$$

if the curve is referred to the x- and y-axes. If the major axis is parallel to the y-axis, the corresponding equation is

$$\frac{(x - h)^2}{b^2} + \frac{(y - k)^2}{a^2} = 1. \qquad (12)$$

Since a translation of axes will change equations (11) and (12) into equations (9) and (10), respectively, any equation of the form of equation (11) or (12) represents an ellipse.

62. Theorem. *The equation*

$$Ax^2 + By^2 + Cx + Dy + E = 0 \qquad (13)$$

represents an ellipse if A and B are of the same sign.

If A and B are of the same sign, the equation may be written so that both are positive. Completing squares, we may write

$$A\left(x^2 + \frac{C}{A}x + \frac{C^2}{4A^2}\right) + B\left(y^2 + \frac{D}{B}y + \frac{D^2}{4B^2}\right) = \frac{C^2}{4A} + \frac{D^2}{4B} - E.$$

not adding same to both sides

By dividing by the expression in the right member of the equation, we may write the equation in the form of equation (11) or (12) (Sec. 61). Equation (13), therefore, represents an ellipse.

If the quantity $C^2/4A + D^2/4B - E = 0$, the locus is a point ellipse.

If the quantity $C^2/4A + D^2/4B - E < 0$, there is no real locus.

EXAMPLE. Find the center, semiaxes, foci, and eccentricity of the ellipse $16x^2 + 25y^2 - 64x + 50y - 311 = 0$.

Completing squares, we may write

$$16(x^2 - 4x + 4) + 25(y^2 + 2y + 1) = 400.$$

Dividing by 400 and rearranging, we obtain

$$\frac{(x-2)^2}{25} + \frac{(y+1)^2}{16} = 1.$$

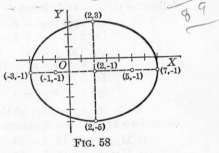

FIG. 58

This equation shows that the center of the ellipse is at $(2, -1)$, that the major axis lies along the line $y = -1$, that the semimajor axis is $a = 5$, and that the semiminor axis is $b = 4$. From $c^2 = a^2 - b^2$ we have $c = 3$. The foci are, therefore, at the points $(-1, -1)$ and $(5, -1)$. The eccentricity is $e = c/a = 3/5$.

63. Scientific applications of the ellipse. The following list is suggestive of the many applications of the ellipse:

(a) The planets move in elliptic orbits about the sun with the sun at a focus.

(b) The arches of stone and concrete bridges are frequently semi-ellipses.

(c) Elliptic gears are used in machines to obtain a slow, powerful movement with a quick return, as in power punches.

(d) Whispering galleries usually have elliptical ceilings arranged so that one may stand at a focus. Thus situated he can hear a slight noise made at the other focus, while an individual standing between the foci hears nothing.

(e) Because of its graceful beauty the elliptic arch is frequently used in architecture.

(f) The locus of the end of the radius vector which represents the magnetic field in a single-phase induction motor is an ellipse, assuming that the motor is operating at less than synchronous speed. This is the normal condition.

(g) In a certain type of map projection, designed to preserve relative areas, the meridians become arcs of ellipses.

EXERCISES

1. Find the center, semiaxes, vertices, and foci of each of the following ellipses and sketch:

(a) $x^2 + 4y^2 - 6x - 16y - 11 = 0$.

(b) $2x^2 + y^2 + 8x - 8y - 48 = 0$.

(c) $9x^2 + 25y^2 + 18x + 150y + 9 = 0$.

(d) $4x^2 + 9y^2 - 48x + 72y + 144 = 0$.

(e) $5x^2 + 3y^2 - 30x - 30y = 0$.

(f) $x^2 + 9y^2 - 8x + 7 = 0$.

2. Write the equations of the ellipses for which the following conditions are given and sketch:

(a) Major axis 10, foci at $(0, 2)$ and $(8, 2)$.

(b) Major axis 12, foci at $(-1, 1)$ and $(-1, 5)$.

(c) Minor axis 6, foci at $(1, -1)$ and $(7, -1)$.

(d) Minor axis 8, foci at $(4, 3 - 2\sqrt{6})$ and $(4, 3 + 2\sqrt{6})$.

3. Write the equations of the two circles one of which has a diameter coincident with the major axis and the other a diameter coincident with the minor axis of the ellipse $9x^2 + 5y^2 - 30y = 0$.

4. Write the equation of the parabola with vertex at the origin which passes through the ends of the minor axis of the ellipse $4x^2 + 25y^2 - 40x = 0$.

5. Find the points of intersection of the loci in (a) and (b) and illustrate graphically:

(a) $x - 3y + 8 = 0$,
$x^2 + 9y^2 - 4x - 18y - 72 = 0$.

(b) $4x^2 + y^2 = 4$,
$4x^2 + 9y^2 - 16x = 20$.

6. Write equation (13), Sec. 62, in a form involving four essential constants.

7. Write the equation of the ellipse which passes through $(-6, 4)$, $(-8, 1)$, $(2, -4)$, and $(8, -3)$ and which has axes parallel to the coördinate axes.

8. Show that the following equations represent point ellipses or no real loci:

(a) $x^2 + 2 y^2 = 0$.   (b) $x^2 + 4 y^2 - 2 x - 16 y + 17 = 0$.
(c) $3 x^2 + y^2 + 12 x - 2 y + 16 = 0$.

9. Find the equation of the ellipse whose foci are $(0, 0)$ and $(1, 1)$ and whose major axis is 2 units. How does the equation differ essentially from equation (13), Sec. 62?

THE HYPERBOLA

64. **Definition and equation of a hyperbola.** *A hyperbola is the locus of points the difference of whose numerical distances from two fixed points is a constant.* The two fixed points are called the **foci** of the hyperbola.

Let the distance between the foci be $2 c$, and let the constant difference be $2 a$, $(a < c)$. Choose the line through the foci as the x-axis and the point midway between the foci as origin. The coördinates of the foci are $(c, 0)$ and $(-c, 0)$. By definition, we have (Fig. 59)

$$F'P - FP = \pm 2 a,$$

where the positive sign is used for a point P on the right of the y-axis and the negative sign is used for a point P on the left of the y-axis. But

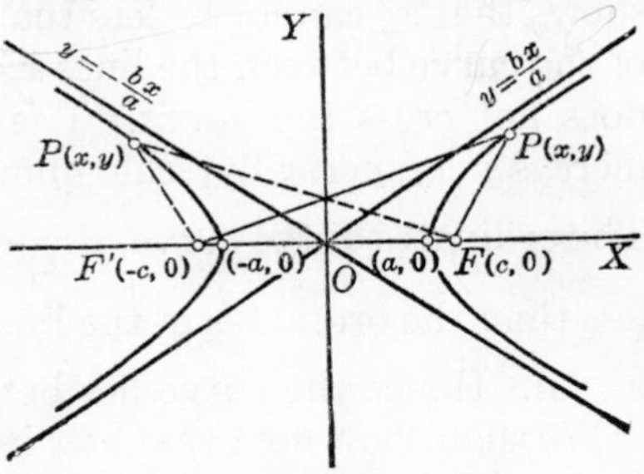

FIG. 59

$$F'P = \sqrt{(x + c)^2 + y^2} \quad \text{and} \quad FP = \sqrt{(x - c)^2 + y^2};$$

hence $\quad \sqrt{(x + c)^2 + y^2} - \sqrt{(x - c)^2 + y^2} = \pm 2 a$.

Transposing the second radical, squaring, and reducing, we have

$$cx - a^2 = \pm a \sqrt{(x - c)^2 + y^2}.$$

Squaring again and reducing, we may write

$$x^2(c^2 - a^2) - a^2 y^2 = a^2(c^2 - a^2).$$

Since $c > a$, let $b^2 = c^2 - a^2$. Making this substitution and dividing by a^2b^2, we obtain the equation of the hyperbola

$$\frac{x^2}{a^2} - \frac{y^2}{b^2} = 1. \tag{14}$$

If the foci are the points $(0, c)$ and $(0, -c)$, the equation of the hyperbola is

$$\frac{y^2}{a^2} - \frac{x^2}{b^2} = 1. \tag{15}$$

Conversely, any equation of the form (14) *or* (15) *represents a hyperbola.* The proof consists in showing that the steps taken in obtaining (14) and (15) can be reversed. The work required involves only simple algebra and will not be set down.

65. Discussion of the equation. We shall now discuss equation (14). The equation shows that the locus is symmetric with respect to both axes and hence is symmetric with respect to the origin. The value of y,

$$y = \pm \frac{b}{a} \sqrt{x^2 - a^2},$$

shows that x^2 cannot be less than a^2; that is, there is no part of the curve between the lines $x = \pm a$. The curve, therefore, does not cross the y-axis. The x-intercepts are $\pm a$. As x increases numerically, the numerical value of y increases. The ordinates of the curve, $y = \pm \frac{b}{a} \sqrt{x^2 - a^2}$, are numerically less than the ordinates of the lines $y = \pm \frac{b}{a} x$, respectively, for $x \geqq a$. Hence the curve lies between these two lines.

We shall show next that as x increases without limit the difference between the ordinates of the line and curve approaches zero as a limit, that is, that the line is the limiting position of the curve as x increases without limit. Because of symmetry it will be sufficient to show this for the first quadrant.

$$\lim_{x \to \infty} \left[\frac{b}{a} x - \frac{b}{a} \sqrt{x^2 - a^2} \right] = \lim_{x \to \infty} \frac{b}{a} \frac{[x - \sqrt{x^2 - a^2}][x + \sqrt{x^2 - a^2}]}{x + \sqrt{x^2 - a^2}}$$

$$= \lim_{x \to \infty} \frac{b}{a} \frac{a^2}{x + \sqrt{x^2 - a^2}} = 0.$$

Hence the curve approaches the line as a limiting position as x increases without limit.

The hyperbola represented by equation (14), therefore, consists of two parts or branches: one branch is to the right of $x = a$ and between the lines $y = \pm bx/a$, and the other branch is to the left of $x = -a$ and between the same lines. These lines $y = \pm bx/a$ are called the **asymptotes** of the hyperbola. The segment of the line of symmetry through the foci from $(-a, 0)$ to $(a, 0)$, of length $2a$, is called the **transverse axis** of the hyperbola. The segment of the line of symmetry at right angles to the transverse axis, from $(0, -b)$ to $(0, b)$, of length $2b$, is called the **conjugate axis**. The lengths a and b are the **semitransverse** and **semiconjugate** axes, respectively. The point of intersection of the transverse and conjugate axes is the **center**, since the hyperbola is symmetric with respect to this point. The ends of the transverse axis are the **vertices** of the hyperbola.

A similar discussion of equation (15) will show that it represents the same curve with transverse axis of length $2a$ along the y-axis and conjugate axis of length $2b$ along the x-axis. In this case the equations of the asymptotes are $y = \pm ax/b$.

EXAMPLE. Graph the hyperbola $9x^2 - 4y^2 = 36$ and find its foci, semiaxes, and asymptotes.

The equation shows symmetry with respect to both axes. Dividing by 36, we obtain

$$\frac{x^2}{4} - \frac{y^2}{9} = 1.$$

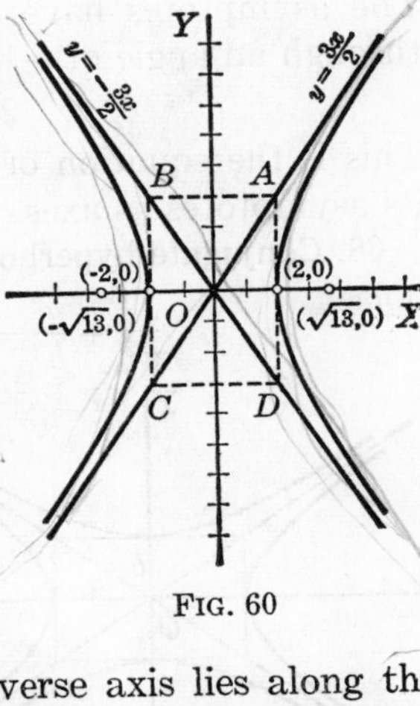

FIG. 60

The equation shows that the transverse axis lies along the x-axis. The semitransverse axis is $a = 2$ and the semiconjugate axis is $b = 3$. The vertices of the hyperbola are at $(\pm 2, 0)$. From $b^2 = c^2 - a^2$ we have $c = \sqrt{13}$. Hence the

foci are at $(\pm \sqrt{13},\ 0)$. The asymptotes are $y = \pm 3\,x/2$.
The asymptotes should be drawn first since they serve as
guiding lines in drawing the hyperbola. We note that the
asymptotes are the diagonals (extended) of the rectangle
$ABCD$, called the **auxiliary rectangle**, shown in Fig. 60.

What information about the axes of the hyperbola could be
obtained directly by investigating for its x- and y-intercepts?

66. Eccentricity. Location of foci. The ratio c/a, denoted
by e, is called the **eccentricity** of the hyperbola. Since
$c^2 = a^2 + b^2$, we may write

$$e = \sqrt{a^2 + b^2}/a.$$

From $c^2 = a^2 + b^2$ we see that c is the hypotenuse of a right
triangle with legs a and b, and hence can be easily constructed
if the semiaxes are known. The distance c laid off on either
side of the center along the transverse axis locates the foci.

67. Equilateral hyperbola. In case $a = b$, the hyperbola is
called an **equilateral** hyperbola. Equation (14), in that case,
reduces to
$$x^2 - y^2 = a^2.$$

The asymptotes have slopes ± 1. If the axes are rotated
through an angle of $-45°$, the equation becomes
$$2\,x'y' = a^2. \quad \text{(See Exercise 14, p. 75.)}$$

This is the equation of an equilateral hyperbola referred to
its asymptotes as axes.

68. Conjugate hyperbolas. Consideration of the two hyperbolas
$$\frac{x^2}{a^2} - \frac{y^2}{b^2} = 1 \quad \text{and} \quad \frac{y^2}{b^2} - \frac{x^2}{a^2} = 1$$

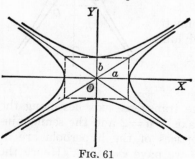

FIG. 61

shows that the transverse
axis of one is the conju-
gate axis of the other,
and that the same
straight lines $y = \pm bx/a$
serve as asymptotes for
both curves. Two hy-
perbolas which are so
related are called conju-
gate hyperbolas.

EXERCISES

1. Find the semiaxes and vertices; draw the auxiliary rectangle, the asymptotes, and the hyperbola; give the equations of the asymptotes, coördinates of the foci, and eccentricity:

(a) $9 x^2 - 16 y^2 = 144$.   (e) $2 x^2 - 3 y^2 - 120 = 0$.
(b) $4 x^2 - 9 y^2 = 36$.   (f) $45 x^2 - 4 y^2 + 180 = 0$.
(c) $y^2 - 3 x^2 = 27$.   (g) $x^2 - y^2 - 16 = 0$.
(d) $4 y^2 - x^2 = 36$.   (h) $x^2 - y^2 + 16 = 0$.

2. Derive the equation of the locus of points the difference of whose distances from $(0, \pm 6)$ is ± 4.

3. Write the equations of the hyperbolas for which the following conditions are given and sketch each curve:

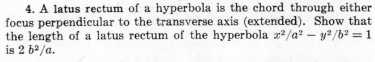

(a) Transverse axis 8, foci at $(\pm 6, 0)$.
(b) Transverse axis 6, foci at $(0, \pm 7)$.
(c) Conjugate axis 4, foci at $(\pm 2\sqrt{5}, 0)$.
(d) Conjugate axis $12\sqrt{2}$, foci at $(0, \pm 3\sqrt{10})$.

4. A latus rectum of a hyperbola is the chord through either focus perpendicular to the transverse axis (extended). Show that the length of a latus rectum of the hyperbola $x^2/a^2 - y^2/b^2 = 1$ is $2 b^2/a$.

5. Write the equation of the ellipse passing through the origin which has for minor axis the latus rectum through the right focus of the hyperbola $x^2 - 3 y^2 = 48$. Draw the figure.

6. Find the equation of the hyperbola with center at the origin and axes on the coördinate axes which passes through (a) $(3, 1)$ and $(9, 5)$; (b) $(1, 5)$ and $(4, 10)$.

7. Write the equation of the hyperbola whose foci are $(\pm 4, 0)$ and which goes through $(14, 24)$.

8. The asymptotes of a hyperbola are $3 y = \pm 4 x$ and the foci are at $(\pm 10, 0)$. Write the equation of the hyperbola.

9. Write the equation of the hyperbola passing through $(4, 6)$ whose asymptotes are $y = \pm \sqrt{3} x$.

10. Show that the eccentricity of the equilateral hyperbola is $\sqrt{2}$.

11. Find the vertices, axes, and foci of the hyperbola $xy = 16$.

12. A variable y varies inversely as a variable x. Write the relationship between x and y in the form of an equation. If $y = 6$ when $x = 2$, find y when $x = 8$. Illustrate graphically.

13. Write the equations of the hyperbolas conjugate to the following hyperbolas. Sketch each pair of conjugate hyperbolas on the same set of axes with their common asymptotes.

(a) $x^2 - 4y^2 = 16$.   (c) $x^2 - y^2 = 25$.
(b) $4y^2 - 9x^2 = 108$.   (d) $xy = 9$.

14. Show that the four foci of two conjugate hyperbolas and the four points of intersection of the tangent lines at the vertices all lie on a circle whose center is the common center of the hyperbolas.

15. In each of the following determine k and l so that the locus $kx^2 + ly^2 = 1$ shall go through the given points, and state whether the locus is an ellipse or a hyperbola:

(a) $(2, 3)$ and $(6, 1)$.   (c) $(-2, 3)$ and $(5, 0)$.
(b) $(-4, 3)$ and $(2, -1)$.   (d) $(2, 3)$ and $(6, -7)$.

16. Find the equation of the locus in each of the following and show that the two loci are identical hyperbolas.

(a) The locus of a point whose distance from $(4, 0)$ is twice its distance from the line $x - 1 = 0$.

(b) The locus of a point whose distance from $(-4, 0)$ is twice its distance from the line $x + 1 = 0$.

17. What are the foci and the eccentricity of the hyperbola in Exercise 16?

69. **Center not at the origin.** By an argument similar to that used for the ellipse one may show that for the center at (h, k) instead of at the origin the equation of a hyperbola is

$$\frac{(x - h)^2}{a^2} - \frac{(y - k)^2}{b^2} = 1 \qquad (16)$$

if the transverse axis is parallel to the x-axis, and is

$$\frac{(y - k)^2}{a^2} - \frac{(x - h)^2}{b^2} = 1 \qquad (17)$$

if the transverse axis is parallel to the y-axis. Since a translation of axes will change equations (16) and (17) to equations (14) and (15), respectively, any equation of the form (16) or (17) represents a hyperbola.

70. Theorem. *In general,* the equation*

Note

$$Ax^2 + By^2 + Cx + Dy + E = 0 \qquad (18)$$

represents a hyperbola if A and B are opposite in sign.

Completing squares, we may write

$$A\left(x^2 + \frac{C}{A}x + \frac{C^2}{4A^2}\right) + B\left(y^2 + \frac{D}{B}y + \frac{D^2}{4B^2}\right) = \frac{C^2}{4A} + \frac{D^2}{4B} - E.$$

Dividing by the expression in the right member of the equation and rearranging, we may write the equation in the form of (16) or (17), since A and B are opposite in sign. Equation (18), therefore, represents a hyperbola.

EXAMPLE. Find the center, semiaxes, asymptotes, foci, and eccentricity of the hyperbola

$$4y^2 - 9x^2 - 36x - 8y - 68 = 0.$$

Completing squares, we may write

$$4(y^2 - 2y + 1) - 9(x^2 + 4x + 4) = 36.$$

Dividing by 36 and rearranging, we obtain

$$\frac{(y-1)^2}{9} - \frac{(x+2)^2}{4} = 1.$$

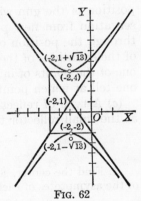

FIG. 62

This equation shows that the center of the hyperbola is at $(-2, 1)$, that the transverse axis lies along the line $x = -2$, that the semitransverse axis is $a = 3$, and that the semiconjugate axis is $b = 2$. From $c^2 = a^2 + b^2$ we have $c = \sqrt{13}$. The foci are, therefore, the points $(-2, 1 + \sqrt{13})$ and $(-2, 1 - \sqrt{13})$. The eccentricity is $e = c/a = \sqrt{13}/3$. The equations of the asymptotes are

$$y - 1 = \pm \tfrac{3}{2}(x + 2),$$

or $\qquad 3x - 2y + 8 = 0 \quad$ and $\quad 3x + 2y + 4 = 0.$

*See footnote, p. 95.

B2

71. Scientific applications of the hyperbola. The following list is suggestive of the applications of the hyperbola:

(a) The equation expressing Boyle's law for a perfect gas under pressure at a constant temperature is of the form of the equation of an equilateral hyperbola referred to its asymptotes as axes.

(b) The hyperbola may be used to locate an invisible source of sound, as in locating an enemy's guns or in range-finding. Two listening posts are established and the difference in time of arrival of the report of the gun at the two posts is measured as accurately as possible. The difference in time multiplied by the rate at which sound travels gives the difference in the distances from the two listening posts to the gun. If the two listening posts are used as foci and the difference in distances from the gun as the transverse axis of a hyperbola, then the position of the gun will lie on the hyperbola. A second observation from new positions will give a second hyperbola through the position of the gun. The simultaneous solution of the equations of the two hyperbolas will locate the gun at one of the points of intersection of the two curves. How can one tell at which point of intersection the gun is located?

(c) A type of reflecting telescope uses a hyperbolic mirror as the small reflector to reflect the image to the eyepiece.

EXERCISES

1. Find the center, semiaxes, vertices, foci, and the equations of the asymptotes of each of the following hyperbolas and sketch:

$$(a) \ x^2 - 3\,y^2 - 4\,x + 18\,y - 50 = 0.$$
$$(b) \ 9\,x^2 - 4\,y^2 + 36\,x + 24\,y + 36 = 0.$$

$(c) \ 3\,x^2 - y^2 - 12\,x - 6\,y = 0.$ $(e) \ 4\,x^2 - y^2 - 8\,x - 12 = 0.$
$(d) \ 16\,x^2 - 9\,y^2 + 90\,y - 81 = 0.$ $(f) \ x^2 - y^2 + 4\,x - 2\,y + 1 = 0.$

2. Write the equations of the hyperbolas for which the following conditions are given and sketch:

(a) Transverse axis 8, foci at $(0, 2)$ and $(10, 2)$.
(b) Transverse axis 4, foci at $(1, 4)$ and $(1, -4)$.
(c) Conjugate axis 4, foci at $(-2, 3)$ and $(10, 3)$.
(d) Conjugate axis 2, foci at $(1, 0)$ and $(1, 6)$.

3. Write the equation of the ellipse which has its major and minor axes coincident, respectively, with the transverse and conjugate axes of the hyperbola $x^2 - 4y^2 - 12x = 0$.

4. Write the equation of the parabola which has its vertex at the center of the hyperbola $x^2 - 3y^2 - 6y = 0$ and which passes through the ends of the latus rectum through the upper focus of the hyperbola.

5. Write equation (18), Sec. 70, in a form involving four essential constants.

6. In each of the following determine a, b, c, and d so that the locus $x^2 + ay^2 + bx + cy + d = 0$ shall go through the given points, and state whether the locus is an ellipse or a hyperbola:

(a) $(-2, -1)$, $(1, 0)$, $(8, 3)$, and $(-4, -3)$.
(b) $(2, 5)$, $(-6, 3)$, $(8, -7)$, and $(10, 1)$.

7. Show that each of the following equations represents two straight lines:

(a) $x^2 - 9y^2 = 0$.   (b) $x^2 - 4y^2 - 4x + 8y = 0$.
(c) $4x^2 - y^2 - 16x + 2y + 15 = 0$.

8. By an appropriate translation of axes eliminate the first-degree terms from $xy + ax + by + c = 0$ and show that the locus is an equilateral hyperbola if $c \neq ab$.

9. Sketch the locus of the equation in Exercise 8 for the cases:

(a) $a = -2$, $b = -1$, $c = 1$.   (b) $a = -2$, $b = -1$, $c = 2$.

10. Find the points of intersection of the loci in each of the following pairs and illustrate graphically:

(a) $4x^2 - 5y^2 = 80$,   (c) $xy - 6 = 0$,
$2x - 3y = 4$. $y = 5 + 2x - x^2$.
(b) $2x^2 - 3y^2 = 24$,   (d) $2x - y = 6$,
$4x^2 + 3y^2 = 192$. $xy - 2x - 2y = 2$.
(e) $9x^2 + 16y^2 - 72x + 64y - 80 = 0$,
$3x^2 - 4y^2 - 24x - 16y + 20 = 0$.

11. Find the equation of the hyperbola whose foci are $(0, 0)$ and $(4, 4)$ and whose transverse axis is 2 units. How does the equation differ essentially from equation (18), Sec. 70?

12. Transform the equation of the hyperbola derived in Exercise 11 by rotating the axes through $45°$.

72. Summary. The types of loci represented by the second degree equation

$$Ax^2 + By^2 + Cx + Dy + E = 0 \qquad (19)$$

may be summarized as follows:

1. If $A = B$, *the locus is a circle* (Sec. 49).

2. If *either* $A = 0$ or $B = 0$, *the locus is a parabola* (Sec. 56).

3. If A *and* B *have the same sign and* $A \neq B$, *the locus is an ellipse* (Sec. 62).

4. If A *and* B *have unlike signs, the locus is a hyperbola* (Sec. 70).

5. *If the left member of the equation can be factored into two first degree factors, the locus is two straight lines.* These lines may be distinct or coincident. This possibility exists for equations of types 2 and 4.

6. *The locus may be a point only.* This possibility exists for equations of types 1 and 3.

The foregoing types of loci are called **conic sections**, or **conics**, because each can be obtained as the curve of intersection of a plane and a conical surface (of two nappes). They were so studied by the early Greeks. Equations of types 1, 2, and 3 represent imaginary loci in some cases.

73. General second degree equation. The general equation of the second degree in x and y can be written in the form

$$Ax^2 + Bxy + Cy^2 + Dx + Ey + F = 0. \qquad (20)$$

It is possible by a proper rotation of axes to obtain an equation of the locus represented by equation (20) in a form which has no xy-term. Rotating the axes through the angle θ by the substitutions $x = x' \cos \theta - y' \sin \theta,$

$$y = x' \sin \theta + y' \cos \theta, \qquad \text{(Sec. 45)}$$

and collecting terms, we transform equation (20) into

$$\begin{aligned}
x'^2 & (A \cos^2 \theta + B \sin \theta \cos \theta + C \sin^2 \theta) \\
& + x'y'[2(C - A) \sin \theta \cos \theta + B(\cos^2 \theta - \sin^2 \theta)] \\
& + y'^2 (A \sin^2 \theta - B \sin \theta \cos \theta + C \cos^2 \theta) \\
& + x'(D \cos \theta - E \sin \theta) + y'(E \cos \theta - D \sin \theta) \\
& + F = 0. \qquad (21)
\end{aligned}$$

Equating the coefficient of $x'y'$ to zero, we have

$$2(C - A) \sin \theta \cos \theta + B(\cos^2 \theta - \sin^2 \theta) = 0,$$

or $\qquad (C - A) \sin 2\theta + B \cos 2\theta = 0,$

whence $\qquad \tan 2\theta = \dfrac{B}{A - C}. \qquad (A \neq C)$

In case $A = C$, we have $\cos 2\theta = 0$ and hence $\theta = 45°$. There is a value of θ for which $\tan 2\theta$ is equal to any given value. Therefore it is always possible to choose an angle through which to rotate the axes, and eliminate the xy-term in the general second degree equation in x and y.

EXAMPLE. Eliminate the xy-term, identify, and draw the conic $11 x^2 - 24 xy + 4 y^2 + 30 x + 40 y - 45 = 0.$

The angle θ through which to rotate the axes in order to eliminate the xy-term is found from

$$\tan 2\theta = \frac{B}{A - C} = -\frac{24}{7}.$$

If we select for 2θ the smallest positive angle with the given tangent, we have $\cos 2\theta = -7/25$, from which

$$\sin \theta = \sqrt{\frac{1 - \cos 2\theta}{2}} = \frac{4}{5}.$$

and $\qquad \cos \theta = \frac{3}{5}.$

The equations for the required rotation are

$$x = \frac{3 x' - 4 y'}{5}, \quad y = \frac{4 x' + 3 y'}{5}.$$

These substitutions transform the equation into

$$11\left(\frac{3 x' - 4 y'}{5}\right)^2 - 24\left(\frac{3 x' - 4 y'}{5}\right)\left(\frac{4 x' + 3 y'}{5}\right)$$
$$+ 4\left(\frac{4 x' + 3 y'}{5}\right)^2 + 30\left(\frac{3 x' - 4 y'}{5}\right)$$
$$+ 40\left(\frac{4 x' + 3 y'}{5}\right) - 45 = 0.$$

Simplifying, we obtain

$$x'^2 - 4 y'^2 - 10 x' + 9 = 0.$$

This equation shows that the conic is a hyperbola. Completing squares and dividing by 16, we may write

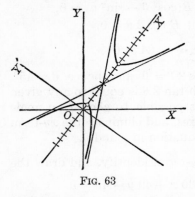

$$\frac{(x'-5)^2}{16} - \frac{y'^2}{4} = 1.$$

The transverse axis of the hyperbola lies on the x'-axis. The semitransverse axis is $a = 4$ and the semiconjugate axis is $b = 2$. With reference to the new axes the center is at $(5, 0)$ and the vertices are at $(1, 0)$ and $(9, 0)$. The value of c is found to be $2\sqrt{5}$ and the eccentricity $e = \sqrt{5}/2$. The foci are at $(5 \pm 2\sqrt{5}, 0)$. The asymptotes are $y' = \pm \frac{1}{2}(x' - 5)$. The figure shows the relation of the curve to both sets of axes. A further simplification of the equation can be effected by a translation of axes.

FIG. 63

EXERCISES

Remove the xy-term by rotation of axes, identify, and sketch the following conics:

1. $8x^2 - 12xy + 17y^2 - 20 = 0$.
2. $9x^2 - 24xy + 16y^2 - 20x - 15y = 0$.
3. $3x^2 + 12xy - 13y^2 - 135 = 0$.
4. $9x^2 + 24xy + 16y^2 - 20x + 15y - 100 = 0$.
5. $41x^2 - 24xy + 34y^2 - 15x - 20y = 0$.
6. $x^2 - xy + y^2 - 6x - 12y + 66 = 0$.
7. $x^2 + 2\sqrt{3}xy + y^2 - 18 = 0$.
8. $3x^2 + 2\sqrt{3}xy + y^2 + 4x - 4\sqrt{3}y + 16 = 0$.

74. Identification of a conic without removing the xy-term.
Designating the coefficients of the terms x'^2, $x'y'$, and y'^2 in equation (21) by A', B', and C' respectively, we have

$$A' = A\cos^2\theta + B\sin\theta\cos\theta + C\sin^2\theta,$$
$$B' = 2(C - A)\sin\theta\cos\theta + B(\cos^2\theta - \sin^2\theta),$$
$$C' = A\sin^2\theta - B\sin\theta\cos\theta + C\cos^2\theta.$$

It can be proved that $B'^2 - 4\,A'C' = B^2 - 4\,AC$ regardless of the value of θ (the student may supply the details of the proof). If θ is chosen so that the xy-term is eliminated, then $B' = 0$, and we have

$$B^2 - 4\,AC = -\,4\,A'C'.$$

If $B^2 - 4\,AC = 0$, either $A' = 0$ or $C' = 0$; hence the conic is a parabola. If $B^2 - 4\,AC < 0$, A' and C' have the same sign; hence the conic is an ellipse. If $B^2 - 4\,AC > 0$, A' and C' are opposite in sign; hence the conic is a hyperbola.

Certain exceptions to the foregoing conclusions may exist as mentioned in Sec. 72, viz., the locus may be two straight lines, a point, or imaginary.

75. Sketching a conic without removing the xy-term. A sketch of a conic whose equation contains the xy-term may be obtained by using the method of composition of ordinates (Sec. 38).

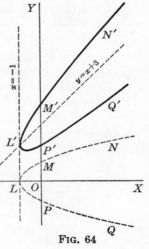

FIG. 64

EXAMPLE. Sketch the conic

$$x^2 - 2\,xy + y^2 + 5\,x - 6\,y + 8 = 0.$$

Solving the equation for y, we have

$$y = x + 3 \pm \sqrt{x + 1}.$$

Let (1) $\quad y_1 = x + 3$

and (2) $\quad y_2 = \pm \sqrt{x + 1}.$

We observe that (1) is a straight line and that (2), which is equivalent to $y^2 = x + 1$, is a parabola. Draw the line and the parabola on the same set of axes (Fig. 64). Adding the positive ordinates y_2 of the arc LMN of the parabola and the ordinates y_1 of the line corresponding to the same abscissas, we obtain the arc $L'M'N'$; adding the negative ordinates y_2 of the arc LPQ and the ordinates of the line, we obtain the arc $L'P'Q'$. That the conic is a parabola could have been determined directly by showing that $B^2 - 4AC = 0$ (Sec. 74). The student is warned against calling the line $y = x + 3$ the axis of the parabola since the parabola is not symmetric to this line.

We could also have determined that the conic is a parabola by studying the quantity under the radical sign in the solution for y. The values of x for which y is real are $x \geqq -1$. Therefore, the equation represents a parabola, since the parabola is the only conic which extends to infinity in one half-plane without doing so in the opposite half-plane.

If when a second degree equation is solved for $y(x)$ and simplified, the value of $y(x)$ is rational in $x(y)$, the equation is factorable and represents two straight lines.

EXERCISES

1. Given the equation $2x^2 + 2xy + y^2 = 9$.

(a) Show that the solution for y is $y = -x \pm \sqrt{9 - x^2}$.

(b) Show that the equation represents an ellipse.

(c) Draw the ellipse by the method of composition of ordinates.

2. Given the equation $y^2 - 2xy + 2x - 2y + 2 = 0$.

(a) Show that the solution for y is $y = x + 1 \pm \sqrt{x^2 - 1}$.

(b) Show that the equation represents a hyperbola.

(c) Draw the hyperbola by the method of composition of ordinates.

3. Identify and draw the following conics without removing the xy-term:

      (a) $x^2 + 2xy + y^2 - 4x - 2y + 1 = 0$.

      (b) $x^2 + 2xy + 2y^2 - 8x - 12y + 18 = 0$.

      (c) $y^2 - 4xy - 4y + 8x = 0$.

      (d) $3x^2 + 2xy + y^2 - 4 = 0$.

      (e) $3x^2 + 2xy - y^2 - 4 = 0$.

      (f) $x^2 - 4xy + 4y^2 - 4x + 16y = 0$.

  (g) $xy - x^2 + 4 = 0$.   (i) $x^2 - xy - x + y - 2 = 0$.

  (h) $xy - x^2 - y = 0$.   (j) $3x^2 + 2xy - y^2 + 4y - 3 = 0$.

4. Find the points of intersection of the loci in each of the following pairs and illustrate graphically:

    (a) $x^2 - xy + y^2 = 3$,   (b) $x^2 + xy + y^2 = 3$,

        $x^2 + y^2 = 6$. $x^2 + y^2 = 3$.

5. Write equation (20), Sec. 73, in a form involving five essential constants.

6. Find the equation of the conic through the points in each of the following and identify the conic:

(a) $(3, 0)$, $(0, -5)$, $(2, 1)$, $(2, -2)$, and $(-3, -2)$.
(b) $(1, 2)$, $(1, 8)$, $(-1, 6)$, $(-5, 0)$, and $(-1, 0)$.
(c) $(2, 4)$, $(3, 4)$, $(-3, -2)$, $(-3, 0)$, and $(-2, 0)$.

7. Show that each of the following equations represents one of the following: two straight lines (distinct or coincident), a point, or an imaginary locus.

(a) $x^2 - 2xy + y^2 + x - y - 2 = 0$.
(b) $x^2 + 4xy + 4y^2 - 2x - 4y + 1 = 0$.
(c) $2x^2 - 5xy + 2y^2 + 3y - 2 = 0$.
(d) $x^2 + 2xy + 2y^2 = 0$.
(e) $x^2 - 2xy + 2y^2 + 1 = 0$.

8. Show that no second-degree equation containing the xy-term represents a circle.

76. General definition of a conic. *A conic is the locus of a point the ratio of whose distance from a fixed point to its distance from a fixed line is a positive constant. The fixed line is called the directrix.*

To find the equation of the locus described, let the constant ratio be r, let the directrix, AB, be the y-axis, and let the line through the fixed point, F, perpendicular to the directrix, be the x-axis (Fig. 65). If we call p the distance from AB to F, the coördinates of F are $(p, 0)$. By definition

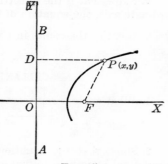

FIG. 65

$$FP = r \cdot DP.$$

But $FP = \sqrt{(x - p)^2 + y^2}$ and $DP = x;$
hence $\sqrt{(x - p)^2 + y^2} = rx,$
or $x^2(1 - r^2) - 2px + y^2 + p^2 = 0.$

If $r = 1$, the locus is a parabola. Why?

If $r < 1$, the locus is an ellipse. Why?

If $r > 1$, the locus is a hyperbola. Why?

It can be shown that the fixed point F is a focus of the conic and that the ratio r is the same as the eccentricity e as previously defined.

Because of the symmetry of the ellipse and the hyperbola it is evident that another line and another point could serve as directrix and as focus, respectively, of the ellipse and of the hyperbola. See Exercises 13 and 16, pp. 102 and 110 respectively.

EXERCISES

1. Derive the equations of the conics for which the following conditions are given. Identify and sketch each conic:

(a) Focus $(2, 1)$, directrix the y-axis, $r = 1$.

(b) Focus $(1, 2)$, directrix the line $x + 2y = 1$, $r = 1$.

(c) Focus $(2, 0)$, directrix the line $x + 6 = 0$, $r = \frac{1}{3}$.

(d) Focus $(1, 1)$, directrix the line $x + y + 4 = 0$, $r = \frac{1}{2}$.

(e) Focus $(0, 3)$, directrix the line $y + 2 = 0$, $r = \frac{3}{2}$.

(f) Focus $(2, -2)$, directrix the line $x - y + 2 = 0$, $r = 2$.

2. Show that if the directrix of a conic is non-parallel to a coordinate axis, the equation of the conic contains an xy-term.

3. Identify the conics in Exercises 9–13, inclusive, p. 70.

MISCELLANEOUS EXERCISES

1. What conic is represented by each pair of equations

$$y = \pm \frac{b}{a} \sqrt{2\,ax - x^2} \text{ and } y = \pm \frac{b}{a} \sqrt{x^2 - 2\,ax}?$$

2. Show that the equation $(x - a)(y - b) = c$ represents an equilateral hyperbola. What are the equations of its asymptotes?

3. Show that each of the equations $x^{\frac{1}{2}} + y^{\frac{1}{2}} = a^{\frac{1}{2}}$, $x^{\frac{1}{2}} - y^{\frac{1}{2}} = a^{\frac{1}{2}}$, and $x^{\frac{1}{2}} - y^{\frac{1}{2}} = -a^{\frac{1}{2}}$ represents a different arc of the same parabola and identify the arc which each equation represents. (*Hint:* Rationalize each equation.)

4. An ellipse with foci $(0, 0)$ and $(9, 15)$ goes through $(4, 3)$. Find (a) its equation, (b) length of its minor axis, (c) its x- and y-intercepts. Sketch the ellipse.

5. Find the points of intersection of the line $3x - 2y = 4$ with the hyperbola $x^2 - 4y^2 + 16 = 0$ and its asymptotes. Illustrate graphically.

6. Find the points of intersection of the curves $xy = 1$ and $x^2 - 2xy + y^2 - 8x - 8y - 16 = 0$ and illustrate graphically.

7. The length of a diagonal of a rectangle inscribed in the ellipse $4x^2 + 7y^2 = 256$ is $4\sqrt{13}$. Find the area of the rectangle.

8. Find the vertices of the square inscribed in the ellipse $4x^2 + 5y^2 = 48x$.

9. Find the equations of the asymptotes of the hyperbola whose foci are $(0, 0)$ and $(2, 2)$ and whose transverse axis is 2 units.

10. Show that the line $y = mx + k$ is tangent to the parabola $y^2 = 2px$ if $k = p/2m$. Show that the point of tangency is $(p/2\,m^2, p/m)$.

11. A line is tangent to the parabola $y^2 = 2px$ at P. Show that the two lines through P, one through the focus and the other parallel to the axis of the parabola, make equal angles with the tangent line.

12. Show that the line $y = mx + k$ is tangent to the ellipse $x^2/a^2 + y^2/b^2 = 1$ if $k = \pm\sqrt{a^2m^2 + b^2}$.

13. Determine k so that the line $y = mx + k$ shall be tangent to the hyperbola $x^2/a^2 - y^2/b^2 = 1$.

14. Any two perpendicular lines are drawn through the vertex of a parabola. Show that the line joining their other intersections with the parabola intersects the axis of the parabola in a fixed point.

15. Chords are drawn through an end of the major axis of the ellipse $b^2x^2 + a^2y^2 = 2ab^2x$. Find the locus of their midpoints.

16. Lines are drawn through the ends of the minor axis of the ellipse $b^2x^2 + a^2y^2 = a^2b^2$ intersecting in a point on the ellipse. Show that the product of their intercepts on the x-axis is a^2.

17. Show that the distance from the center to a point on an equilateral hyperbola is a mean proportional between the focal distances of the point.

18. Let P be any point on a hyperbola. Show that the product of the distances from the asymptotes to P is constant.

19. If a line is drawn intersecting a hyperbola, show that the two segments of the line included between the hyperbola and its asymptotes are equal.

20. Show that the area of the circle whose diameter is the segment joining the foci of an ellipse is equal to the difference of the areas of the major and minor auxiliary circles of the ellipse.

21. Show that the area of a circle whose diameter is the segment joining the foci of a hyperbola is equal to the sum of the areas of the circles whose diameters are the transverse and conjugate axes, respectively, of the hyperbola.

22. The base of a triangle is fixed in length and position. Find the locus of its vertex if the tangents of the base angles have (a) a constant sum; (b) a constant difference; (c) a constant product; (d) a constant quotient.

23. Given the line $y = ax + b$. A curve is constructed whose ordinates for a given abscissa are the positive and negative square roots of the ordinate of the line for the same abscissa. Show that the curve is a parabola and discuss its position relative to the line.

24. Given the parabola $y = ax^2 + bx + c$. A curve is constructed whose ordinates for a given abscissa are the positive and negative square roots of the ordinate of the parabola corresponding to the same abscissa. Discuss the curve for each of the following cases: (1) $a > 0$; (2) $a < 0$, subjecting the discussion in each of the cases (1) and (2) to the conditions (a) $b^2 - 4ac > 0$; (b) $b^2 - 4ac = 0$; (c) $b^2 - 4ac < 0$.

CHAPTER VI

OTHER TYPES OF CURVES IN RECTANGULAR COÖRDINATES

77. Algebraic and transcendental curves. Equations of the form $f(x, y) = 0$ (or which can be reduced to this form), where $f(x, y)$ is a polynomial* in x and y are called **algebraic.** The equations $2x^3 - 3x^2y + y^2 - x + 5 = 0$, $y = (x-1)/(x+1)$, and $y = x^{\frac{3}{2}}$, for example, are algebraic equations. Equations which cannot be so expressed are called **transcendental.** The equations $y = e^x$, $y = \log x$, and $x + \sin x = y^2$, for example, are transcendental equations.

The graph of an algebraic equation in two variables is called an **algebraic curve** and the graph of a transcendental equation in two variables is called a **transcendental curve.** Curves in a plane represented by algebraic equations of degree greater than two, or by transcendental equations, are called **higher plane curves.**†

The curves discussed in the preceding chapters are algebraic curves of which several in Chapter III are higher plane curves. The curves discussed in Chapters VI, VII, and VIII are higher plane curves, with a few exceptions, and these are grouped into chapters according to the method of treatment.

---

*From algebra we recall that a polynomial (also called a rational and integral function) in x and y is the algebraic sum of a finite number of terms of the type kx^ry^s, where k is a constant and each of the exponents, r and s, is either a positive integer or zero; the degree of a term is $r + s$ and the degree of the polynomial is the degree of the term or terms of highest degree.

†Exceptions may occur in the case of algebraic equations if the left member of $f(x, y) = 0$ is factorable. For example, $x^3 + xy^2 - x = 0$ can be written $x(x^2 + y^2 - 1) = 0$. Hence the locus consists of the line $x = 0$ and the circle $x^2 + y^2 - 1 = 0$, neither of which is a higher plane curve.

ALGEBRAIC CURVES

78. Illustrations. EXAMPLE 1. Discuss and graph

$$y^2 = (x - 1)(x - 2)(x - 3).$$

The equation shows the locus to be symmetric with respect to the x-axis. The x-intercepts are 1, 2, and 3. For $x = 0$, $y^2 = -6$, and hence the curve does not intersect the y-axis.

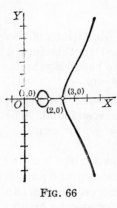

For $x < 1$, each factor in the right member is negative and there is no real value for y. For $1 < x < 2$, the first factor is positive and the other two are negative; y^2 is therefore positive and there are two real values of y. For $2 < x < 3$, y^2 is negative and there are no real values for y. For $x > 3$, there are real values for y. As x increases without limit y also increases without limit. Assigning a few values to x between 1 and 2 and values to x greater than 3 we find a few points on the curve, such as $(\frac{5}{4}, .5 +)$, $(\frac{3}{2}, .6 +)$, $(\frac{7}{4}, .5 -)$, $(4, 2.4 +)$, and $(5, 4.9 -)$. The curve is shown in Fig. 66.

FIG. 66

EXAMPLE 2. Sketch the curve $x^3 - x^2y + y = 0$.
Solving for y, we have

$$y = \frac{x^3}{x^2 - 1}.$$

For $x = \pm 1$, the denominator of the fraction is zero, and hence the lines $x = 1$ and $x = -1$ are vertical asymptotes.

As x approaches -1 from the left (right) y decreases (increases) without limit. As x approaches 1 from the left (right) y decreases (increases) without limit.

As x increases numerically without limit y also increases numerically without limit. Hence there is no horizontal asymptote. Dividing the numerator by the denominator, we have

$$y = x + \frac{x}{x^2 - 1}.$$

As x increases numerically without limit the fraction $x/(x^2-1)$ approaches zero. Hence the curve approaches the line $y = x$ as an asymptote. One branch of the curve is above the line $y = x$ for $x > 1$ and another branch is below it for $x < -1$.

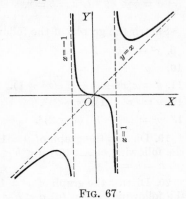

FIG. 67

The curve goes through the origin and is symmetric with respect to the origin (Fig. 67).

It is an interesting exercise to draw the curve in Fig. 67 by addition of ordinates. To do this let (1) $y_1 = x$ and (2) $y_2 = x/(x^2-1)$. Draw the graphs of (1) and (2) on the same set of axes and add the ordinates, y_1 and y_2, corresponding to the same abscissas.

EXERCISES

1. The graph of $y = f(x) = a_0x^n + a_1x^{n-1} + \cdots + a_{n-1}x + a_n$, if $f(x)$ is a polynomial in x, is called a polynomial curve. Discuss how the sketching of the curve is facilitated if $f(x)$ is written in the factored form $f(x) = a_0(x - r_1)(x - r_2) \cdots (x - r_n)$.

2. Sketch the following polynomial curves:

(a) $y = x^3 - 6x^2 + 8x$. (c) $3y = x^4 + 4x^3 - 4x^2 - 16x$.
(b) $4y = x^3 - 9x^2 + 24x$. (d) $y = x^4 + x^3 - x^2 + x - 2$.

3. Sketch the graph of $y = (x - 1)(x - 2)(x - 3)$ and show how it can be used to aid in obtaining the graph of the equation in Example 1, p. 124.

Sketch the graphs of the following equations:

4. (a) $y = x(x - 3)^2$; (b) $y^2 = x(x - 3)^2$.
5. (a) $y = x^2(x - 3)$; (b) $y^2 = x^2(x - 3)$.
6. (a) $y = (x - 3)^3$; (b) $y^2 = (x - 3)^3$.
7. Discuss the graph of the equation $y = (x - a)(x - b)(x - c)$ in each of the following cases: (a) $a < b < c$; (b) $a < b = c$; (c) $a = b < c$; (d) $a = b = c$.

8. Discuss the graph of the equation $y^2 = (x - a)(x - b)(x - c)$ in each of the following cases: (a) $a < b < c$; (b) $a < b = c$; (c) $a = b < c$; (d) $a = b = c$.

Sketch the graphs of the following equations:

9. $x^3 - x^2y - 1 = 0$.

10. $x^3y - x^2 - y = 0$.

11. $y = x(x^2 + x + 1)/(x^2 - 1)$.

12. $y = (x^2 - 1)/(x - 2)^2$.

13. $y^2 = (x^2 - 1)/(x - 2)^2$.

14. $xy^2(x - 2)^2 = 1$.

15. $x^4 - x^2y - y = 0$.

16. $x^3 - x^2y - y = 0$.

17. $x^5 + 3\,x^4 - y^2 = 0$.

18. $x^3 + y^3 = 2\,x^2y$.

19. Discuss the graph of $y = 1/(x - a)(x - b)(x - c)$ in each of the following cases: (a) $a < b < c$; (b) $a < b = c$; (c) $a = b < c$; (d) $a = b = c$.

20. Discuss the graph of $y^2 = 1/(x - a)(x - b)(x - c)$ in each of the following cases: (a) $a < b < c$; (b) $a < b = c$; (c) $a = b < c$; (d) $a = b = c$.

TRANSCENDENTAL CURVES

79. The trigonometric functions $\sin x$, $\cos x$, and $\tan x$. From trigonometry we know that as x increases from 0 to $\pi/2$, $\sin x$ varies from 0 to 1; as x increases from $\pi/2$ to π, $\sin x$ varies from 1 to 0; as x increases from π to $3\,\pi/2$, $\sin x$

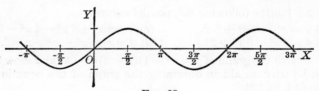

FIG. 68

varies from 0 to -1; as x increases from $3\,\pi/2$ to $2\,\pi$, $\sin x$ varies from -1 to 0; as x increases from $2\,\pi$ to $4\,\pi$, $\sin x$ goes through the same cycle of values as when x increases from 0 to $2\,\pi$. We find exactly how $\sin x$ varies by consulting a table of sines. The curve $y = \sin x$ is represented in Fig. 68. The function $\cos x$ goes through the same cycle of values as sin x, starting with the value 1 at $x = 0$. The curve $y = \cos x$ is shown in Fig. 69. The function tan x varies from $- \infty$ to $+ \infty$ as x increases from $- \pi/2$ to $\pi/2$, and again as x increases from $\pi/2$ to $3 \pi/2$, etc. (See Fig. 70.)

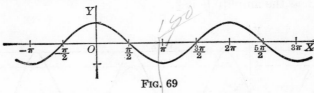

FIG. 69

Since the values of sin x repeat on each successive x-interval of 2π we say that the function sin x is **periodic** with **period** 2π. The functions cos x and tan x have periods of 2π and π respectively.

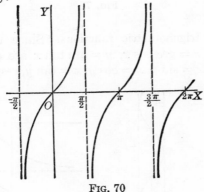

FIG. 70

80. **The curve $y = a \sin bx$.** The curve $y = \sin bx$ crosses the x-axis at points where $bx = 0, \pm \pi, \pm 2 \pi, \pm 3 \pi, \cdots$. The abscissas of these points are $x = 0, \pm \dfrac{\pi}{b}, \pm \dfrac{2 \pi}{b}, \pm \dfrac{3 \pi}{b}, \cdots$.

Since $\sin bx = \sin (bx + 2 \pi) = \sin b \left(x + \dfrac{2 \pi}{b} \right)$ it is evident that the values of sin bx repeat on each successive x-interval of $\dfrac{2 \pi}{b}$. Hence the period of sin bx is $\dfrac{2 \pi}{b}$. This quantity is sometimes called the **wave length.**

The ordinate of the curve $y = a \sin bx$ for any x is a times the ordinate of the curve $y = \sin bx$ for the same x. The maximum height a of an arch or wave is called the **amplitude**. The curve is shown in Fig. 71 for $a = \frac{3}{2}$ and $b = 2$. The period is π and the amplitude is $\frac{3}{2}$.

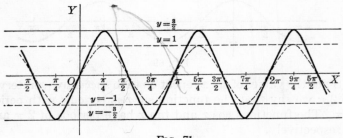

FIG. 71

81. Inverse trigonometric functions. Since the equations $y = $ arc sin x, $y = $ arc cos x, $y = $ arc tan x are equivalent to the equations $x = \sin y$, $x = \cos y$, $x = \tan y$, respectively, the

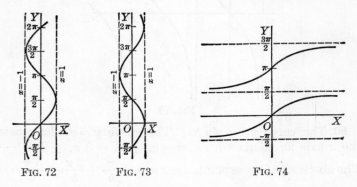

FIG. 72   FIG. 73   FIG. 74

inverse trigonometric functions graph like the corresponding direct functions with the x- and y-axes interchanged. See Figs. 72, 73, and 74, respectively. What is the graphical interpretation of the definitions, given in trigonometry, of the principal values of arc sin x, arc cos x, and arc tan x?

EXERCISES

1. Sketch the following curves on the same set of axes, using for each curve an x-interval of at least one period:

(a) $y = \sin x$; (b) $y = 2 \sin x$; (c) $y = \sin 2 x$; (d) $y = \sin \dfrac{x}{2}$.

2. Discuss the curve $y = a \cos bx$.

3. Sketch the following curves on the interval $x = 0$ to $x = 2\pi$:

(a) $y = \sin 3 x$.   (c) $y = \sin \dfrac{2 x}{3}$.   (e) $y = 3 \cos \dfrac{x}{3}$.

(b) $y = \cos 3 x$.   (d) $y = \tfrac{1}{2} \cos 2 x$.   (f) $y = 2 \sin \dfrac{3 x}{2}$.

4. Sketch the following curves: *omit*
(a) $y = \tan 2 x$; (b) $y = \tfrac{1}{2} \tan x$; (c) $y = \tan^2 x$.

5. Using the reciprocals of the ordinates of the curves $y = \sin x$, $y = \cos x$, and $y = \tan x$ obtain respectively the sketches of the curves $y = \csc x$, $y = \sec x$, and $y = \cot x$.

6. Sketch the following curves:

(a) $y = \sin \left(x - \dfrac{\pi}{6} \right)$; (b) $y = \cos \left(x + \dfrac{\pi}{4} \right)$; (c) $y = \tan (x + \pi)$. *omit*

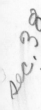

7. Sketch the following curves by composition of ordinates:

(a) $y = \sin x + \cos x$.   (e) $y = 2 \sin x + \cos 2 x$.

(b) $y = \sin x - \cos x$.   (f) $y = \cos x + \tfrac{1}{2} \cos 2 x$.

(c) $y = \sin x + \sin 2 x$.   (g) $y = \tfrac{1}{2} \sin 2 x + 2 \sin \dfrac{x}{2}$.

(d) $y = 2 \sin x + \sin 2 x$.   (h) $y = \sin x + \tfrac{1}{3} \sin 3 x$.

8. Sketch the curves (a) $y = x + \sin x$; (b) $y = x + \sin 2 x$.

9. Discuss the curve $y = a \sin (bx + c)$.

10. Sketch the curve $y = \tfrac{2}{3} \sin \left(3 x - \dfrac{\pi}{3} \right)$.

11. Reduce the equation $y = k_1 \sin mx + k_2 \cos mx$ to the form $y = a \sin (bx + c)$.

Solution. Multiply and divide the right member by $h = \sqrt{k_1{}^2 + k_2{}^2}$. Let θ be an angle such that $\tan \theta = k_2/k_1$. Then

$\cos \theta = k_1/\sqrt{k_1{}^2 + k_2{}^2}$ and $\sin \theta = k_2/\sqrt{k_1{}^2 + k_2{}^2}$.

Hence the equation can be written

$$y = h (\sin mx \cos \theta + \cos mx \sin \theta) = h \sin (mx + \theta),$$

which is in the form $y = a \sin (bx + c)$, where $a = h = \sqrt{k_1{}^2 + k_2{}^2}$, $b = m$, and $c = \theta$.

12. What are the amplitude and the period of the curve represented by the equation in Exercise 11?

13. Sketch the curve $y = \sin 2x + \sqrt{3} \cos 2x$: (a) by composition of ordinates; (b) after changing the equation to the form $y = a \sin (bx + c)$.

14. Reduce the equation $y = k \cos (mx + n)$ to the form $y = a \sin (bx + c)$. *Hint.* $\cos A = \sin \left(\dfrac{\pi}{2} - A\right)$.

15. Sketch the following curves on the interval $x = 0$ to $x = 2\pi$. (a) $y = \dfrac{x}{2} \sin x$; (b) $y = \dfrac{x^2}{10} \cos x$.

16. Sketch the curves: (a) $y = \sin \pi x$; (b) $y = \sin \dfrac{\pi}{x}$.

17. Sketch the curves: (a) $y = \arcsin 2x$; (b) $y = \arccos \dfrac{x}{2}$; (c) $y = 2 \arcsin x$; (d) $y = \frac{1}{2} \arccos x$.

82. The exponential function $y = a^x$ $(a > 0)$. The curve crosses the y-axis at $y = 1$, but does not cross the x-axis. There are no values of x for which y is negative or zero, and hence the curve is entirely above the x-axis. For further dis-

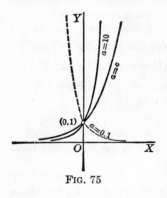

FIG. 75

cussion it is necessary to distinguish the cases where $a > 1$, $a = 1$, and $a < 1$.

For $a > 1$, as x increases through positive values y increases very rapidly. Hence the curve turns away from the x-axis much more rapidly, in the first quadrant, than it recedes from the y-axis. For x negative, y is less than 1. As x decreases without limit y approaches 0 and the curve approaches the x-axis as an asymptote.

In case $a = 1$, $y = 1$ for every x and the curve is a straight line.

Since $a^x = (1/a)^{-x}$, it follows that for $0 < a < 1$ the curve is symmetric with respect to the y-axis to the curve $y = a_1{}^x$, where $a_1 = 1/a$. In Fig. 75, the curve $y = a^x$ is shown for $a = e = 2.718 \cdots$, for $a = 10$, and for $a = 0.1$.

83. **Scientific applications of the exponential function.** The exponential relation occurs frequently and in many fields.

(*a*) Bacterial growth takes place according to an exponential law.

(*b*) Some chemical actions, such as the conversion of sugar under certain conditions, follow an exponential law.

(*c*) Radium decomposes according to an exponential law.

(*d*) The friction of a rope around a post, automobile braking, and a slipping belt involve an exponential law.

(*e*) Newton's law of cooling is exponential.

(*f*) The relation between atmospheric pressure and the height above the surface of the earth is exponential.

(*g*) The growth of current immediately after closing a circuit with constant electromotive force, resistance, and inductance is exponential.

(*h*) The amplitude of a damped vibration under certain restrictions decreases according to an exponential law.

(*i*) If we think of interest as being compounded continuously the amount is an exponential function of the time. For this reason the law expressed by an exponential relation is often called the "compound interest law."

84. The logarithmic function $y = \log_a x \ (a > 1)$. Since $y = \log_a x$ is equivalent to $x = a^y$, the graph of the logarithmic function will be like that of the exponential function with the x- and y-axes interchanged. The broken curve in Fig. 76,

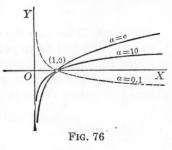

FIG. 76

representing $y = \log_{0.1} x$, illustrates the case $0 < a < 1$.

85. The graph of $y = e^{-x/2} \sin \pi x$. We draw the graphs of the equations $y_1 = e^{-x/2}$, $y_2 = \sin \pi x$, and $y_3 = -e^{-x/2}$ (Fig. 77). For integral values of x, $\sin \pi x = 0$, hence the curve $y = e^{-x/2} \sin \pi x$ crosses the x-axis at each point whose abscissa is an integral value of x. For $x = (4n + 1)/2$ (n an integer) $\sin \pi x = 1$, and the value of y coincides with the value of y_1.

And for $x = (4n+3)/2$ (n an integer) $\sin \pi x = -1$, and the value of y coincides with the value of y_3. For $0 < \sin \pi x < 1$, $y < y_1$, and for $-1 < \sin \pi x < 0$, $y > y_3$. Hence the curve $y = e^{-x/2} \sin \pi x$ lies between the boundary curves $y_1 = e^{-x/2}$ and $y_3 = -e^{-x/2}$, touching the curve $y_1 = e^{-x/2}$ whenever $\sin \pi x = 1$ and touching the curve $y_3 = -e^{-x/2}$ whenever $\sin \pi x = -1$. The ordinate y for any abscissa is the product of the ordinates y_1 and y_2 for the same abscissa.

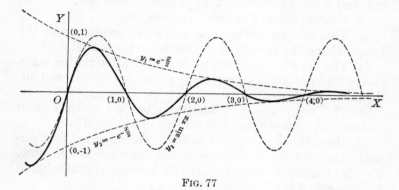

FIG. 77

The curve illustrates the effect of a damped vibration and is commonly called a **damped vibration curve**. The factor $e^{-x/2}$ is called the damping factor. As x increases without limit y approaches zero. A more general form of the equation of a damped vibration curve is

$$y = ae^{-kx} \sin (bx + c). \quad (k > 0)$$

EXERCISES

1. Sketch the following curves on the same set of axes:

   (a) $y = 2^x$; (b) $y = 2^{-x}$; (c) $y = 2^{x/2}$; (d) $y = 2^{2x}$.

2. Sketch on the same set of axes the members of the family of curves $y = a^x$ for $a = 2$, e, 3, and 10.

3. Sketch the curves: (a) $y = 2^{x+1}$; (b) $y = 2^{x-1}$.

4. Sketch the curves: (a) $y = 2^{1/x}$; (b) $y = 2^{-x^2}$.

5. Sketch the curves: (a) $y^2 = 2^x - 1$; (b) $y^2 = 2^{x-1}$.

6. Sketch by composition of ordinates the curves:

$$(a)\ y = \tfrac{1}{2}(e^x + e^{-x}); \quad (b)\ y = \tfrac{1}{2}(e^x - e^{-x}).$$

7. Sketch the members of the family of curves $y = x^n e^{-x}$ for $n = 1$ and $n = 2$.

8. Sketch on the same set of axes the members of the family of curves $y = \log_a x$ for $a = 2$, e, 3, and 10.

9. Sketch each of the following curves:

(a) $y = \log_e 2\,x$.

(b) $y = \log_e \dfrac{x}{2}$.

(c) $y = \log_e x^2$.

(d) $y = \log_e \sqrt{x}$.

(e) $y = \log_e \dfrac{1}{x}$.

(f) $y = \log_e (-x)$.

(g) $y = \log_e^2 x$.

(h) $y = \log_e (\log_e x)$.

(i) $y^2 = \log_e x$.

10. Sketch the curves: (a) $y = \log_e (x + 1)$; (b) $y = \log_e (x - 1)$; (c) $y = \log_e (x^2 - 1)$.

11. Sketch the curves: (a) $y = \log_e (1 + x^2)$; (b) $y = \log_e (1 - x^2)$.

12. Sketch the curves: (a) $y = x + \log_{10} x$; (b) $y = x \log_{10} x$.

13. Sketch the following "damped vibration" curves:

(a) $y = 2\,e^{-x} \sin \dfrac{\pi x}{2}$.

(b) $y = e^{-x/4} \sin 2\,x$.

(c) $s = 2\,e^{-t/5} \cos (\pi t/3)$.

(d) $s = 3\,e^{-t/3} \sin \left(2\,t - \dfrac{\pi}{3} \right)$.

14. Discuss the curve $y = e^{x/2} \sin \pi x$.

MISCELLANEOUS EXERCISES

1. Sketch the graphs of the following equations:

(a) $y = ax^3$ (the cubical parabola). Let $a = \tfrac{1}{8}$.

(b) $y^2 = ax^3$ (the semicubical parabola). Let $a = \tfrac{1}{4}$.

(c) $y = a^3/(x^2 + a^2)$ (the witch). Let $a = 2$.

(d) $y = a^2 x/(x^2 + b^2)$ (the serpentine). Let $a = b = 2$.

(e) $y^2 = x^3/(2\,a - x)$ (the cissoid). Let $a = 3$.

2. Sketch the graphs of the following equations:

(a) $a^2y^2 = 2ax^3 - x^4$. Let $a = 1$.

(b) $\dfrac{x^2}{a^2} + \left(\dfrac{y}{b}\right)^{\frac{2}{3}} = 1$. Let $a = b = 5$.

3. Sketch the members of the family of curves $cy = x^c(x^2 - c^2)$ corresponding to (a) $c = 1, 2, 3$; (b) $c = -1, -2, -3$.

4. Sketch the curve $y^2 = x(x - 1)^2(x + 2)(x - 2)$.

5. Sketch the following curves on the same set of axes:

(a) $y = \sin x$; (b) $y = \sin^2 x$; (c) $y = \sin^3 x$; (d) $y^2 = \sin x$.

6. Sketch the following curves: (a) $y = (\sin x)/x$; (b) $y = e^x/x$; (c) $y = (\log_{10} x)/x$.

7. Sketch the curves: (a) $y = x \sin \pi/x$; (b) $y = \sin x^2$.

8. Sketch the following curves: (a) $y = \log_{10} (x + 1)/(x - 1)$; (b) $y = \log_{10} x\sqrt{x - 1}$.

9. Draw the graph of $y = (1 + x)^{1/x}$ on the interval $-1 \leqq x \leqq 1$. (It is shown in more advanced mathematics that $\lim\limits_{x \to 0} (1 + x)^{1/x} = e$. The number $e = 2.71828 \cdots$ is used as the base in a system of logarithms called the natural, or Napierian, system.)

10. Sketch the graphs of the following equations:

(a) $y = \dfrac{a}{2} (e^{x/a} + e^{-x/a})$ (the catenary). Let $a = 2$.

(b) $y = \dfrac{1}{\sqrt{2\pi}} e^{-x^2/2}$ (the probability curve).

11. Show that the curves $y = \log_a nx$ $(n \neq 0)$ have the same shape as the curve $y = \log_a x$. What is the relation of the curves $y = \log_a x^n$ to the curve $y = \log_a x$?

12. In the equation of the catenary, Exercise 10 (a), solve for x in terms of y.

13. Solve the equation $x = \log_e (y + \sqrt{y^2 \pm 1})$ for y in terms of x and graph.

14. Estimate from the graph the value of x for which y is zero: (a) $y = x + e^x$; (b) $y = x + \log_e x$; (c) $y = x - \cos x$.

15. Draw on the same set of axes the loci in each of the following pairs and estimate the coördinates of their points of intersection:

(a) $y = e^{-x}$,   (b) $y = \log_{10} x$,   (c) $y = 2^x$,   (d) $y = \sin x$,
$y = x$. $y = -x$. $y = 2^{1/x}$. $x = 2y$.

16. Find the points of intersection of the loci in (a) and (b) and illustrate graphically:

(a) $x + y = 1$, (b) $3x - 4y + 15 = 0$,
    $y^2(5 - x) = 5 + x$. $y^2(5 - x) = x^2(5 + x)$.

17. Sketch the locus of $(x^2 - 1)^2 + (y^2 - 1)^2 = 1$. Is the locus a higher plane curve?

18. Find the equation of the locus of a point which moves so that the product of its distances from two fixed points is a constant. Call the distance between the fixed points $2c$ and the constant a^2. (This locus is called the **ovals of Cassini**.)

19. What does the equation of the locus in Exercise 18 become if $a = c$? (This curve is called the **lemniscate of Bernoulli**.)

20. Draw on the same axes the ovals of Cassini for $a = 5$, $c = 4$; $a = 4$, $c = 4$; $a = 3$, $c = 4$.

21. The triangle ABC has a fixed base $AB = 2c$. Find the locus of the vertex C in each of the following cases:

(a) The sum of the sides AC and BC is constant.
(b) The difference of the sides AC and BC is constant.
(c) The product of the sides AC and BC is constant.
(d) The quotient of the sides AC and BC is constant.

CHAPTER VII

PARAMETRIC EQUATIONS

86. Parameters. It is sometimes convenient to express the rectangular coördinates of a point in terms of a third variable, or parameter.* Each rectangular coördinate is expressed in terms of the auxiliary variable and hence two equations are necessary to represent a locus. These equations are called **parametric equations** of the locus. The elimination of the parameter between the two equations gives the equation in x and y. For example, the equations $y = t + 2$, $x = t^2 + 2t$

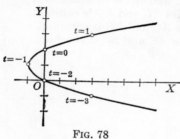

FIG. 78

represent the curve shown in the accompanying figure. Points on the curve are found by assigning values to the parameter t and calculating the coördinates x and y from the given equations. Eliminating the parameter, we have $x = y^2 - 2y$. The curve is a parabola (Fig. 78).

An equation in x and y may be replaced by two parametric equations in an unlimited number of ways. It is sufficient to express one of the coördinates, x or y, in terms of a parameter in any way we choose, substitute in the equation, and solve for the other coördinate in terms of the parameter. The equations for x and y thus obtained are parametric equations of the same locus (or a portion of the same locus) as that defined by the equation in x and y. For example, if we put $y = t + 1$ in the equation $x = y^2 - 2y$, we obtain $x = t^2 - 1$.

*The word "parameter" is used to mean either an auxiliary variable or an arbitrary constant.

Hence $x = t^2 - 1$, $y = t + 1$ is another parametric representation of the parabola in Fig. 78.

Parameters are frequently used in deriving equations of loci. Often the parameter is time or a geometric quantity, such as an angle. It should be observed that the locus is independent of the parameter used.

87. Parametric equations of a circle. If we look upon the circle (Fig. 79) as traced by the point P moving continuously around the circumference, we may choose $\angle XOP = \theta$ as the parameter and write

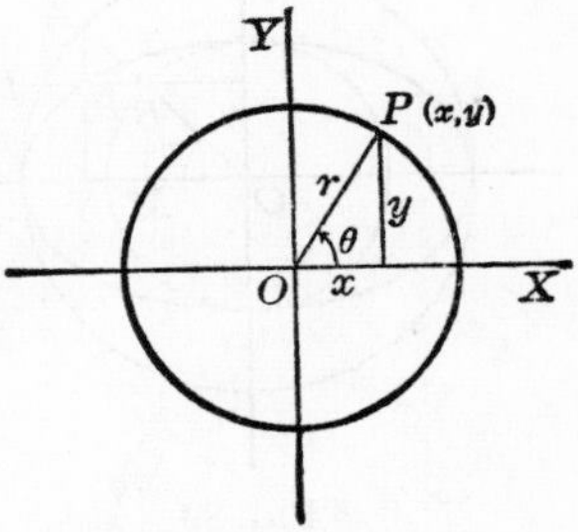

$$x = r \cos \theta \quad \text{and} \quad y = r \sin \theta \quad (1)$$

These are parametric equations of a circle with center at the origin.

FIG. 79

Squaring and adding the equations (1), we have

$$x^2 + y^2 = r^2(\sin^2 \theta + \cos^2 \theta) = r^2.$$

This is the rectangular equation of a circle with center at the origin and radius r. This equation and the parametric equations represent the same circle.

If we suppose that the point P moves at a constant rate, so that OP turns through an angle ω each second, then at the end of t seconds $\theta = \omega t$. Substituting this value for θ in equations (1), we have

$$x = r \cos \omega t \quad \text{and} \quad y = r \sin \omega t.$$

The parametric equations in the latter form enable us to locate the position of the point P in terms of the time during which it has been moving.

88. Parametric equations of an ellipse. Two circles with centers at the origin have radii a and b $(a > b)$. A line is drawn from O cutting the outer circle at A and the inner circle at B. The line AN is drawn parallel to the y-axis and the line BD is drawn parallel to the x-axis. The lines AN and BD intersect at P. We shall show that the locus of P is an ellipse.

From the figure we have for the coördinates of P

$$x = ON = a \cos \phi \quad \text{and} \quad y = NP = MB = b \sin \phi.$$

Dividing by a and b, respectively, squaring, and adding, we have

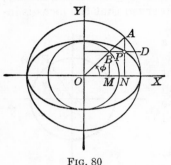

$$\frac{x^2}{a^2} + \frac{y^2}{b^2} = \sin^2 \phi + \cos^2 \phi = 1.$$

This equation represents an ellipse with semiaxes a and b. Hence

$$x = a \cos \phi,$$
$$y = b \sin \phi$$

are parametric equations of an ellipse.

Fig. 80

89. The path of a projectile. Let us assume that no forces other than the attraction of the earth and the initial impulse affect the motion of the projectile. Choose the horizontal and vertical lines through the point at which the projectile leaves the propelling apparatus as the x- and y-axes, respectively.

Call the initial velocity v_0, the angle the initial direction makes with the horizontal α, and the measure of the attraction of the earth g. If g is expressed in feet, then x, y, and v_0 must be expressed in feet.

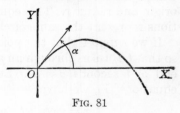

Fig. 81

The horizontal component of the initial velocity is $v_0 \cos \alpha$, and the vertical component is $v_0 \sin \alpha$. The horizontal distance traveled by the projectile in t seconds will be $v_0 t \cos \alpha$, and the vertical distance traveled will be $v_0 t \sin \alpha - \frac{1}{2} g t^2$. The vertical distance is made up of the distance traveled due to the initial velocity minus the distance the attraction of the earth pulls the projectile down. Hence the coördinates of P, after t seconds, will be

$$x = v_0 t \cos \alpha,$$
$$y = v_0 t \sin \alpha - \frac{1}{2} g t^2.$$

These are parametric equations of the path of the projectile. That the path is a parabola is shown by the elimination of the parameter t, which gives

$$y = x \tan \alpha - \frac{gx^2}{2\,v_0{}^2} \sec^2 \alpha.$$

EXERCISES

1. Construct the loci represented by the following parametric equations by assigning values to the parameter and computing the values of x and y:

(a) $x = 1 - t$, $y = 1 + t$.
(b) $x = 1 - t^2$, $y = 1 + t^2$.
(c) $x = 2\,t$, $y = t^2$.
(d) $x = 2\,t$, $y = t^3$.

(e) $x = t^2$, $y = t^3$.
(f) $x = t$, $y = 4/t$.
(g) $x = 4 \cos \theta$, $y = 4 \sin \theta$.
(h) $x = 4 \cos \theta$, $y = 3 \sin \theta$.

2. Eliminate the parameter and show that $x = a \sec \theta$, $y = b \tan \theta$ represent a hyperbola.

3. Eliminate the parameter, identify, and sketch the following loci:

(a) $x = 3 \cos \theta + 4$, $y = 3 \sin \theta - 2$.
(b) $x = 4 \cos \theta + 1$, $y = 2 \sin \theta + 3$.
(c) $x = 2 \tan t$, $y = \sec^2 t$. (e) $x = t + 1/t$, $y = t - 1/t$.
(d) $x = \log_e t$, $y = t + 1$. (f) $x = t/(t+1)$, $y = t/(t-1)$.
(g) $x = (1-t)/(1+t)$, $y = (1-t^2)/(1+t^2)$.

4. Show that $x = \cos^2 \theta - 1$, $y = \cos \theta + 1$ represent a part only of the parabola in Fig. 78 and identify this part.

5. Show that the following parametric equations represent a part only of the locus represented by the equation obtained by eliminating the parameter and identify this part:

(a) $x = \sin^2 \theta$, $y = 2 \cos \theta$. (d) $x = 4 \tan^2 \theta$, $y = 2 \sec \theta$.
(b) $x = 2 \sin \theta$, $y = 2 \cos 2\theta$. (e) $x = \cos^2 \theta$, $y = \cos^3 \theta$.
(c) $x = 2 \cos^2 \theta$, $y = 3 \sin^2 \theta$. (f) $x = e^t$, $y = e^{-t}$.

6. Show that $x = a + bt$, $y = a' + b't$ represent a straight line with slope b'/b.

7. Draw the line $x = 2 + 3\,t$, $y = 3 + 2\,t$.

8. Show that $x = a \cos t + b \sin t$, $y = a \sin t - b \cos t$ represent a circle. Find its center and radius.

9. Show that $x = a \cos nt + c$, $y = b \sin nt + d$ represent an ellipse. Find its center and semiaxes.

10. Find the parametric equations of the parabola $y^2 = 2\,px$ if the parameter is the slope of the line joining the origin to the point (x, y) on the parabola.

11. Find parametric equations of a point on the rim of a wheel 6 feet in diameter which turns on its axle at the rate of 30 revolutions per minute if the point starts from (a) the x-axis; (b) the y-axis; (c) the line $y = x$. (*Hint.* Use origin at center of wheel.)

12. What will the equations of the path of a projectile become if the projectile is fired horizontally?

13. A bullet is fired at an angle of elevation of 30° with an initial velocity of 1600 feet per second. Assuming that the bullet leaves the gun at the ground level and that $g = 32$, find how far away the bullet strikes the earth (assumed to be level). How far above the earth is the highest point of its path?

14. If the bullet in the preceding exercise strikes a target 784 feet above the earth, how far away in a horizontal direction is the target from the gun?

15. If a baseball leaves the hand of a pitcher $5\frac{1}{2}$ feet above the ground in a horizontal direction, what must be its initial velocity to cross the plate 18 inches above the ground? Is this a possible velocity? (Distance from pitcher's box to plate is 60 feet 6 inches.)

16. The parametric equations of the path of a projectile are $x = 100\,t$, $y = 100\,t - 16\,t^2$. Plot the path of the projectile.

90. The cycloid.* *The cycloid is the path traced by a fixed point on the circumference of a circle as the circle rolls along a straight line.*

Let the line along which the circle rolls be the x-axis, and let one of the points at which the fixed point on the circle comes in contact with the x-axis be the origin. Choose for the parameter the angle $\theta = \angle ACP$ (measured in radians) in Fig. 82. This is the angle through which the circle, of

---

*Galileo (1564–1642) first called attention to the cycloid in 1630, suggesting that it be used for the arches of bridges.

radius a, has rolled from its position when the point P was at O. The coördinates x and y of P are

$$x = OB = OA - BA = OA - PD,$$
$$y = BP = AD = AC - DC.$$

But $OA = \text{arc } AP = a\theta$, $PD = a \sin \theta$, $AC = a$,   and $DC = a \cos \theta$. Substituting these values, we have

$$x = a\theta - a \sin \theta = a(\theta - \sin \theta),$$
$$y = a - a \cos \theta = a(1 - \cos \theta),$$

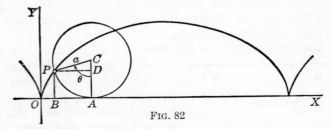

Fig. 82

as parametric equations of the cycloid. Eliminating θ between these equations, we have

$$x = a \text{ arc cos } \frac{a - y}{a} \pm \sqrt{2ay - y^2}$$

as the equation in x and y. This is a transcendental equation.

91. Prolate and curtate cycloids. If the point P of the previous section is not on the circumference, the equation of the locus is obtained in a similar manner. Let b represent the distance of the tracing point from the center of the rolling circle. Then the coördinates of the point P are

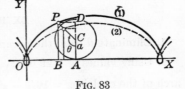

Fig. 83

$$x = OA - BA = a\theta - b \sin \theta,$$
$$y = AC - DC = a - b \cos \theta.$$

If $b > a$, the curve is called a **prolate** cycloid (Fig. 83, curve numbered (1)). If $b < a$, the curve is called a **curtate** cycloid (Fig. 83, curve numbered (2)).

92. Properties of the cycloid. The cycloid has many interesting properties. Some of these properties which can be obtained by more advanced mathematics are:

(a) The length of one arch is 8 a, that is, eight times the radius of the rolling circle.

(b) The area inclosed between one arch and the x-axis is $3 \pi a^2$, that is, three times the area of the rolling circle.

(c) The teeth of gears are often cut with faces which are arcs of cycloids so that there is a rolling contact when the gears are in mesh. The epicycloid, the hypocycloid, and the involute of a circle (discussed in following sections) are also used by the designer of gears.

If the circle rolls along the lower side of the fixed line the

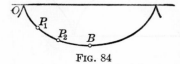

FIG. 84

cycloid will be inverted, as in Fig. 84, and in this position has the additional properties:

(d) If two particles sliding without friction start from any two points of the curve, P_1 and P_2, at the same time, they will reach the lowest point B at the same instant.

(e) A particle sliding without friction will travel from O to B in less time than along any other curve connecting O and B. Hence the cycloid is sometimes called the curve of quickest descent.

The cycloid was the first transcendental curve to be rectified, that is, to have the length of its arc determined by mathematical means.*

EXERCISES

1. Eliminate θ from the parametric equations of the cycloid.

2. Using values of θ at intervals of every $\frac{\pi}{4}$ radians, sketch one arch of the cycloid $x = 10(\theta - \sin \theta)$, $y = 10(1 - \cos \theta)$.

3. What are the lengths of the base and altitude of an arch of the cycloid in Exercise 2?

*This was done by Sir Christopher Wren (1632–1723) in 1658.

4. Derive the equations of the cycloid if the circle rolls along the under side of the fixed line.

5. Derive the equations of the cycloid if the origin is at the top of an arch.

6. Plot the curtate cycloid $x = 9\,\theta - 6\sin\theta$, $y = 9 - 6\cos\theta$.

7. Plot the prolate cycloid $x = 9\,\theta - 12\sin\theta$, $y = 9 - 12\cos\theta$.

93. The epicycloid. *If a circle rolls on the outside of another circle in the same plane, a fixed point on the circumference of the rolling circle will trace a path called an epicycloid.*

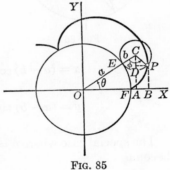

FIG. 85

Let a be the radius of the fixed circle and b the radius of the rolling circle. The angle that the line of centers makes with the x-axis is denoted by θ (Fig. 85) and the angle through which the radius CP turns from the line of centers is denoted by ϕ ($\phi = \angle OCP$). Then $\angle ACO = \pi/2 - \theta$, and $\angle ACP = \phi - (\pi/2 - \theta) = \theta + \phi - \pi/2$. Arcs FE and PE are equal, hence $a\theta = b\phi$. The coördinates of the point P are

$$x = OA + AB = OA + DP = (a + b)\cos\theta + b\sin(\theta + \phi - \pi/2),$$

$$y = BP = AC - DC = (a + b)\sin\theta - b\cos(\theta + \phi - \pi/2).$$ But

$$\sin(\theta + \phi - \pi/2) = -\cos(\theta + \phi),$$
$$\cos(\theta + \phi - \pi/2) = \sin(\theta + \phi),$$
$$\phi = a\theta/b.$$

Making these substitutions, we obtain the parametric equations of the epicycloid,

$$x = (a + b)\cos\theta - b\cos\frac{a + b}{b}\,\theta,$$

$$y = (a + b)\sin\theta - b\sin\frac{a + b}{b}\,\theta.$$

94. The hypocycloid. *If a circle rolls on the inside of a fixed circle in the same plane, a fixed point on the circumference of*

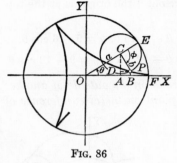

the rolling circle traces a curve called a hypocycloid.

The equations are obtained in a manner similar to that used for the epicycloid and differ from those equations only in the sign of b. Replacing b in the equations of the epicycloid by $-b$, we have the equations of the hypocycloid,

FIG. 86

$$x = (a - b) \cos \theta + b \cos \frac{a - b}{b} \theta,$$

$$y = (a - b) \sin \theta - b \sin \frac{a - b}{b} \theta.$$

The special case where $a = 4\,b$ is of interest. The equations become

$$x = 3\,b \cos \theta + b \cos 3\,\theta = b(3 \cos \theta + 4 \cos^3 \theta - 3 \cos \theta)$$
$$= 4\,b \cos^3 \theta = a \cos^3 \theta,$$

$$y = 3\,b \sin \theta - b \sin 3\,\theta = b(3 \sin \theta - 3 \sin \theta + 4 \sin^3 \theta)$$
$$= 4\,b \sin^3 \theta = a \sin^3 \theta.$$

Eliminating θ, we get

$$x^{\frac{2}{3}} + y^{\frac{2}{3}} = a^{\frac{2}{3}}(\cos^2 \theta + \sin^2 \theta),$$

or $$x^{\frac{2}{3}} + y^{\frac{2}{3}} = a^{\frac{2}{3}},$$

where a is the radius of the fixed circle. This curve is known as the hypocycloid of four cusps (Fig. 87) and is frequently called

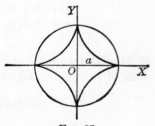

FIG. 87

the **astroid**. The astroid is an algebraic higher plane **curve.**

EXERCISES

1. Sketch the epicycloid for

(a) $b = \dfrac{a}{3}$;   (b) $b = \dfrac{a}{2}$;   (c) $b = \dfrac{2\,a}{3}$;   (d) $b = a$.

2. Sketch the hypocycloid for

(a) $b = \dfrac{a}{3}$;   (b) $b = \dfrac{a}{2}$;   (c) $b = \dfrac{2\,a}{3}$;   (d) $b = a$.

3. Derive the parametric equations of the 4-cusped hypocycloid directly from a figure. (In Fig. 86 let $\phi = 4\,\theta$).

4. Show that the four-cusped hypocycloid is an algebraic curve.

5. Find the coördinates of the points of intersection of the circle $x^2 + y^2 = 25$ with the epicycloid whose equations are $x = 4\cos\theta - \cos 4\,\theta$, $y = 4\sin\theta - \sin 4\,\theta$ and check graphically.

95. The involute of a circle. *If a thread is unwound from around a fixed circle, a point on the thread traces a curve called the involute of the circle.*

Axes are chosen as indicated in Fig. 88, the point P on the thread having been in contact with the circle at A. The coördinates of P, expressed in terms of θ, give the parametric equations of the involute,

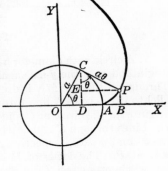

$$x = OD + DB = a\cos\theta + a\theta\sin\theta,$$

$$y = DC - EC = a\sin\theta - a\theta\cos\theta.$$

FIG. 88

MISCELLANEOUS EXERCISES

1. Eliminate the parameter and sketch:

(a) $x = \cos(t/2)$, $y = 1 + \cos t$.   (d) $x = t/(1 + t^2)$, $y = t/(1 - t^2)$.

(b) $x = e^{-t}$, $y = e^{2t}$.   (e) $x = t/(t - 1)$, $y = t^2/(t - 1)$.

(c) $x = \tan t$, $y = \sin t$.   (f) $x = e^{2t}$, $y = e^t + 1$.

(g) $x = \sin t$, $y = \cos 4\,t$.

2. Show that $x = \dfrac{a(1 - t^2)}{1 + t^2}$, $y = \dfrac{2\,bt}{1 + t^2}$ represent an ellipse.

3. Show that $x = e^t + e^{-t}$, $y = e^t - e^{-t}$ represent a branch of an equilateral hyperbola.

4. Show that $x = t^2 + t$, $y = t^2 - t$ represent a parabola.

5. Show that $x = a \log_e t$, $y = \dfrac{a}{2}\Big(t + \dfrac{1}{t}\Big)$ represent the catenary $y = \dfrac{a}{2}\Big(e^{\frac{x}{a}} + e^{-\frac{x}{a}}\Big)$.

6. Show that each of the following sets of parametric equations, (1) $x = a\,\cos^4 t$, $y = a \sin^4 t$, (2) $x = a \sec^4 t$, $y = a \tan^4 t$, and (3) $x = a \tan^4 t$, $y = a \sec^4 t$, represents a different arc of the same parabola.

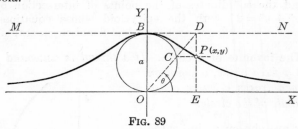

FIG. 89

7. A circle with diameter a is drawn tangent to the x-axis at the origin and cuts the y-axis again at B. Through B the line MN is drawn parallel to the x-axis. A line through the origin cuts the circle at C and MN at D. Lines through C and D parallel to the x- and y-axes, respectively, intersect at P. The locus of P is called the witch of Agnesi (Fig. 89). Find its equations. (Let $\theta = \angle EOC$ be the parameter.)

8. From the fixed point $A(-a, 0)$ a line is drawn intersecting the y-axis at B. In either direction from B along AB the distance $BP = OB$ (numerically) is laid off. The locus of P is called the strophoid (Fig. 90). Find its parametric equations, using θ as the parameter.

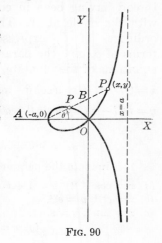

FIG. 90

9. Eliminate θ from the parametric equations of the witch (Exercise 7).

10. Eliminate θ from the parametric equations of the strophoid (Exercise 8).

11. The curve whose parametric equations are $x = 3\,at/(1 + t^3)$, $y = 3\,at^2/(1 + t^3)$ is called the folium of **Descartes** (Fig. 91). Show that (*a*) its equation in x and y is $x^3 + y^3 - 3\,axy = 0$;   (*b*) the line $x + y + a = 0$ is an asymptote of the curve. (*Hint.* Show that as t approaches -1, x and y increase numerically without limit but their sum, $x + y$, approaches $-a$.)

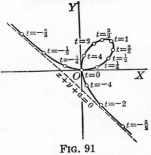

FIG. 91

12. If a ring with polished inner surface is laid on a table and the light shines from one side and above, a brightly illuminated curve is seen on the table within the ring. A similar curve may be observed in a glass of milk. Such a curve is called a **caustic.** If the ring has a radius of 1, the equations of the caustic are $x = \frac{3}{4}\cos\theta - \frac{1}{4}\cos 3\,\theta$, $y = \frac{3}{4}\sin\theta - \frac{1}{4}\sin 3\,\theta$. Draw the curve. Show that this curve is an epicycloid for which $a = \frac{1}{2}$ and $b = \frac{1}{4}$.

13. The rod OAB is pivoted at O and hinged at A. The part of the rod OA turns about O at a constant rate, while AB turns about A at a rate twice as great. Find the equations of B if $OA = AB$ and the turning begins when OAB is a straight line.

14. The parallelogram $OQPQ'$ is hinged and OQ and OQ' turn about O at constant rates. Find the equations of the locus of P.

15. A crank OP, 2 feet in length, turns around O at a uniform rate. A rod 6 feet long is attached at P and the other end Q moves along a fixed line OB. Find the equations of the path of P, and the equations of the path of Q, if the origin is at O and the line OB is the x-axis. (Let $\theta = \angle BOP$ be the parameter.)

16. Find the equations of the locus of the midpoint of the rod PQ in Exercise 15.

17. Eliminate the parameter from the equations derived in Exercise **16** and show that the locus is an algebraic higher plane curve.

18. The ends A and B of the segment AB of a rigid rod ABP move on the x- and y-axes respectively (Fig. 92). The lengths of AB and BP are a units and b units respectively. Find the locus of P. (Let $\theta = \angle OAB$ be the parameter.)

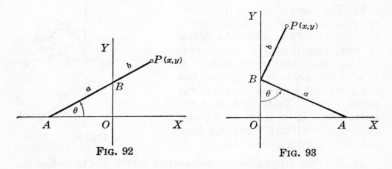

FIG. 92   FIG. 93

19. The ends A and B of a rod of length a units move on the x- and y-axes respectively. A rod BP of length b units is rigidly attached to AB at B and is perpendicular to AB (Fig. 93). Find the locus of P. (Let $\theta = \angle OBA$ be the parameter.)

20. An insect crawls out along the spoke of a wheel 4 feet in diameter at the rate of 1 foot per minute. The wheel is rolling along the ground at the rate of 2 revolutions per minute. Find the equations of the path of the insect. Draw the graph showing the path of the insect for the first 2 minutes. (Assume that the insect starts to crawl vertically downward from the center of the wheel at time $t = 0$. Choose for origin the bottom point of the wheel when $t = 0$.)

CHAPTER VIII

POLAR EQUATIONS

96. Polar coördinates. Another method of locating a point
P in a plane is obtained by giving its distance OP (Fig. 94)

from a fixed point O and the
angle MOP which OP makes
with a fixed line OM through
O. OM is called the **polar axis**,
OP the **radius vector** of the
point P, and O the **pole**. The
polar coördinates of P are designated by (ρ, θ), where ρ is the
distance OP and θ the vectorial
angle MOP. The distance ρ is

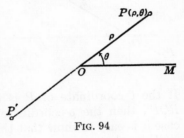

Fig. 94

measured from the pole; it is considered positive if measured
along the terminal side of θ, and negative if measured in the
opposite direction. Thus in Fig. 94
the point P could be located by giving θ the value of the positive angle
MOP' and making ρ negative; or by
giving θ the value of the negative
angle MOP and making ρ positive.

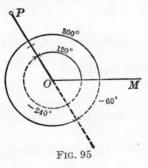

Fig. 95

In Fig. 95 the point P may be
represented by any one of the four
sets of coördinates—(a) $(2, 120°)$;
(b) $(2, -240°)$; (c) $(-2, -60°)$;
(d) $(-2, 300°)$—in which the angle
is numerically less than 360°. Any of these angles may be
increased or decreased by a multiple of 360° and the point
will not be changed. Hence there are an indefinite number of
sets of polar coördinates for any point. There is, however, just
one point corresponding to a given set of polar coördinates.

Are there four distinct polar representations of a point on the polar axis with θ numerically less than 360°?

97. Relations between rectangular and polar coördinates. If we make the pole of the polar system coincide with the origin of the rectangular system, and place the polar axis on the positive x-axis, it is easy to find relations between

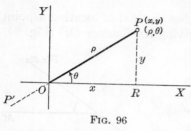

FIG. 96

the rectangular coördinates (x, y) and the polar coördinates (ρ, θ) of any point P. From the $\triangle OPR$ we have

$$x = \rho \cos \theta,$$
$$y = \rho \sin \theta,$$
and $$\rho = \sqrt{x^2 + y^2},$$
$$\theta = \arctan \frac{y}{x}.$$

If the θ-coördinate of P is the positive or negative angle ROP', then the ρ-coördinate of P is $-\sqrt{x^2 + y^2}$. In this case it is easy to show that the remaining three formulas are unchanged.

EXERCISES

1. Plot the following points on the same diagram: $(4, 30°)$; $(-4, 30°)$; $(4, -30°)$; $(-4, -30°)$; $(-4, 210°)$; $(-4, 150°)$; $(4, 150°)$.

2. Plot the following points on the same diagram: $(6, \pi/4)$; $(-2, \pi/3)$; $(5, \pi/2)$; $(-5, -\pi/2)$; $(3, \pi)$; $(-3, -\pi)$; $(a, 2n\pi)$, where $a > 0$ and n is any integer positive or negative.

3. What point is represented by $(0, \theta)$? *pole*

4. A regular hexagon with sides each 6 units in length has its center at the pole and one vertex on the polar axis. Give a pair of polar coördinates of each of its vertices.

5. Give at least three more distinct pairs of polar coördinates representing the point $(1, \pi/3)$.

6. Give the rectangular coördinates of each of the points in Exercises 1 and 2.

7. Give a pair of polar coördinates of the points whose rectangular coördinates are $(2, 2)$; $(-2, 2)$; $(-2, -2)$; $(2, -2)$; $(2, 0)$; $(0, 2)$; $(-1, \sqrt{3})$; $(1, -\sqrt{3})$.

8. Plot on one diagram $(3, 0)$; $(2\sqrt{3}, \pi/6)$; $(3\sqrt{2}, \pi/4)$; $(6, \pi/3)$; $(2\sqrt{3}, -\pi/6)$; $(-3\sqrt{2}, 3\pi/4)$; $(-6, 2\pi/3)$. Show that these points lie on a straight line perpendicular to the polar axis.

9. Show that $(4, 5\pi/6)$, $(12 - 4\sqrt{3}, \pi/2)$, and $(12, \pi/3)$ lie on a straight line.

10. Find the distance between $(5, 2\pi/3)$ and $(8, \pi/3)$. (*Hint.* Use the cosine law.) Check the answer by using rectangular coordinates.

11. Find the area of the triangle whose vertices are $(0, 0)$, $(10, \pi/6)$, and $(8, \pi/3)$. (*Hint.* Use formula area $= \frac{1}{2} ab \sin C$ where a and b are two sides of a triangle and C is their included angle.)

12. Find the area of the triangle whose vertices are

(*a*) $(4, \pi/3)$, $(6, 2\pi/3)$, and $(8, 4\pi/3)$.
(*b*) $(6, \pi/6)$, $(8, 5\pi/6)$, and $(10, -\pi/2)$.
(*c*) $(12, \pi/6)$, $(8, 5\pi/6)$, and $(5, 5\pi/6)$.

98. Graphs of polar equations. EXAMPLE 1. Draw the graph of $\rho = 2 \sin \theta$.

Assigning values* to θ and finding corresponding values of ρ, we make a table of values:

$\theta =$	0°	30°	45°	60°	90°	120°	135°	150°	180°
$\rho =$	0	1	$\sqrt{2}$	$\sqrt{3}$	2	$\sqrt{3}$	$\sqrt{2}$	1	0

Plotting the corresponding points and drawing a smooth curve through them in the order of increasing θ, we have the graph shown in Fig. 97. It is to be noted that if θ is allowed to vary from 180° to 360°, the corresponding values of ρ will be numerically equal to those

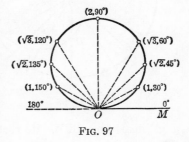

FIG. 97

*The student should not overlook those values of θ for which ρ has its numerically largest and zero values.

obtained above but will be negative. Hence these additional points will coincide with those already found and no new part of the curve will be obtained. The graph is, therefore, completed as θ varies from 0° to 180°.

We can readily show that this curve is a circle by transforming its polar equation to rectangular form. Using formulas in Sec. 97, the equation $\rho = 2 \sin \theta$ can be written

$$\rho = 2\,y/\rho \quad \text{or} \quad \rho^2 = 2\,y \quad \text{or} \quad x^2 + y^2 = 2\,y,$$

which represents a circle.

EXAMPLE 2. Draw the graph of $\rho = 4(1 + \cos \theta)$.
Making a table of values,

$\theta =$	0°	30°	45°	60°	90°	120°	135°	150°	180°
$\rho =$	8	7.5	6.8	6	4	2	1.2	0.5	0

plotting the corresponding points, and drawing a smooth curve through them in the order of increasing θ, we obtain the branch MBO of the curve in Fig. 98. If θ is allowed to vary from 180° to 360° the corresponding values of ρ will be equal, in reverse order, to those obtained above and will be positive. Hence additional points are found and the branch $OB'M$ is drawn. The curve is called a **cardioid** (meaning "heart-shaped"). Its rectangular equation is:

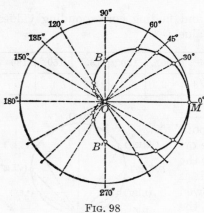

FIG. 98

$$x^4 + 2\,x^2y^2 + y^4 - 8\,xy^2 - 8\,x^3 - 16\,y^2 = 0.$$

Obviously the polar equation is simpler.

EXAMPLE 3. Draw the graph of $\rho = a\theta$.

Assigning positive values (in radian measure) to θ and finding the corresponding values of ρ, we plot points and draw the curve as shown in Fig. 99 for $a = 1$. Since ρ varies directly as θ, ρ will increase indefinitely as θ increases. Hence the curve will recede in spiral form farther and farther from the pole.

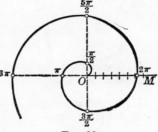

The student should draw that part of the graph corresponding to negative values of θ.

Discuss the graph for $a = -1$.

FIG. 99

EXERCISES

1. Draw the graphs of the following equations:

(a) $\rho = 2 \cos \theta$.

(b) $\rho = 4(1 - \cos \theta)$.

(c) $\rho = -6 \sin \theta$.

(d) $\rho = 2(1 + \sin \theta)$.

(e) $\rho = 5$.

(f) $\theta = 1$.

(g) $\rho \cos \theta = 3$.

(h) $\rho \sin \theta = 2$.

(i) $\rho = 2 \sin^2 \theta$.

(j) $\rho^2 = 4 \cos \theta$.

(k) $\rho = 2 + 4 \cos \theta$.

(l) $\rho = 3 + \sin \theta$.

(m) $\rho = 4 \cos (\theta/2)$.

(n) $\rho^2 = 9 \sin 2 \theta$.

(o) $\rho = 2 \tan \theta$.

2. Draw the graphs of the following equations:

(a) $2 \rho = \theta$; (b) $2 \rho = -\theta$; (c) $\rho\theta = 2$; (d) $\rho\theta = -2$.

3. Transform the following equations to rectangular form and sketch:

(a) $\rho = 4 \sec \theta \tan \theta$.

(b) $\rho^2 = 4 \tan \theta \sec^2 \theta$.

(c) $\rho^2 = 2 \csc 2 \theta$.

(d) $\rho = 4 \csc \theta \cot \theta$.

(e) $\rho = 4 \tan^2 \theta \sec \theta$.

(f) $\rho \sin 2 \theta = 2(\sin \theta + \cos \theta)$.

4. Identify the locus $\rho(2 \cos \theta + 3 \sin \theta) = 6$.

5. Change to rectangular form and show that $\rho = 4(\sin \theta + \cos \theta)$ represents a circle. Give a pair of polar coördinates of its center.

6. Sketch the loci of the following equations:

(a) $\rho(1 - \cos \theta) = 2$; (b) $\rho(2 - \cos \theta) = 3$; (c) $\rho(1 - 2 \cos \theta) = 3$.

7. Change the equations in (a), (b), and (c), Exercise 6, to rectangular form and identify the loci.

8. Change the equations in (a) and (b) to rectangular form. Which form, polar or rectangular, would be easier to use in sketching the curve?

(a) $\rho = 1 + 2 \sin \theta$. (b) $\rho^2 = \cos 2\,\theta$.

9. Transform to polar form:

(a) $x^2 + y^2 - 8\,x = 0$. (c) $x^2 + y^2 = 9$.
(b) $x^2 + y^2 + 8\,y = 0$. (d) $x^2 - y^2 = 9$.

10. Transform to polar form and sketch:

(a) $x^4 + x^2y^2 = y^2$; (b) $x^3 + xy^2 = y$; (c) $x^6 + x^4y^2 = y^4$.

11. Show that $\rho = f(\theta)$, $\rho = f(\theta + 2\,\pi)$, and $-\rho = f(\theta + \pi)$ represent the same curve.

12. Verify that the equations in each of the following pairs represent the same curve:

(a) $\rho = 2 + \cos \theta$, (b) $\rho = 1 + 2 \sin \theta$, (c) $\rho = a$,
$\rho = \cos \theta - 2$. $\rho = 2 \sin \theta - 1$. $\rho = -a$.

13. Show that each of the four equations $\rho = \pm \sin \dfrac{\theta}{2}$, $\rho = \pm \cos \dfrac{\theta}{2}$ represents the same curve.

99. Polar equation of a straight line. In the figure, $OC = p$ (considered positive as in Sec. 22) is drawn from the pole

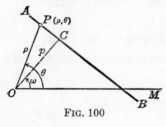

Fig. 100

perpendicular to the line AB whose equation we are seeking and making an angle ω with the polar axis. Let $P\,(\rho,\ \theta)$ be any point on the line AB and draw OP. Then $\angle COP = \theta - \omega$, and from the figure we have

$$\rho \cos (\theta - \omega) = p.$$

This is the polar equation of the line AB, since it is a relation between ρ and θ that is true for every point on the line AB and for no other point.

There are some important special cases of the polar equation of the straight line. For a line perpendicular to the polar axis $\omega = 0°$ or $180°$ and the equation becomes

$$\rho \cos \theta = p \quad \text{or} \quad \rho \cos \theta = -p.$$

For a line parallel to the polar axis $\omega = 90°$ or $270°$ and the equation becomes

$$\rho \sin \theta = p \quad \text{or} \quad \rho \sin \theta = -p.$$

A line through the pole has for its equation

$$\theta = k. \quad (k \text{ a constant})$$

100. Polar equation of a circle. Let (ρ_1, θ_1) be the polar coordinates of the center and (ρ, θ) the polar coördinates of any point on a circle of radius r.

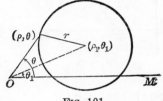

Equating the square of the distance from (ρ_1, θ_1) to (ρ, θ) to r^2, we have for the polar equation of a circle

$$\rho^2 + \rho_1{}^2 - 2\,\rho\rho_1 \cos (\theta - \theta_1) = r^2.$$

The polar equation is, in general, more complicated than the equa-

FIG. 101

tion of the circle in rectangular coördinates. Some special cases of the equation of the circle in polar coördinates are quite simple and useful.

(a) If the center is the pole the equation becomes

$$\rho = \pm r.$$

(b) If the center is $(r, 0°)$ or $(r, 180°)$ the equation becomes

$$\rho = 2\,r \cos \theta \quad \text{or} \quad \rho = -2\,r \cos \theta.$$

(c) If the center is $(r, 90°)$ or $(r, 270°)$ the equation becomes

$$\rho = 2\,r \sin \theta \quad \text{or} \quad \rho = -2\,r \sin \theta.$$

101. Polar equation of a conic. The polar equation of a conic can easily be obtained from the definition in Sec. 76. Choose the focus for the pole and the line through the focus perpendicular to the directrix for the polar axis. The ratio of the definition is the eccentricity of the conic.

By definition, $FP = eDP.$ (Fig. 102)

But $FP = \rho$ and $DP = p + \rho \cos \theta.$ Hence

$$\rho = ep + e\rho \cos \theta.$$

Solving for ρ, we have

$$\rho = \frac{ep}{1 - e \cos \theta}.$$

Figs. 103, 104, and 105 are drawn for $e = 1$, $e = \frac{1}{2}$, and $e = 2$, respectively, and represent a parabola, an ellipse, and a hyperbola.

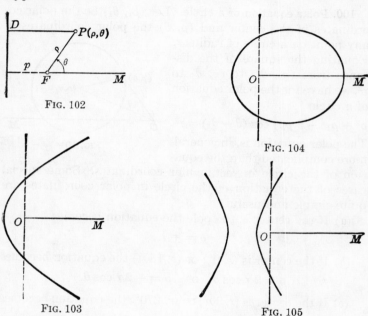

Fig. 102

Fig. 104

Fig. 103

Fig. 105

EXERCISES

1. A line is perpendicular to the polar axis at a point 5 units to the right of the pole. Derive its polar equation directly from a figure.

2. A line is parallel to the polar axis and 3 units above it. Derive its polar equation directly from a figure.

3. Change to polar form: (a) $x = \pm 6$; (b) $y = \pm 2$.

4. Draw the following lines:

   (a) $\rho \cos \theta = 3$.

   (b) $\rho \sin \theta = -1$.

   (c) $\theta = \pi/3$.

   (d) $\theta = \arctan \frac{3}{4}$.

   (e) $\rho = 2\sqrt{2} \sec (\theta - \pi/4)$.

   (f) $\rho = 3 \sec (2 \pi/3 - \theta)$.

5. Transform the equations of Exercise 4 to rectangular coördinates.

6. Change equation (6), Sec. 22, to polar form.

7. A square of side 6 units has one vertex at the pole and the lower side extending to the right along the polar axis. Write the polar equations of its four sides and its two diagonals.

8. Show that $\rho = 2\,r\cos\theta$ represents a circle (a) directly from a figure; (b) by changing the equation to rectangular form.

9. Show that $\rho = 2\,r\sin\theta$ represents a circle.

10. Draw the following circles:

(a) $\rho = 10\cos\theta$.	(c) $\rho = -8\cos\theta$.	(e) $\rho = 5$.
(b) $\rho = 6\sin\theta$.	(d) $\rho = -4\sin\theta$.	(f) $\rho = -5$.

11. Show that $\rho = a\cos\theta + b\sin\theta$ represents a circle.

12. Identify the arc of the circle $\rho = 6(\cos\theta + \sin\theta)$ which is obtained as θ varies from $3\,\pi/4$ to π. Give other intervals for θ which correspond to the same arc.

13. Find the locus of the midpoints of all chords passing through a fixed point on a given circle.

14. Show that the polar equation of the conic with focus at the pole to the left of the directrix is $\rho = ep/(1 + e\cos\theta)$.

15. Show that the polar equation of the conic with focus at the pole and directrix parallel to and below the polar axis is $\rho = ep/(1 - e\sin\theta)$. How will the equation differ if the directrix is above the polar axis?

16. Graph the following equations:

(a) $\rho = \dfrac{6}{1 - \cos\theta}$.

(b) $\rho = \dfrac{6}{1 - \sin\theta}$.

(c) $\rho = \dfrac{4}{2 + \cos\theta}$.

(d) $\rho = \dfrac{4}{2 + \sin\theta}$.

(e) $\rho = \dfrac{8}{1 + 3\cos\theta}$.

(f) $\rho = \dfrac{8}{1 + 3\sin\theta}$.

17. Show that $\rho = a/(\cos\theta + 1)$ and $\rho = a/(\cos\theta - 1)$ represent the same parabola.

18. Show that $\rho = a\sec^2\dfrac{\theta}{2}$ is a parabola, and sketch.

102. The rose-leaved curves $\rho = a \sin n\theta$ **and** $\rho = a \cos n\theta$.
These families of curves are very much alike. We shall dis-

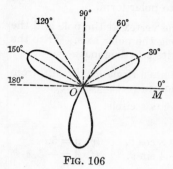

FIG. 106

cuss the curve $\rho = a \sin 3\,\theta$.

The radius vector ρ will be zero whenever $3\,\theta$ is $0°$, $180°$, or some multiple of $180°$. This will occur when θ is $0°$, $60°$, $120°$, $180°$, $240°$, $300°$, etc. Numerically ρ will be greatest when $3\,\theta$ is some odd multiple of $90°$, that is, when θ is $30°$, $90°$, $150°$, $210°$, $270°$, $330°$, etc. As θ varies from $0°$ to $30°$, $3\,\theta$ varies from $0°$ to $90°$, $\sin 3\,\theta$ varies from 0 to 1,

and ρ varies from 0 to a. As θ varies from $30°$ to $60°$, ρ decreases from a to 0; as θ varies from $60°$ to $90°$, ρ decreases from 0 to $-a$; as θ varies from $90°$ to $120°$, ρ increases from $-a$ to 0; as θ varies from $120°$ to $150°$, ρ increases from 0 to a; and as θ varies from $150°$ to $180°$, ρ decreases from a to 0. As θ varies from $180°$ to $360°$, the same curve is retraced. The graph of the equation is shown in Fig. 106.

In case n is an even number, the curve will have $2\,n$ loops, as is illustrated in Fig. 107 for $\rho = a \cos 2\,\theta$.

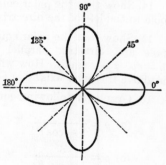

FIG. 107

103. The limaçon of Pascal. If to each radius vector of the circle, located with respect to the pole and the polar axis as shown in Fig. 108, is added a positive constant b, the locus of P, the end of the new radius vector, is a limaçon.

The equation of a circle thus located is (Sec. 100) $\rho = 2\,a \cos \theta$, where a is the radius.

The equation of the locus of P is evidently

$$\rho = 2\,a \cos \theta + b.$$

(1) If $b > 2\,a$, ρ is always positive and the graph of the equation is shown in Fig. 108 as the curve numbered (1).

(2) If $b = 2\,a$, $\rho = 0$ for $\theta = \pi$ and is positive for other values of θ, and the resulting curve is shown as the curve numbered (2). This form of the limaçon is called the **cardioid**.

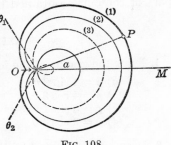

FIG. 108

(3) If $b < 2\,a$, $\rho = 0$ for $\theta_1 = \text{arc} \cos (-\,b/2\,a)$ in the second quadrant and for $\theta_2 = \text{arc} \cos (-\,b/2\,a)$ in the third quadrant, and $\rho < 0$ for values of θ such that $\theta_1 < \theta < \theta_2$. The curve is shown as the curve numbered (3). For $b = a$, the curve is called the **trisectrix**.

104. The spirals. The spirals are curves for which the radius vector continuously increases or decreases as the vectorial angle changes. The curve makes a circuit of the pole for each change of $2\,\pi$ in the vectorial angle. The spirals are transcendental curves.

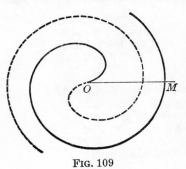

FIG. 109

Some of the spirals have names suggested by the fact that the polar coördinates enter into the equation in the same way as rectangular coördinates enter into the equation of the curve for which the spiral is named. For example, the graph of the equation $\rho^2 = a\theta$ is called the parabolic spiral. There is no analogy between the loci. A well-known spiral is the **spiral of Archimedes**, shown in Fig. 99, page 153.

The spirals can be readily graphed by locating a few points on each turn of the curve about the pole. Fig. 109 shows the graph of $\rho^2 = 4\,\theta$. Solving for ρ, we have $\rho = \pm\,2\sqrt{\theta}$. The solid line represents the part of the curve obtained by using positive values of ρ and the dotted line represents that part of the curve obtained by using negative values of ρ.

EXERCISES

1. Draw the graphs of the following equations:

(a) $\rho = 4 \sin 2\,\theta$.

(b) $\rho = 4 \cos 3\,\theta$.

(c) $\rho = 3 \sin 4\,\theta$.

(d) $\rho = 3 \cos 4\,\theta$.

(e) $\rho = 2 \sin 5\,\theta$.

(f) $\rho = 3 \cos 6\,\theta$.

(g) $\rho = 5 \sin 9\,\theta$.

(h) $\rho = 7 \cos 10\,\theta$.

2. Draw only that part of the graph of each of the following equations which corresponds to the specified interval of θ:

(a) $\rho = 3 \sin 2\,\theta,\ 0 \leqq \theta \leqq 3\,\pi/4$.

(b) $\rho = 4 \sin 3\,\theta,\ \dfrac{\pi}{6} \leqq \theta \leqq \dfrac{2\,\pi}{3}$.

(c) $\rho = 3 \cos 2\,\theta,\ \dfrac{\pi}{4} \leqq \theta \leqq \pi$.

(d) $\rho = 2 \cos 6\,\theta,\ 0 \leqq \theta \leqq \dfrac{\pi}{2}$.

3. Draw the limaçons corresponding to the following equations:

(a) $\rho = 2 \cos \theta + 3$.

(b) $\rho = 3 \sin \theta + 5$.

(c) $\rho = 3(1 + \cos \theta)$.

(d) $\rho = 4(1 - \sin \theta)$.

(e) $\rho = 2 + 4 \cos \theta$.

(f) $\rho = 1 - 2 \sin \theta$.

4. Draw the following spirals:

(a) $\rho = a\theta$ (spiral of Archimedes). Let $a = \frac{1}{3}$.

(b) $\rho\theta = a$ (hyperbolic spiral). Let $a = 1$.

(c) $\rho = e^{a\theta}$ (logarithmic spiral). Let $a = \frac{1}{2}$.

(d) $\rho^2\theta = a$ (lituus). Let $a = 4$.

5. Sketch the graphs of the following equations:

(a) $\rho + \theta = \pi$.

(b) $\rho - \theta = \pi$.

(c) $\rho^2 + \theta^2 = \pi^2$.

(d) $\rho^2 - \theta^2 = \pi^2$.

6. Change to rectangular form:

(a) $\rho\theta = a$; (b) $\rho = a \sin 2\,\theta$; (c) $\rho = a \cos 2\,\theta$; (d) $\rho = a + b \cos \theta$.

105. The intersection of polar curves. Care must be exercised in the simultaneous solution of polar equations. It is usually desirable to check the solutions found by solving the equations simultaneously with the solutions found by drawing the two loci on the same diagram. The following example illustrates the difficulty.

EXAMPLE. Find the intersections of the curves $\rho = \sin \theta$ and $\rho = 2 \cos \theta + 1$.

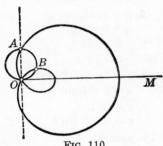

FIG. 110

Eliminating ρ, we have

$$\sin \theta = 2 \cos \theta + 1.$$

Replacing $\sin \theta$ by $\pm \sqrt{1 - \cos^2 \theta}$, squaring, and solving, we obtain

$$\cos \theta = 0 \quad \text{and} \quad \cos \theta = -\tfrac{4}{5}.$$

For $\cos \theta = 0$, we have from each equation $\rho = 1$ when $\theta = \pi/2$, and $\rho = -1$ and $\rho = 1$, respectively, when $\theta = 3 \pi/2$. Hence $A(1, \pi/2)$ is an intersection. For $\cos \theta = -\tfrac{4}{5}$, θ in the second quadrant, $\rho = \tfrac{3}{5}$ in one case and $\rho = -\tfrac{3}{5}$ in the other. Hence there is no intersection for this value of θ. For $\cos \theta = -\tfrac{4}{5}$, θ in the third quadrant, $\rho = -\tfrac{3}{5}$ in each equation, and the point $B(-\tfrac{3}{5}, 216° 52')$ is an intersection. The pole should be checked independently, since it is represented by $\rho = 0$ no matter what value θ may have.

In some cases there are points other than the pole at which the curves evidently intersect but whose coördinates are not given by the simultaneous solutions of the equations. The coördinates of these points may be found by using other pairs of equations which represent the same curves.

EXERCISES

Find the points of intersection of the loci in each of the following pairs and illustrate graphically:

1. $2 \rho \cos \theta = 3$,
   $\rho = 6 \cos \theta$.

2. $\rho = 4(1 + \sin \theta)$,
   $\rho \sin \theta = 3$.

3. $\rho = 4 \sin^2 \theta,$
$\rho = 3.$

4. $\rho = 3 \cos \theta,$
$\rho = 1 + \cos \theta.$

5. $\rho = 1,$
$\rho = 2 \cos 2 \theta.$

6. $\rho = \sin \theta,$
$\rho = \cos 2 \theta.$

7. $\rho = 4 \cos \theta,$
$\rho = 4 \sin \theta.$

8. $\rho = 1,$
$\rho = 4 + 6 \cos \theta.$

9. $\rho \sin \theta = 1,$
$\rho = 3 - 2 \sin \theta.$

10. $\rho \sin \theta = 1,$
$\rho = 2 - \sin \theta.$

11. $\rho = 2 \cos \theta,$
$2 \rho(1 + \cos \theta) = 3.$

12. $\rho = 2(1 + \cos \theta),$
$\rho(1 - \cos \theta) = 1.$

13. $\rho = 3 \sin \theta,$
$\rho = 3 \sin 2 \theta.$

14. $\rho = 6 \sin 2 \theta,$
$\rho = 6 \cos 2 \theta.$

15. $\rho^2 = \sin 2 \theta,$
$\rho^2 = \cos 2 \theta.$

16. $\rho = 1,$
$\rho = 2 \cos \dfrac{\theta}{2}.$

17. $\rho = 1,$
$\rho = \tan \theta.$

18. $\rho = \sqrt{2},$
$\rho^2 = \tan \theta \sec^2 \theta.$

19. $\rho = a\theta,$
$\rho\theta = a.$

20. $\rho = a\theta,$
$(\rho - a)^2 = a^2(1 - \theta^2).$

MISCELLANEOUS EXERCISES

1. Draw the curves corresponding to the following equations:

(a) $\rho = 2 + \sin 2 \theta.$ (d) $\rho = 2 + \sin^2 4 \theta.$
(b) $\rho = 2 - \sin (\theta/2).$ (e) $(\rho - 2)^2 = \sin^2 2 \theta.$
(c) $\rho = 2 + \sin 4 \theta.$ (f) $(\rho - 2)^2 = \sin 6 \theta.$

2. Sketch the following curves:
(a) $\rho \sin (\theta/2) = 2;$ (b) $\rho \sin (\theta/3) = 1;$ (c) $\rho \sin 2 \theta = 2.$

3. Sketch the following curves:

(a) $\rho \sin 2 \theta = 2 \sin \theta.$ (c) $\rho^2 \sin 2 \theta = 2 \cos \theta.$
(b) $\rho \cos 2 \theta = 2 \cos \theta.$ (d) $\rho^2 \sin \theta = \cos 2 \theta.$

4. Sketch the curves: (a) $\rho = 4 \cos (3 \theta/2);$ (b) $\rho = 4 \cos (2 \theta/3).$

5. Show that each of the following equations represents an equilateral hyperbola: (a) $\rho^2 \sin 2 \theta = a;$ (b) $\rho^2 \cos 2\theta = a.$

6. Sketch the curves: (a) $\rho = 4/(\theta^2 + 1);$ (b) $\rho = 4/(\theta^2 - 1);$ (c) $\rho = \pi^2/\theta^2.$

7. Find the points of intersection of the loci in each of the following pairs and illustrate graphically:

(a) $\rho = a \sec^2 \dfrac{\theta}{2}$, (b) $\rho = 1 + \sin \theta$, (c) $\rho = 1 + 2 \sin \theta$,

$\rho = a \csc^2 \dfrac{\theta}{2}$. $\rho = 1 + \sin 2\theta$. $\rho^2 = 1$.

8. Change to polar form and sketch:

(a) $(x^2 + y^2)^3 = 16 \, x^2 y^2 (x^2 - y^2)^2$; (b) $x = e^t \cos t$, $y = e^t \sin t$.

9. Show that the same curve is represented by:

(a) $x = 2(t + 1)$, $y = t(t + 2)$, and $\rho(1 - \sin \theta) = 2$.

(b) $x = 4 \cos t + 2$, $y = 2\sqrt{3} \sin t$ and $\rho(2 - \cos \theta) = 6$.

10. From the parametric equations of the strophoid obtained in Exercise 8, page 146, obtain its polar equation.

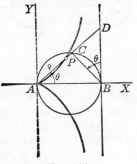

11. See Fig. 111. To a circle of radius a, with a diameter AB, a tangent is drawn at B. Any line is drawn from A cutting the circle at C and the tangent at D. The locus of P, where $AP = CD$, is called the cissoid of Diocles. Find its polar equation and transform it to rectangular form.

FIG. 111

12. See Fig. 112. Through a fixed point A, any line AB is drawn cutting a fixed line CD at M. The points P and P' are located so that $P'M = MP = b$, a constant. The locus of P and P' is called the conchoid of Nicomedes. Find its polar equation.

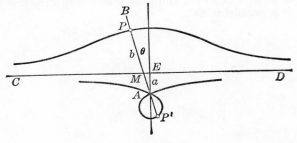

FIG. 112

13. A moving line of constant length has its ends on the x- and y-axes. Find the polar equation of the locus of its midpoint.

14. A moving line of constant length has its ends on the x- and y-axes. Find the polar equation of the locus of the foot of the perpendicular from the origin to the line.

15. A moving line segment of variable length has its ends on two fixed perpendicular lines and is at a constant distance from their point of intersection. Find the equation of the locus of its midpoint.

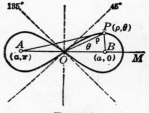

FIG. 113

16. Find the equation of the locus of the vertex of a triangle with a fixed base if the product of the other two sides is equal to the square of one half the base. This curve is the **lemniscate of Bernoulli** and is illustrated in Fig. 113.

17. If a line is drawn from a fixed point O outside a circle, cutting the circle in the points P and Q, show that $OP \cdot OQ$ is a constant.

18. A family of chords of a conic has the focus in common. Show that the focus divides each member into two segments the sum of whose reciprocals is constant.

19. In a triangle the base AB is a fixed length a. Find the equation of the locus of the vertex C if the exterior angle at B formed by producing AB is $\frac{3}{2} \angle CAB$. (*Hint.* Choose A for the pole and use the law of sines.)

20. Show that the epicycloid of one cusp is a cardioid. (*Hint.* Let $b = a$ in the equations of the epicycloid, Sec. 93; translate origin to point F, Fig. 85, and note that if $a = b$ the line joining F and P is parallel to OC.)

Solid Analytic Geometry

CHAPTER IX

POINTS, PLANES, AND LINES

106. Rectangular coördinates. In a space of three dimensions a point can be definitely located by giving its directed distances from three mutually perpendicular planes, called coördinate planes. In the figure
the three planes XOY, YOZ, and
XOZ are called the **xy-, yz-,** and
xz-planes, respectively, and their
lines of intersection OX, OY, and
OZ are called the **x-, y-,** and
z-axes, respectively. The point O
is the origin. The directed distances of a point P from the

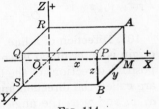

Fig. 114

yz-plane, the xz-plane, and the xy-plane are called the **x-, y-,**
and z-coördinates, respectively, of the point P. Thus the
coördinates of $P(x, y, z)$ are represented by

$$x = QP, \qquad y = AP, \qquad z = BP.$$

It is frequently convenient to locate P by drawing

$$x = OM, \qquad y = MB, \qquad z = BP.$$

The three coördinate planes divide space into eight divi-
sions called octants. The octant in which the coördinates are
all positive is called the first octant and the others are seldom
numbered. They are distinguished by the signs of the coordinates. The student should draw axes and locate the
points (3, 2, 4), (3, − 2, 4), (3, 0, 4), (− 3, 2, − 4), and
(− 3, − 2, 4).

165

107. Distance between two points. Drawing lines through $P_1(x_1, y_1, z_1)$ and $P_2(x_2, y_2, z_2)$ parallel to each of the coördi-

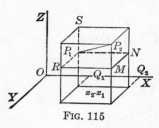

FIG. 115

nate axes, and other lines as indicated in the figure, we have a rectangular parallelepiped of which the distance between P_1 and P_2 is a diagonal. The length of the diagonal in terms of the sides is

$$P_1P_2 = \sqrt{\overline{P_1N}^2 + \overline{NM}^2 + \overline{MP_2}^2}.$$

But $P_1N = Q_1Q_2 = x_2 - x_1$, and similarly, $NM = y_2 - y_1$ and $MP_2 = z_2 - z_1$. Hence

$$P_1P_2 = \sqrt{(x_2 - x_1)^2 + (y_2 - y_1)^2 + (z_2 - z_1)^2}.$$

In particular, the distance from the origin $(0, 0, 0)$ to a point $P_1(x_1, y_1, z_1)$ is

$$OP_1 = \sqrt{x_1{}^2 + y_1{}^2 + z_1{}^2}.$$

108. Direction of a line. The direction of a line through the origin is determined if we know the angles it makes with the positive directions of the three coördinate axes. These angles are called the **direction angles** of the line and are denoted by α, β, and γ as the angles made with the x-, y-, and z-axes, respectively. It is found that the cosines of the angles are more useful than the angles, and the direction of a line is usually given by the cosines of its direction angles. The cosines of the direction angles are called the **direction cosines** of the line. If the direction cosines of a line AB are $\cos \alpha$,

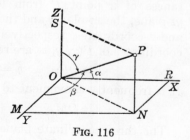

FIG. 116

$\cos \beta$, and $\cos \gamma$, the direction cosines of the line BA are $\cos (180° - \alpha)$, $\cos (180° - \beta)$, and $\cos (180° - \gamma)$.

The direction cosines of a line through the origin are related. In the figure we see that

$$OR = OP \cos \alpha. \quad RN = OM = OP \cos \beta, \quad NP = OS = OP \cos \gamma.$$

Squaring and adding, we have

$$\overline{OR}^2 + \overline{RN}^2 + \overline{NP}^2 = \overline{OP}^2 (\cos^2 \alpha + \cos^2 \beta + \cos^2 \gamma).$$

But

$$\overline{OR}^2 + \overline{RN}^2 + \overline{NP}^2 = \overline{OP}^2;$$

hence

$$\cos^2 \alpha + \cos^2 \beta + \cos^2 \gamma = 1.$$

The direction cosines of a line not through the origin are defined to be the same as the direction cosines of a line parallel to the given line and passing through the origin. Thus in Fig. 115 we have

$$\cos \alpha = \frac{P_1 N}{P_1 P_2}, \quad \cos \beta = \frac{P_1 R}{P_1 P_2}, \quad \cos \gamma = \frac{P_1 S}{P_1 P_2},$$

or $$\cos \alpha = \frac{x_2 - x_1}{P_1 P_2}, \quad \cos \beta = \frac{y_2 - y_1}{P_1 P_2}, \quad \cos \gamma = \frac{z_2 - z_1}{P_1 P_2}. \quad (1)$$

Squaring and adding, we have

$$\cos^2 \alpha + \cos^2 \beta + \cos^2 \gamma = \frac{(x_2 - x_1)^2 + (y_2 - y_1)^2 + (z_2 - z_1)^2}{\overline{P_1 P_2}^2} = 1.$$

This verifies the fact that *for any line the sum of the squares of the direction cosines is 1.*

In particular, the direction cosines of the line joining the origin to any point (x, y, z) are

$$\cos \alpha = \frac{x}{\sqrt{x^2 + y^2 + z^2}}, \quad \cos \beta = \frac{y}{\sqrt{x^2 + y^2 + z^2}},$$

$$\cos \gamma = \frac{z}{\sqrt{x^2 + y^2 + z^2}}.$$

Any three numbers a, b, and c (not all zero) are proportional to the direction cosines of some line. Let (a, b, c) be any point P (Fig. 116). We have

$$OP = \sqrt{a^2 + b^2 + c^2},$$

and $$\cos \alpha = \frac{a}{\sqrt{a^2 + b^2 + c^2}}, \quad \cos \beta = \frac{b}{\sqrt{a^2 + b^2 + c^2}},$$

$$\cos \gamma = \frac{c}{\sqrt{a^2 + b^2 + c^2}}.$$

Hence a, b, and c are proportional to the direction cosines of the line OP, or of any line parallel to OP. Numbers propor-

B2

tional to the direction cosines of a line are called **direction numbers** of the line. A set of direction cosines may be obtained from the direction numbers by dividing each number by the square root of the sum of the squares of the three direction numbers.

It is important to note from equations (1) that

$$x_2 - x_1, \quad y_2 - y_1, \quad \text{and} \quad z_2 - z_1$$

are proportional to the direction cosines of the line through (x_1, y_1, z_1) and (x_2, y_2, z_2) and hence may serve as a set of direction numbers of the line.

EXAMPLE. Find the distance between the points $(9, 2, -1)$ and $(-3, 5, -5)$ and the direction of the line through them.

The distance between the points is

$$d = \sqrt{[9 - (-3)]^2 + (2 - 5)^2 + [-1 - (-5)]^2} = \sqrt{169} = 13.$$

Considering the direction of the line as that from the first point to the second, the direction cosines are

$$\cos \alpha = \frac{-3 - 9}{13} = -\frac{12}{13}, \quad \cos \beta = \frac{5 - 2}{13} = \frac{3}{13},$$

$$\cos \gamma = \frac{-5 - (-1)}{13} = -\frac{4}{13}.$$

If we consider the direction of the line as that from the second point to the first, the direction cosines are

$$\cos \alpha = \frac{12}{13}, \quad \cos \beta = -\frac{3}{13}, \quad \cos \gamma = \frac{4}{13}.$$

The numbers 12, -3, and 4, or any three numbers proportional to them, will serve as direction numbers of the line through the two points.

EXERCISES

1. Find the distance between the two points in each of the following:

(a) $(2, 1, 3)$ and $(6, 2, 11)$.   (c) $(6, 4, 0)$ and $(0, 0, 12)$.
(b) $(-2, -3, 1)$ and $(3, 0, 5)$.   (d) $(0, 0, 0)$ and $(9, 2, 6)$.

2. Find the perimeter of the triangle whose vertices are $(6, 1, 5)$, $(0, 3, 2)$, and $(6, 1, -7)$.

3. Show that (a) $(5, 1, 5)$, $(4, 3, 2)$, and $(-3, -2, 1)$ are the vertices of a right triangle; (b) $(3, 7, -2)$, $(-1, 8, 3)$, and $(-3, 4, -2)$ are the vertices of an isosceles triangle; (c) $(4, 2, 4)$, $(10, 2, -2)$, and $(2, 0, -4)$ are the vertices of an equilateral triangle

4. Find the direction cosines of the line segment directed from the origin to each of the following points:

(a) $(4, 4, 2)$; (b) $(-8, 4, -1)$; (c) $(4, 3, 0)$; (d) $(0, 0, 5)$.

5. Find the direction cosines of the line segment directed from the first point to the second in each of the following:

(a) $(-2, 2, 1)$ and $(4, 5, -1)$. (d) $(10, 9, -2)$ and $(3, 4, -3)$.
(b) $(5, -2, 3)$ and $(-2, 3, 7)$. (e) $(3, 1, 2)$ and $(-1, -3, 2)$.
(c) $(4, 5, 7)$ and $(-2, 3, 7)$. (f) $(-3, 4, 5)$ and $(7, 4, 5)$.

6. (a) If $\alpha = \beta = 60°$, find γ (two solutions).
(b) If $\alpha = \beta = 30°$, find γ.

7. Draw the line through the origin which has $\cos \alpha = \cos \beta = \sqrt{2}/2$.

8. Find the direction angles of a line which makes equal angles with the coördinate axes.

9. Find a set of direction cosines of the lines whose direction numbers are

(a) 1, 2, and 2. (c) 5, 6, and -8. (e) 2, 3, and 6.
(b) 2, -6, and 9. (d) 1, 1, and 0. (f) 1, 0, and 0.

10. Give a set of direction numbers of the line through the two points in each of the following:

(a) $(5, 2, 3)$ and $(11, 6, 5)$. (c) $(2, 1, -3)$ and $(7, -1, 1)$.
(b) $(-3, 2, 4)$ and $(6, -1, 1)$. (d) $(0, 5, 0)$ and $(5, 0, 0)$.

11. Find the equation of the locus of points equidistant from $(-3, 1, 2)$ and $(7, 5, 10)$. What is this locus?

12. Find the equation of the locus of points 7 units distant from $(3, 2, 6)$. What is this locus?

13. Find the equation of the locus of points in the xy-plane 7 units distant from $(3, 2, 6)$. What is this locus?

14. Find the points on the x-axis 7 units distant from $(3, 2, 6)$.

15. Show that the midpoint of the line segment joining (x_1, y_1, z_1) and (x_2, y_2, z_2) is

$$\left(\frac{x_1 + x_2}{2}, \; \frac{y_1 + y_2}{2}, \; \frac{z_1 + z_2}{2}\right).$$

109. Angle between two lines. Let $P(x, y, z)$ and $P_1(x_1, y_1, z_1)$ be two points and let the direction cosines of OP and OP_1 be $\cos \alpha$, $\cos \beta$, and $\cos \gamma$, and $\cos \alpha_1$, $\cos \beta_1$, and $\cos \gamma_1$, respectively. In the triangle OPP_1 we have

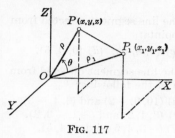

Fig. 117

$$\overline{PP_1}^2 = \rho^2 + \rho_1^2 - 2\,\rho\rho_1 \cos \theta,$$

or $\quad \cos \theta = \dfrac{\rho^2 + \rho_1^2 - \overline{PP_1}^2}{2\,\rho\rho_1}.$

But (Sec. 107) $\rho^2 = x^2 + y^2 + z^2$, $\quad \rho_1^2 = x_1^2 + y_1^2 + z_1^2$, and $\overline{PP_1}^2 = (x - x_1)^2 + (y - y_1)^2 + (z - z_1)^2.$

Making these substitutions and reducing, we have

$$\cos \theta = \frac{xx_1 + yy_1 + zz_1}{\sqrt{x^2 + y^2 + z^2} \cdot \sqrt{x_1^2 + y_1^2 + z_1^2}}.$$

The direction cosines of OP are

$$\cos \alpha = \frac{x}{\sqrt{x^2 + y^2 + z^2}}, \quad \cos \beta = \frac{y}{\sqrt{x^2 + y^2 + z^2}},$$

and

$$\cos \gamma = \frac{z}{\sqrt{x^2 + y^2 + z^2}},$$

and the direction cosines of OP_1 are

$$\cos \alpha_1 = \frac{x_1}{\sqrt{x_1^2 + y_1^2 + z_1^2}}, \quad \cos \beta_1 = \frac{y_1}{\sqrt{x_1^2 + y_1^2 + z_1^2}},$$

and

$$\cos \gamma_1 = \frac{z_1}{\sqrt{x_1^2 + y_1^2 + z_1^2}}.$$

Hence we may write

$$\cos \theta = \cos \alpha \cos \alpha_1 + \cos \beta \cos \beta_1 + \cos \gamma \cos \gamma_1. \quad (2)$$

If the lines do not pass through the origin or do not intersect, the angle between them is defined to be the same as the angle between lines through the origin parallel to the given lines. Hence the cosine of the angle between any two lines is given in terms of the direction cosines of the two lines by equation (2).

The condition that the two lines are perpendicular is that $\cos \theta = 0$, that is,

$$\cos \alpha \cos \alpha_1 + \cos \beta \cos \beta_1 + \cos \gamma \cos \gamma_1 = 0.$$

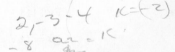

EXAMPLE. Find the angle between the line joining the origin to $(3, 4, 5)$ and the line joining the points $(2, 1, 4)$ and $(10, 5, 5)$.

The direction cosines of the first line are $\dfrac{3}{5\sqrt{2}}$, $\dfrac{4}{5\sqrt{2}}$, and $\dfrac{5}{5\sqrt{2}}$, and the direction cosines of the second line are $\frac{8}{9}$, $\frac{4}{9}$, and $\frac{1}{9}$. Hence

$$\cos \theta = \frac{8 \cdot 3 + 4 \cdot 4 + 1 \cdot 5}{9 \cdot 5\sqrt{2}} = \frac{\sqrt{2}}{2},$$

and the angle between the lines is $45°$.

EXERCISES

1. If two lines are parallel how do their direction cosines compare? How do their direction numbers compare?

2. Show that the line through $(1, 5, 8)$ and $(3, 2, 4)$ is parallel to the line through the origin and $(-4, 6, 8)$.

3. Show that the points $(1, -2, 3)$, $(-4, -6, 1)$, and $(11, 6, 7)$ are collinear.

4. Find the acute angle between the line through $(6, 2, 6)$ and $(4, -1, 1)$ and the line through $(5, 0, 5)$ and $(0, 2, 2)$.

5. Find the acute angle between the line through $(5, -1, 7)$ and $(1, -3, 3)$ and a line which has $\cos \alpha = \frac{11}{15}$, $\cos \beta = \frac{2}{3}$, and $\cos \gamma = \frac{2}{15}$.

6. Find the acute angle between a line whose direction numbers are 2, -1, and 0 and the line through $(2, 3, -2)$ and $(-5, -2, -6)$.

7. If the direction numbers of two lines l_1 and l_2 are a_1, b_1, c_1 and a_2, b_2, c_2, respectively, show that l_1 and l_2 are perpendicular if
$$a_1a_2 + b_1b_2 + c_1c_2 = 0$$
and conversely.

8. Show that the line through $(3, 5, 7)$ and $(5, 2, 3)$ is perpendicular to the line through $(-1, 9, -2)$ and $(-7, 1, 1)$.

9. Show that the line through $(5, 1, -2)$ and $(-4, -5, 13)$ is a perpendicular bisector of the line segment joining $(-5, 2, 0)$ and $(9, -4, 6)$.

10. Work Exercise 3, p. 169, in a different way.

110. Equation of a plane. Let ON be the line from the origin perpendicular to the plane, and let its length be p and

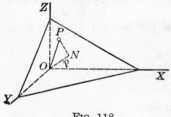

Fig. 118

its direction cosines be $\cos \alpha_1$, $\cos \beta_1$, and $\cos \gamma_1$. Let $P(x, y, z)$ be any other point in the plane, and let the direction cosines of OP be $\cos \alpha$, $\cos \beta$, and $\cos \gamma$. The triangle ONP is a right triangle for all points P which lie in the plane and for no other points. We have

$$p = ON = OP \cos \theta. \quad (\theta = \angle NOP)$$

But $\cos \theta = \cos \alpha \cos \alpha_1 + \cos \beta \cos \beta_1 + \cos \gamma \cos \gamma_1$, $\cos \alpha = x/OP$, $\cos \beta = y/OP$, and $\cos \gamma = z/OP$. Making these substitutions and reducing, we have

$$x \cos \alpha_1 + y \cos \beta_1 + z \cos \gamma_1 = p \qquad (3)$$

as the equation of a plane, in which the constants are the length and the direction cosines of the perpendicular from the origin to the plane. The length p is positive when measured from the origin to the plane.

Conversely, any equation of the form of equation (3) represents a plane.

By retracing the steps by which equation (3) is obtained, we see that equation (3) is satisfied by the coördinates of points P for which the angle ONP is a right angle, and by the coördinates of no other points. All such points lie in a plane. Hence any equation in the form of (3) represents a plane.

111. Theorem. *The equation*

$$Ax + By + Cz + D = 0 \tag{4}$$

represents a plane, provided that A, B, and C are not all zero.

Transposing D and dividing by $\pm\sqrt{A^2 + B^2 + C^2}$, we have

$$\frac{A}{\pm\sqrt{A^2 + B^2 + C^2}}x + \frac{B}{\pm\sqrt{A^2 + B^2 + C^2}}y$$
$$+ \frac{C}{\pm\sqrt{A^2 + B^2 + C^2}}z = \frac{-D}{\pm\sqrt{A^2 + B^2 + C^2}}. \tag{5}$$

By Sec. 108, the quantities

$$\frac{A}{\pm\sqrt{A^2 + B^2 + C^2}}, \frac{B}{\pm\sqrt{A^2 + B^2 + C^2}}, \text{ and } \frac{C}{\pm\sqrt{A^2 + B^2 + C^2}}$$

are the direction cosines of a line. Equation (5) is, therefore, in the form of equation (3), and hence equation (4) represents a plane perpendicular to the line whose direction cosines are

$$\cos\alpha_1 = \frac{A}{\pm\sqrt{A^2 + B^2 + C^2}}, \qquad \cos\beta_1 = \frac{B}{\pm\sqrt{A^2 + B^2 + C^2}},$$
$$\cos\gamma_1 = \frac{C}{\pm\sqrt{A^2 + B^2 + C^2}}. \tag{6}$$

The distance p from the origin to the plane is

$$p = \frac{-D}{\pm\sqrt{A^2 + B^2 + C^2}},$$

where the sign before the radical is chosen so that p is positive.

A line perpendicular to a plane is often called a **normal** to the plane.

It is important to note from equations (6) that the numbers A, B, and C are proportional to the direction cosines of a normal to the plane

$$Ax + By + Cz + D = 0$$

and hence may serve as a set of direction numbers of any line perpendicular to the plane.

Planes parallel to coördinate axes or parallel to coördinate planes have equations which are special cases of equation (4).

In case a plane is parallel to a coördinate axis, say the x-axis, the direction angle made by a normal with that axis is 90° and the corresponding direction cosine, $\cos \alpha_1$, is zero. Hence, in equation (4), $A = 0$. Similarly, the equation of a plane parallel to the y-axis has no y-term, and a plane parallel to the z-axis has no z-term. Thus the equations

$$2\,y - 3\,z = 5, \quad x + 7\,z - 2 = 0, \quad 3\,x + 2\,y + 4 = 0$$

represent planes parallel to the x-, y-, and z-axes, respectively.

In case a plane is parallel to a coördinate plane, a normal is at right angles to the two axes lying in that coördinate plane. Hence two direction cosines are zero. The only variable in the equation of such a plane is the one corresponding to that axis to which the given plane is perpendicular. Thus the equations

$$2\,x = 7, \quad y + 3 = 0, \quad z = 9$$

represent planes parallel to the yz-, the xz-, and the xy-planes, respectively.

EXAMPLE. Discuss the locus of the equation

$$2\,x + 3\,y + 4\,z = 12.$$

The equation represents a plane since it is of first degree. Direction numbers of a normal to the plane are 2, 3, and 4. The direction cosines are found from the direction numbers to be $\cos \alpha_1 = 2/\sqrt{29}$, $\cos \beta_1 = 3/\sqrt{29}$, and $\cos \gamma_1 = 4/\sqrt{29}$.

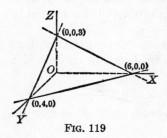

FIG. 119

The distance from the origin to the plane is $12/\sqrt{29}$. The intercepts on the x-, y-, and z-axes are 6, 4, and 3, respectively.

The lines in which the plane intersects the coördinate planes are called the **traces** of the plane.

In the xy-plane, $z = 0$. Hence, to find the equation of the trace in the xy-plane set $z = 0$ in the equation of the plane. Similarly, to find the xz-trace set $y = 0$, and to find the yz-trace set $x = 0$. The equations of the xy-, yz-, and xz-traces of the plane under discussion are

$$2 x + 3 y = 12, \quad 3 y + 4 z = 12, \quad x + 2 z = 6,$$

respectively. The traces and intercepts are shown in Fig. 119.

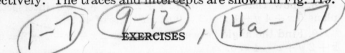

EXERCISES

1. Find the intercepts on the axes and the traces in the coördinate planes of each of the following planes, and sketch the portion of each plane which is intercepted by the coördinate planes:

    (a) $2 x + 2 y + z = 12$.   (c) $2 x + 5 y - 4 z = 15$.
    (b) $2 x - 3 y - 6 z + 14 = 0$.   (d) $x - 2 y + z = 6$.

2. Find the distance from the origin to each of the planes in Exercise 1.

3. Sketch the following planes:

    (a) $x + 2 y = 8$.   (e) $x + y = 0$.   (i) $y = - 3$.
    (b) $3 x + z = 6$.   (f) $2 z = x$.   (j) $z^2 = 4$.
    (c) $4 z - y = 4$.   (g) $z = 2 y$.   (k) $y = kx$.
    (d) $x - y = 0$.   (h) $x = 5$.   (l) $x^2 - x = 6$.

4. Picture the volume in the first octant bounded by the planes in each of the following:

    (a) $x + y + z = 10$, $2 y + z = 10$, and the coördinate planes.
    (b) $x + y = z$, $x + y = 4$, and the coördinate planes.
    (c) $x + y + z = 6$, $2 y = x$, $y = 2 x$, $z = 0$, and $z = 3$.
    (d) $2 z = x$, $y = x$, $x = 4$, $y = 0$, and $z = 0$.
    (e) $2 y + z = 4$, $3 y = x$, $x = 6$, $z = 2$, $y = 0$, and $z = 0$.

5. Find the point of intersection of the following planes:
$x + 2 y + z - 6 = 0$, $3 x - y - 2 z + 5 = 0$, $4 x + 3 y - z + 1 = 0$.

6. Find a set of direction cosines of a normal to each of the following planes:

    (a) $6 x - 2 y + 9 z = 7$.   (c) $3 x - 4 y = 0$.
    (b) $11 x + 10 y - 2 z = 20$.   (d) $z = k$.

7. If θ is the angle between the planes $a_1x + b_1y + c_1z + d_1 = 0$ and $a_2x + b_2y + c_2z + d_2 = 0$, show that

$$\cos \theta = \pm \frac{a_1a_2 + b_1b_2 + c_1c_2}{\sqrt{a_1{}^2 + b_1{}^2 + c_1{}^2} \cdot \sqrt{a_2{}^2 + b_2{}^2 + c_2{}^2}}.$$

use for 9–12

(*Hint.* Consider the angle between two lines perpendicular to the planes, respectively.)

8. Show that the plane $2x + 2y + z + 5 = 0$ intersects the plane $5x + 4y - 3z - 2 = 0$ at an angle of 45°.

9. Find the angle between the planes $2x + y - z + 8 = 0$ and $x + 2y + z - 4 = 0$.

10. Determine the angle which the plane $x + y + z - d = 0$ makes with each of the coördinate planes.

11. Show that the planes in Exercise 7 are perpendicular if $a_1a_2 + b_1b_2 + c_1c_2 = 0$ and conversely.

12. Show that the plane $3x - y + 2z = 6$ is perpendicular to the plane $6x + 4y - 7z + 2 = 0$.

plug into

13. Show that the distance from the plane whose equation is $x \cos \alpha + y \cos \beta + z \cos \gamma - p = 0$ to the point (x_1, y_1, z_1) is equal to $x_1 \cos \alpha + y_1 \cos \beta + z_1 \cos \gamma - p$. (See the method for finding the distance from a line to a point, Sec. 24.)

14. Find the distance from the plane $8x + 4y + z - 16 = 0$ to (a) $(5, 2, 4)$; (b) $(1, 1, 1)$; (c) $(3, -1, -4)$.

15. Show that the planes in Exercise 7 are parallel and distinct if $a_2 = ka_1$, $b_2 = kb_1$, $c_2 = kc_1$, $d_2 \neq kd_1$ (k any constant $\neq 0$).

16. What is the condition that the planes in Exercise 7 be coincident? *parallel distance is zero.*

17. Show that the plane $9x - 6y + 2z - 11 = 0$ is parallel to the plane $18x - 12y + 4z - 55 = 0$. Find the distance between the two planes.

18. Show analytically that the locus of points equidistant from $P_1(x_1, y_1, z_1)$ and $P_2(x_2, y_2, z_2)$ is a plane which bisects at right angles the line segment joining P_1 and P_2.

112. To find the equation of a plane satisfying given conditions. Planes are usually determined by three given points or by the direction of a normal and one point.

In case three points are given, substitute their coördinates in turn in equation (4). We thus obtain three equations from which three of the numbers A, B, C, and D may be determined in terms of the fourth. Or, by dividing each of the equations by one of the numbers, say A, we have three equations in the unknowns B/A, C/A, and D/A which may be solved simultaneously.

EXAMPLE 1. Find the equation of the plane through the points $(1, 1, 1)$, $(-2, -1, 2)$, and $(3, 9, 3)$.

Equation (4) may be divided by D* and written

$$A'x + B'y + C'z + 1 = 0,$$

where $A' = A/D$, $B' = B/D$, and $C' = C/D$. The equations expressing the condition that the points are in the plane are

$$A' + B' + C' + 1 = 0,$$
$$-2A' - B' + 2C' + 1 = 0,$$
$$3A' + 9B' + 3C' + 1 = 0.$$

Solving simultaneously, we have $A' = -\frac{1}{2}$, $B' = \frac{1}{3}$, and $C' = -\frac{5}{6}$. Substituting these values and reducing, we have the desired equation,

$$3x - 2y + 5z - 6 = 0.$$

In case the direction of a normal and one point are given, we may use equation (4). The numbers A, B, and C are direction numbers of a normal to the plane. From the given direction of a normal we obtain direction numbers which are used for A, B, and C; and D is determined so that the plane passes through the given point.

EXAMPLE 2. Find the equation of the plane through the point $(3, 5, -1)$ perpendicular to the line through $(-1, 3, 7)$ and $(4, 2, 5)$.

Direction numbers of the line through the given points are 5, -1, and -2. Hence we may take $A = 5$, $B = -1$, $C = -2$, and write

$$5x - y - 2z + D = 0$$

*Division must be by a quantity not zero. In case $D = 0$, it will be impossible to solve the set of conditional equations. In such a case, we should have to divide by one of the other numbers.

as the equation of a plane perpendicular to the given line. Substituting the coördinates of the point $(3, 5, -1)$, we find the value of D, $D = -12$, for which the plane passes through the given point. The required equation is, therefore,

$$5x - y - 2z - 12 = 0.$$

EXERCISES

1. In each of the following find the equation of the plane determined by the given points:

    (a) $(5, 3, -1)$, $(3, -2, 3)$, $(2, 0, 2)$.
    (b) $(2, -2, 3)$, $(1, -1, 2)$, $(0, 4, -1)$.
    (c) $(0, 0, 0)$, $(2, 6, 3)$, $(5, -7, 2)$.
    (d) $(2, 3, 5)$, $(4, -1, 3)$, $(3, -2, 1)$.

2. Find the equation of the plane containing the z-axis and the point $(3, 2, 5)$.

3. Find the equation of the plane parallel to the x-axis whose intercepts on the y- and z-axes are 3 and 5, respectively.

4. Write the equation of the plane parallel to the y-axis whose trace in the xz-plane contains the points $(2, 0, 9)$ and $(6, 0, 1)$.

5. The base of a pyramid is a rectangle three of whose vertices are $(0, 0, 0)$, $(6, 0, 0)$, and $(0, 4, 0)$. The vertex of the pyramid is $(0, 0, 8)$. Write the equations of the lateral faces of the pyramid.

6. Show that the equation of a plane whose x-, y-, and z-intercepts are a, b, and c, respectively, is $x/a + y/b + z/c = 1$.

7. Find the equation of the plane through $(3, 6, 2)$ perpendicular to the line joining that point to the origin.

8. Write the equation of the plane bisecting at right angles the line segment joining $(3, 6, -2)$ and $(5, -2, 4)$.

9. Find the point equidistant from $(0, 0, 0)$, $(2, 1, -5)$, $(1, 0, -3)$, and $(-1, 4, 1)$.

10. Write the equation of the plane through $(8, 3, 6)$ parallel to the plane $x - 3y + 2z = 1$.

11. Find the equation of the plane through $(1, 1, 1)$ and $(2, -2, -1)$ perpendicular to the plane $x + 3y - 8z + 2 = 0$.

12. Find the equation of the plane through $(1, -3, 2)$ perpendicular to the planes $x - 2y - 3z = 6$ and $3x + 4y - 4z = 1$.

113. Equations of a straight line. A straight line is determined by the intersection of two planes. An indefinite number of planes pass through any straight line. The equations of any two of the planes through the line, considered as simultaneous equations, represent the line. It is usually convenient to represent a line by planes which are parallel to coördinate axes. The equations representing such planes have but two variables each.

114. Projecting planes. A plane parallel to the z-axis and passing through a given line is perpendicular to the xy-plane and cuts that plane in a line which is the projection of the given line upon the xy-plane. Similarly, planes through the given line and parallel to the y-axis and to the x-axis, respectively, cut the xz-plane and the yz-plane in lines which are the projections of the given line upon those planes. Such planes are called **projecting planes** of the line. Each line not parallel to an axis has three projecting planes and any two of them determine the line. The method of finding the projecting planes of a line whose equations are in the general form is illustrated in the following example.

EXAMPLE. Find the equations of the projecting planes of the line whose equations are

$$2x + 2y + 3z = 23$$
and $4x + 3y + 9z = 52.$

Eliminating z, y, and x in turn from the given equations, we obtain

$$2x + 3y = 17, \ 2x + 9z = 35,$$
and $y - 3z + 6 = 0$

FIG. 120

as the three required equations. They represent the planes which project the given line upon the xy-, xz-, and yz-planes, respectively.

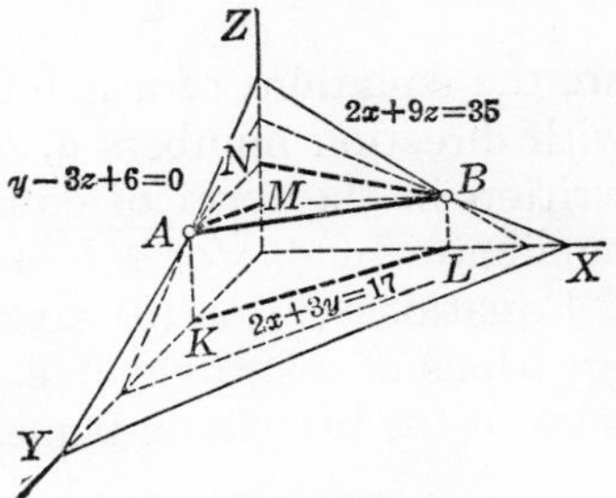

The segment AB in the figure represents a part of the given line, and AM, BN, and KL are segments of the traces of the three projecting planes in the coördinate planes.

115. Equations of a line through a point and in a given direction. Let (x_1, y_1, z_1) be the given point and let the direction cosines of the line be $\cos \alpha$, $\cos \beta$, and $\cos \gamma$. Let (x, y, z) be any other point on the line and call d the distance from (x_1, y_1, z_1) to (x, y, z). Then

$$d = \frac{x - x_1}{\cos \alpha} = \frac{y - y_1}{\cos \beta} = \frac{z - z_1}{\cos \gamma}.$$

These equalities exist for every d; hence the equations of the line through the point (x_1, y_1, z_1) and with direction cosines $\cos \alpha$, $\cos \beta$, and $\cos \gamma$ are

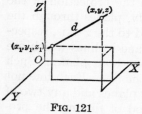

FIG. 121

$$\frac{x - x_1}{\cos \alpha} = \frac{y - y_1}{\cos \beta} = \frac{z - z_1}{\cos \gamma}. \quad (7)$$

Since equations (7) may be multiplied by the same constant without destroying the equality, it is not necessary that the denominators be the direction cosines of the line.

It is sufficient that the denominators be proportional to the direction cosines. Thus the equations

$$\frac{x - x_1}{a} = \frac{y - y_1}{b} = \frac{z - z_1}{c} \quad (8)$$

are the equations of a line through the point (x_1, y_1, z_1) and with direction numbers a, b, and c. Equations (8) may be written in the form of equations (7) by dividing each denominator by $\pm \sqrt{a^2 + b^2 + c^2}$.

Equations (7) or (8) are frequently called the **symmetric** equations of a straight line. Either (7) or (8) are the equations of the projecting planes of the line.

EXAMPLE. Find symmetric equations of the line through the point $(2, 1, -3)$ and parallel to the line through the points $(5, 2, 3)$ and $(0, 6, 2)$.

The direction cosines of a line are proportional to the differences of corresponding coördinates of two points on the line. Hence the direction cosines of the line through $(5, 2, 3)$

and $(0, 6, 2)$ are proportional to $5, -4,$ and 1. The required equations are, therefore,

$$\frac{x-2}{5} = \frac{y-1}{-4} = \frac{z+3}{1}.$$

116. Equations of a line through two given points. Let the given points be $P_1(x_1, y_1, z_1)$ and $P_2(x_2, y_2, z_2)$. The direction cosines are proportional to $x_2 - x_1$, $y_2 - y_1$, and $z_2 - z_1$. The equations of the line through P_1 and P_2 are, therefore, from equations (8) of the last section,

$$\frac{x-x_1}{x_2-x_1} = \frac{y-y_1}{y_2-y_1} = \frac{z-z_1}{z_2-z_1}.$$

117. Transformation of the general equations of a line to symmetric form.

EXAMPLE. Transform the equations of the line

$$2x + 2y + 3z = 23 \quad \text{and} \quad 4x + 3y + 9z = 52,$$

in the example of Sec. 114, to symmetric form.

First method. In that example we found the projecting planes of the given line to be

$$2x + 3y = 17, \quad 2x + 9z = 35, \quad \text{and} \quad y - 3z + 6 = 0. \quad (9)$$

Any two of these planes determine the line. Solving the first two equations of (9) for $2x$ (or for the common variable of any two of the equations), we may write

$$2x = -3y + 17 = -9z + 35.$$

Dividing by 18, and writing each variable with a positive sign, we have

$$\frac{x}{9} = \frac{y - \frac{17}{3}}{-6} = \frac{z - \frac{35}{9}}{-2}. \quad (10)$$

These are symmetric equations of a line through the point $(0, \frac{17}{3}, \frac{35}{9})$ and with direction numbers $9, -6,$ and -2.

Second method. Let us find any two distinct points on the line. Suppose we let $z = 1$ in each of the given equations of the planes. We have then the equations

$$2x + 2y = 20 \quad \text{and} \quad 4x + 3y = 43$$

whose simultaneous solution is $x = 13$, $y = -3$.   Hence the point $P_1(13, -3, 1)$ is on the line.   Similarly letting $z = 3$, we find a second point $P_2(4, 3, 3)$ on the line.   By Sec. 116 symmetric equations of the line are

$$\frac{x-13}{9} = \frac{y+3}{-6} = \frac{z-1}{-2}. \tag{11}$$

The student may readily verify that either set of equations (10) or (11) represents the same line.

EXERCISES

1. Find the projecting planes of the following lines:

(a) $x + 2y + 2z = 10$, $x + 3y + z = 9$.
(b) $x + y + z = 15$, $y + 3z = 9$.
(c) $x + y + z = 12$, $2y = x$.
(d) $x + y = z$, $y = x$.
(e) $\dfrac{x-4}{2} = \dfrac{y-1}{-2} = \dfrac{z-3}{-1}$.

2. Find the points where each line of Exercise 1 pierces the coördinate planes.

3. Write symmetric equations of each of the following lines:

(a) Through $(6, 2, 4)$ and with $\cos \alpha = \frac{8}{9}$, $\cos \beta = \frac{4}{9}$, $\cos \gamma = \frac{1}{9}$.
(b) Through $(-1, 3, -2)$ and with direction numbers $6, -3, 2$.
(c) Through $(0, -3, 8)$ and $(7, 2, 9)$.
(d) Through $(5, 2, 0)$ and parallel to the line joining the origin and $(8, 5, 1)$.
(e) Through $(3, 2, 0)$ and with $\cos \alpha = \frac{4}{5}$, $\cos \beta = \frac{3}{5}$.

4. Write symmetric equations of the line through $(2, 6, 1)$ parallel to the line

$$\frac{x-3}{11} = \frac{y-1}{2} = \frac{z-2}{10}.$$

5. Write symmetric equations of the line through the origin making equal angles with the positive directions of the coördinate axes.

6. Show that the line determined by the points $(3, 1, 0)$ and $(1, 4, -3)$ is perpendicular to the line

$$\frac{x}{3} = \frac{y-3}{8} = \frac{z+7}{6}.$$

7. Show that the line $\dfrac{x-7}{3} = \dfrac{y+2}{1} = \dfrac{z-6}{-2}$ is parallel to the plane $5x - 11y + 2z = 9$ and find the ~~distance from the plane~~ to the line.

8. Show that the line $\dfrac{x-4}{-3} = \dfrac{y-1}{3} = \dfrac{z+1}{2}$ lies in the plane $5x - y + 9z = 10$.

9. Write symmetric equations of the line through $(5, 4, 8)$ perpendicular to the plane $2x + 3y + 6z = 18$.

10. Find the foot of the perpendicular dropped from the point $(-8, 5, 2)$ upon the plane $3x - 2y - z + 8 = 0$.

11. Find the point on the line $\dfrac{x-5}{2} = \dfrac{y-11}{6} = \dfrac{z-12}{9}$ equidistant from $(4, -1, 2)$ and $(-2, 3, 6)$.

12. How far must the line segment directed from $(-2, 3, 1)$ to $(2, -1, 3)$ be extended to pierce the plane $3x - 4y - 3z = 12$?

13. Show that the lines

$$\frac{x-3}{2} = \frac{y+1}{-1} = \frac{z-1}{3} \quad \text{and} \quad \frac{x-7}{-6} = \frac{y-8}{3} = \frac{z-6}{-9}$$

are parallel and find the distance between them.

14. Find symmetric equations of each of the following lines:

    (a) $x - 6y + 6z + 35 = 0$, $2x - 2y - 3z = 0$.
    (b) $2x - y - 2z = 13$, $x - 2y + 2z + 7 = 0$.
    (c) $4x - y - z = 12$, $2x + y - 2z + 6 = 0$.

MISCELLANEOUS EXERCISES

1. Find the equation of the plane parallel to the y-axis and containing the points $(7, 2, 1)$ and $(3, -4, 3)$.

2. Find the point equidistant from $(6, 0, 0)$, $(0, 6, 0)$, and $(0, 0, 12)$ and lying in the plane of these points.

3. Show that the planes $2x + y + z - 3 = 0$, $5x - y - 2 = 0$, $x + 2y + 2z - 3 = 0$, and $3x - 3y - 4z - 2 = 0$ meet in a common point.

4. Show that $(1, 4, 1)$, $(-3, 1, 0)$, $(5, 0, 1)$, and $(5, 7, 2)$ lie in a common plane.

5. Determine the angle which the line

$$\frac{x-3}{1} = \frac{y+1}{2} = \frac{z-4}{-1}$$

makes with the plane $2x + y + z = 7$.

6. Find the equation of the plane containing the line

$$\frac{x+3}{2} = \frac{y-2}{-2} = \frac{z+2}{3}$$

and the point $(1, -3, 6)$.

7. Show that the lines

$$\frac{x+1}{3} = \frac{y-6}{1} = \frac{z-3}{2} \quad \text{and} \quad \frac{x-6}{2} = \frac{y-11}{2} = \frac{z-3}{-1}$$

lie in a common plane, and find the equation of the plane.

8. Write the equations of the two lines through $(6, 4, 1)$ with $\cos \alpha = \frac{2}{3}$ and parallel to the plane $x + y - 4z - 12 = 0$.

9. Find the distance from $(6, 1, 2)$ to the line

$$\frac{x-5}{3} = \frac{y+3}{-2} = \frac{z-8}{4}.$$

10. Two lines are **skew lines** if they do not lie in a common plane. The shortest distance between two skew lines is the length of their common perpendicular. Show that the lines

$$\frac{x-2}{1} = \frac{y+1}{-4} = \frac{z-3}{-3} \quad \text{and} \quad \frac{x-2}{5} = \frac{y-8}{-4} = \frac{z+1}{9}$$

are skew lines and find the shortest distance between them.

11. Show that the equation

$$a_1x + b_1y + c_1z + d_1 + k(a_2x + b_2y + c_2z + d_2) = 0$$

(k any constant) represents a plane containing the line of intersection of the planes

$$a_1x + b_1y + c_1z + d_1 = 0 \quad \text{and} \quad a_2x + b_2y + c_2z + d_2 = 0.$$

12. Write the equation of the plane containing the line of intersection of the planes $x - 6y + 2z + 1 = 0$ and $2x + y - 7z + 3 = 0$ and passing through $(2, -1, 3)$.

13. Write the equation of the plane containing the line of intersection of the planes $x + 2y - z - 8 = 0$ and $3x - y + 4z + 2 = 0$ and perpendicular to the first of these planes.

14. Show that the following planes meet in a common line: $x - 3y + 5z - 2 = 0, 2x + y - 6z - 4 = 0, 9x + y - 19z - 18 = 0.$

15. Show that the following planes taken two at a time determine three parallel lines:

$$x - 2y + 6z = 12, \quad x + y - 2z = 4, \quad 2x - y + 4z = 8.$$

CHAPTER X

SURFACES AND CURVES

118. Equation of a cylindrical surface with elements parallel to an axis. Let us consider an equation in two variables only, say in x and y, $$x^2 + y^2 = 25. \tag{1}$$

In the xy-plane the equation represents a circle of radius 5 and with center at the origin. Let $P(x, y, 0)$ be a point on

the curve and draw through P a line AB parallel to the z-axis. The coördinates of any point on this line will satisfy equation (1) since each point on AB has the same x- and y-coördinates as P. Hence the coördinates of every point on the surface generated by moving P around the circle, keeping AB parallel to the z-axis, will satisfy equation (1). A surface which can be generated by

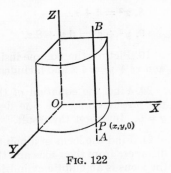

Fig. 122

moving a line parallel to a fixed position is called a **cylindrical surface.** Hence equation (1) represents a cylindrical surface with elements parallel to the z-axis and with any cross-section parallel to the xy-plane a circle of radius 5. The circle (1) is called a **directrix** of the cylindrical surface.

In a similar manner it can be shown that any equation in two variables represents a cylindrical surface with elements parallel to the axis corresponding to the variable which is lacking in the equation. Cylindrical surfaces are frequently given names corresponding to the directrix, such as elliptic, parabolic, etc. A plane may be looked upon as a cylindrical surface whose directrix is a straight line.

185

EXERCISES

Sketch the following cylindrical surfaces and in each case state what curve will serve as a directrix.

1. $y^2 = 4x$.

2. $y^2 + z^2 = 16$.

3. $x^2 + y^2 - 6x = 0$.

4. $9x^2 + 16y^2 = 144$.

5. $x^2 - 4y^2 = 16$.

6. $3x^2 + 8z = 48$.

7. $x^2 + 4z^2 = 4x$.

8. $x^2 = 4 + z$.

9. $y^2 + z^2 = 6y + 8z$.

10. $3x + 4y = 12$.

11. $x^2 = 8y$.

12. $xz = 6$.

13. $y^3 = x$.

14. $y^3 = x^2$.

15. $y = \sin x$.

16. $z = e^x$.

17. $z = \log_e y$.

18. $y(x^2 + 1) = 2x$.

19. Picture the volume inside both of the surfaces $x^2 + y^2 = 4$ and $x^2 + y^2 = 4x$ and included between the planes $z = 0$ and $z = 4$.

20. Find the equation of the locus of points equidistant from the yz-plane and the line determined by the planes $x = 4$ and $y = 0$. Interpret the result.

21. Find the locus of a point which moves so that the sum of its distances from the z-axis and the line $y = 0$, $x = 6$ is 10. Show that the locus is an elliptic cylindrical surface.

119. Surfaces of revolution. A surface formed by revolving a plane curve about some line in its plane has the property that cross-sections perpendicular to the axis of revolution are circles. The radius of the circle in each case is the distance from the axis to the point on the curve which is in the plane of the cross-section. This enables us to obtain the equation of the surface when we know the equation of the generating curve, as is illustrated in the following examples.

EXAMPLE 1. The circle in the xz-plane whose equation is $x^2 + z^2 = a^2$ is revolved about the z-axis. Find the equation of the spherical surface thus generated.

Any point P on the given circle will generate a circle with center at Q and with radius QP. The plane of QMP is parallel to the xy-plane. For any point M we have

$$x^2+y^2=\overline{ON}^2=\overline{QM}^2=\overline{QP}^2.$$

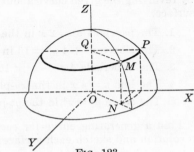

But QP is the x-coördinate of the point P in the xz-plane. From the given equation we have

$$QP = x = \sqrt{a^2 - z^2}.$$

Hence the equation of the locus of P is

FIG. 123

$$x^2 + y^2 = a^2 - z^2, \quad \text{or} \quad x^2 + y^2 + z^2 = a^2. \tag{2}$$

But P is any point on the circle, hence equation (2) represents the spherical surface formed by revolving the circle about the z-axis. The student may derive the equation of the surface generated by revolving the given circle about the x-axis and show that it is identical with (2).

EXAMPLE 2. The line in the xy-plane whose equation is $x + y = 6$ is revolved about the x-axis. Find the equation of the conical surface thus generated.

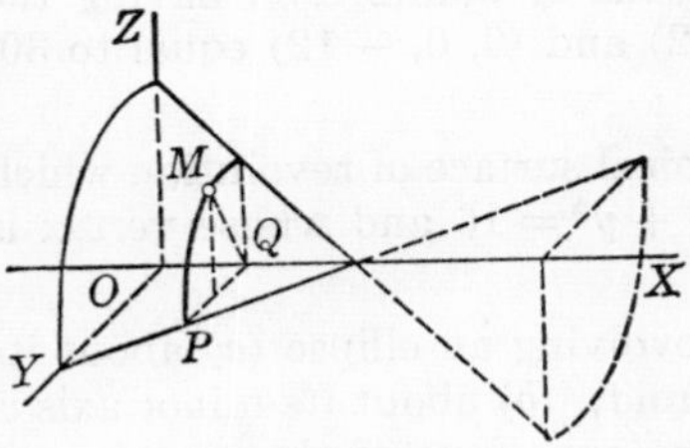

Any point P on the line generates a circle whose plane is parallel to the yz-plane. For any point M on this circle

$$y^2 + z^2 = \overline{QM}^2 = \overline{QP}^2.$$

FIG. 124

But in the xy-plane $QP = y$, hence $QP = y = 6 - x$. The required equation of the conical surface is, therefore,

$$y^2 + z^2 = (6 - x)^2, \quad \text{or} \quad x^2 - y^2 - z^2 - 12\,x + 36 = 0.$$

EXERCISES

Find the equation of each of the following surfaces generated by revolving the given curve about the given line, and sketch each surface:

1. The parabola $z^2 = 2\,x$ in the xz-plane; the x-axis.
2. The ellipse $x^2 + 4\,y^2 = 16$ in the xy-plane; the x-axis.
3. The hyperbola $4\,x^2 - z^2 = 16$ in the xz-plane; the z-axis.
4. The line $y = 4\,x$ in the xy-plane; the y-axis.
5. The curve $y^2 = z^3$ in the yz-plane; the z-axis.

Find a generating curve for each of the following surfaces of revolution and sketch each surface:

6. $x^2 + y^2 = 3\,z.$
7. $y^2 + z^2 = 6\,x.$
8. $x^2 + y^2 + z^2 = 25.$
9. $x^2 + y^2 + z^2 - 8\,z = 0.$
10. $4\,x^2 + 9\,y^2 + 9\,z^2 = 144.$
11. $x^2 + y^2 = 6\,x.$

12. $x^2 + z^2 + 2\,y = 16$
13. $4\,x^2 - 9\,y^2 - 9\,z^2 = 144.$
14. $9\,x^2 + 9\,y^2 - z^2 = 0.$
15. $y^2 + z^2 = e^{-x}.$
16. $z = e^{-(x^2 + y^2)}.$
17. $x^2 + y^2 = \log^2 z.$

18. Find the equation of the locus of points at a constant distance d from the point (x_1, y_1, z_1). Can this surface be interpreted as a surface of revolution? What is this locus?

19. Find the equation of the locus of points equidistant from the yz-plane and the point $(a, 0, 0)$. Interpret the result.

20. Find the equation of the locus of points each having the sum of its distances from $(0, 0, 12)$ and $(0, 0, -12)$ equal to 30. Interpret the result.

21. Find the equation of the conical surface of revolution which cuts the xy-plane in the curve $x^2 + y^2 = 16$ and whose vertex is $(0, 0, 4)$.

22. The surface generated by revolving an ellipse (a) about its major axis is called a **prolate spheroid**; (b) about its minor axis is called an **oblate spheroid**. Find the equations of the prolate and oblate spheroids generated by the ellipse $x^2/a^2 + y^2/b^2 = 1$ $(a > b)$.

23. Find the equation of the surface generated by revolving the circle $(x - b)^2 + z^2 = a^2$ $(a < b)$ in the xz-plane about the z-axis. (Such a surface is called a **torus**.)

120. Traces of a surface in the coördinate planes and in planes parallel to the coördinate planes. The curve in which a surface intersects a plane is called the *trace* of the surface in that plane. The trace of a surface in the xy-plane is found by intersecting the surface with the xy-plane, that is, by making $z = 0$ in the equation of the surface. Similarly, the xz- and yz-traces are found by making $y = 0$ and $x = 0$, respectively, in the equation of the surface. Thus the traces of the surface $4\,x^2 + y^2 - 2\,z = 8$

in the xy-, yz-, and xz-planes, respectively, are

$$4\,x^2 + y^2 = 8, \quad y^2 - 2\,z = 8, \quad \text{and} \quad 4\,x^2 - 2\,z = 8.$$

The equation of any plane parallel to the xy-plane is of the form $z = k$. If we let $z = k$ in the equation of a surface, we have the equation of the trace of that surface in the plane $z = k$. Traces of a surface in planes parallel to the other coördinate planes are found in a similar manner.

121. Discussion of a surface. The discussion of a surface whose equation is given should include the following points:

(a) *Symmetry.* The same tests apply for symmetry with respect to the coördinate planes as those used in the plane for symmetry with respect to the axes.

(b) *Intercepts on the axes.*

(c) *Traces in the coördinate planes.*

(d) *Traces in planes parallel to each of the coördinate planes.* If all traces in planes parallel to a coördinate plane are circles, with centers on a line perpendicular to this coördinate plane, the surface is a surface of revolution. Find the generating curve.

(e) *Extent of the surface.*

Very little can be learned concerning a surface by locating points on the surface.

EXAMPLE 1. Discuss the locus of the equation

$$\frac{x^2}{a^2} + \frac{y^2}{b^2} + \frac{z^2}{c^2} = 1.$$

The surface is symmetric with respect to each of the co-ordinate planes. The intercepts are $\pm a$ on the x-axis, $\pm b$ on the y-axis, and $\pm c$ on the z-axis. The trace in the xy-plane is

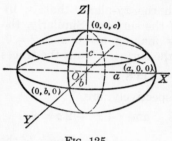

FIG. 125

$$\frac{x^2}{a^2} + \frac{y^2}{b^2} = 1.$$

This equation represents an ellipse with semiaxes a and b. Similarly, traces in the yz- and xz-planes are ellipses. Transposing z^2/c^2, we have

$$\frac{x^2}{a^2} + \frac{y^2}{b^2} = 1 - \frac{z^2}{c^2}.$$

Letting $z = \pm k(k > 0)$ and dividing by $1 - k^2/c^2$, we obtain

$$\frac{x^2}{a^2\left(1 - \dfrac{k^2}{c^2}\right)} + \frac{y^2}{b^2\left(1 - \dfrac{k^2}{c^2}\right)} = 1.$$

The last equation shows that the sections of the surface by planes $z = \pm k$ are ellipses for $k < c$. The semiaxes $a\sqrt{1 - k^2/c^2}$ and $b\sqrt{1 - k^2/c^2}$ decrease as k approaches c in value. For $k = c$ the section is a point; and for $k > c$ the planes do not intersect the surface. Hence the surface lies between the planes $z = \pm c$, and each trace in a plane parallel to the xy-plane is an ellipse. Similarly, we can show that the sur-face lies between the planes $y = \pm b$ and between the planes $x = \pm a$, and that traces in planes parallel to the xz- and yz-planes, respectively, are ellipses. Such a surface is called an **ellipsoid**.

If $a = b$, traces in planes parallel to the xy-plane are circles and the surface is an ellipsoid of revolution. The generating curve is either the ellipse in the xz-plane,

$$\frac{x^2}{a^2} + \frac{z^2}{c^2} = 1,$$

or the ellipse in the yz-plane,

$$\frac{y^2}{b^2} + \frac{z^2}{c^2} = 1.$$

Similarly, if $b = c$ or if $a = c$, the surface is an ellipsoid of revolution.

If $a = b = c$, traces in planes parallel to the coördinate planes are circles and the surface is a sphere whose equation is $$x^2 + y^2 + z^2 = a^2.$$

EXAMPLE 2. Discuss the locus of the equation

$$\frac{x^2}{a^2} + \frac{y^2}{b^2} - \frac{z^2}{c^2} = 1.$$

The surface is symmetric with respect to each of the coördinate planes. The intercepts are $\pm a$ on the x-axis and $\pm b$ on the y-axis. The surface does not cross the z-axis. The trace in the xy-plane is an ellipse and the traces in the yz- and xz-planes are hyperbolas with transverse axes along the y- and x-axes, respectively. Traces in planes $z = \pm k$ are ellipses whose semiaxes, $a\sqrt{1 + k^2/c^2}$ and $b\sqrt{1 + k^2/c^2}$, increase as k increases. Traces in the planes $y = \pm h$ are hyperbolas,

$$\frac{x^2}{a^2} - \frac{z^2}{c^2} = 1 - \frac{h^2}{b^2},$$

with transverse axes in the xy-plane for values of h less than b. Traces in the planes $y = \pm h = \pm b$ are the straight lines $$\frac{x}{a} \pm \frac{z}{c} = 0.$$

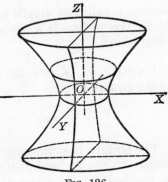

FIG. 126

For values of h greater than b the traces are hyperbolas with transverse axes in the yz-plane. Similarly, traces in planes parallel to the yz-plane are hyperbolas or straight lines. Such a surface is called an **elliptic hyperboloid of one sheet**. In case $a = b$ the surface is a surface of revolution.

EXAMPLE 3. Discuss the locus of the equation

$$\frac{x^2}{a^2} - \frac{y^2}{b^2} - \frac{z^2}{c^2} = 1.$$

The surface is symmetric with respect to each of the coördinate planes. The intercepts are $\pm a$ on the x-axis.

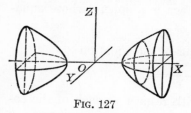

FIG. 127

The surface does not intersect the other axes. Traces in planes $x = \pm k$ parallel to the yz-plane are given by the equation

$$\frac{y^2}{b^2} + \frac{z^2}{c^2} = \frac{k^2}{a^2} - 1.$$

This equation shows that for $k < a$ the planes do not intersect the surface and hence the surface is outside the two planes $x = \pm a$. For $k > a$ the sections are ellipses whose semiaxes increase as k increases. Traces in planes parallel to the xy- and xz-planes, respectively, are hyperbolas. This surface is called an **elliptic hyperboloid of two sheets**. In case $b = c$, the surface is a surface of revolution.

EXAMPLE 4. Discuss the locus of the equation

$$\frac{x^2}{a^2} + \frac{y^2}{b^2} = cz.$$

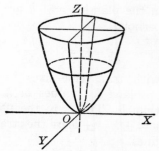

FIG. 128

The surface is symmetric with respect to the xz- and yz-planes. It touches the xy-plane at the origin but does not extend below that plane if c is positive, nor above that plane if c is negative. The traces in the xz- and yz-planes are the parabolas $x^2 = a^2cz$ and $y^2 = b^2cz$, respectively. Traces in planes parallel to the xy-plane are ellipses with increasing semiaxes as the intersecting plane is moved farther and farther from the xy-plane. The surface is called an **elliptic paraboloid** if $a \neq b$, and a paraboloid of revolution if $a = b$. The figure is drawn for c positive.

EXAMPLE 5. Discuss the locus of the equation

$$\frac{x^2}{a^2} - \frac{y^2}{b^2} = cz.$$

The surface is symmetric with respect to the xz- and yz-planes. The origin is on the surface and the axes intersect the surface in no other point. The traces in the xy-, the yz-, and the xz-plane, respectively, are the lines $x/a \pm y/b = 0$, the parabola $y^2 = -b^2cz$, and the parabola $x^2 = a^2cz$. Traces of the surface in planes parallel to the xy-plane are hyperbolas with the transverse axes in the xz-plane when the intersecting planes are above the xy-plane and with the transverse axes in the yz-plane when the intersecting planes are below the xy-plane. For c positive, as in Fig. 129, traces of the surface in planes parallel to the xz-plane are found to be parabolas, concave upward, with vertices on the parabola which is the trace of the surface in the yz-plane. Similarly, the traces in planes parallel to the yz-plane are found to be parabolas, concave downward, with vertices on the parabola which is the trace of the surface in the xz-plane. This surface is called a **hyperbolic paraboloid**.

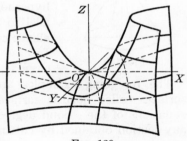

FIG. 129

EXAMPLE 6. Discuss the locus of the equation

$$\frac{x^2}{a^2} + \frac{y^2}{b^2} - \frac{z^2}{c^2} = 0.$$

The surface is symmetric with respect to each of the three coördinate planes. The origin is on the surface and

there are no other intercepts on the axes. The trace in the
xy-plane is a point; the trace in the xz-plane is the lines

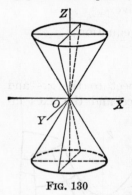

$x/a \pm z/c = 0$; and the trace in the
yz-plane is the lines $y/b \pm z/c = 0$.
Traces in planes parallel to the xy-plane
are ellipses with increasing semiaxes
as the intersecting plane is moved
farther and farther from the xy-plane.
Traces of the surface in planes parallel to the xz- and the yz-planes are
hyperbolas with transverse axes parallel to the z-axis. The surface is an
elliptic cone with axis along the z-axis.
In case $a = b$, the surface is a right
circular cone.

FIG. 130

The foregoing examples are illustrations of a class of
surfaces called **quadric** surfaces. They are represented by
equations of the second degree and have the property that
any section obtained by cutting the surface with a plane is
a conic.

EXERCISES

Discuss and sketch the following surfaces:

1. $\dfrac{x^2}{25} + \dfrac{y^2}{16} + \dfrac{z^2}{9} = 1.$ 3. $\dfrac{x^2}{25} - \dfrac{y^2}{16} - \dfrac{z^2}{9} = -1.$

2. $\dfrac{x^2}{25} - \dfrac{y^2}{16} - \dfrac{z^2}{9} = 1.$ 4. $\dfrac{x^2}{25} - \dfrac{y^2}{16} - \dfrac{z^2}{9} = 0.$

Sketch the following surfaces:

5. $x^2 + y^2 + z^2 = 25.$ 11. $x^2 + y^2 + z^2 = 10\,x.$

6. $2\,y^2 + z^2 = 8\,x.$ 12. $x^2 + y^2 = 10\,x.$

7. $x^2 + 4\,z^2 = 2\,y.$ 13. $x^2 - 4(y^2 + z^2) = 16.$

8. $4\,x^2 - 9\,y^2 = 0.$ 14. $x^2 - 4(y^2 + z^2) = 0.$

9. $4\,x^2 + 9\,y^2 + z^2 = 36.$ 15. $4(x^2 + y^2) - z^2 = 16.$

10. $9\,y^2 + 4\,z^2 = x^2.$ 16. $4\,z = 36 - x^2 - y^2.$

17. $\dfrac{x^2}{16} + \dfrac{y^2}{9} + \dfrac{(z-6)^2}{36} = 1.$ 18. $\dfrac{x^2}{16} + \dfrac{y^2}{9} - \dfrac{(z-6)^2}{36} = 0.$

Show that the following equations represent cylindrical surfaces and sketch each surface:

19. $x^2 = 16 - 2y - 4z.$ **20.** $(x + y)^2 + z^2 = 9.$

21. Discuss fully and sketch the surface $x^2 - 4y^2 = 8z.$

22. Show that $x^2 - y^2 = az$ becomes $2x'y' = az$ by rotating the x- and y-axes through an angle of $-45°$, keeping the z-axis fixed.

23. The equation of state of a perfect gas is $PV = kT$, wherein P, V, and T are pressure, volume, and temperature respectively, and k is a constant. Show that P, V, and T are related in the same way as the coördinates of a point on a hyperbolic paraboloid surface.

122. The locus of an equation in three variables. The elimination of z between the equations $f(x, y, z) = 0$ and $z = c$ results in the equation

$$f(x, y, c) = 0.$$

This equation represents a cylindrical surface with elements parallel to the z-axis. This surface cuts the xy-plane in a curve which is congruent to the curve cut from the plane $z = c$ by the same surface. Hence we may look upon $f(x, y, c) = 0$ as the equation of a cylindrical surface or as the equation of the curve in which that cylindrical surface cuts the xy-plane. But the equation $f(x, y, c) = 0$ is satisfied by all the points whose coördinates satisfy the equations $f(x, y, z) = 0$ and $z = c$ simultaneously. Hence the plane $z = c$ intersects the locus represented by $f(x, y, z) = 0$ in a plane curve which is congruent to the curve in the xy-plane represented by $f(x, y, c) = 0$. It was pointed out in Sec. 39 that an equation in two variables, such as $f(x, y, c) = 0$, represents in a plane either a curve, isolated points, or no real locus. Hence the plane $z = c$ may intersect the locus of $f(x, y, z) = 0$ in a plane curve, in isolated points, or in no real locus. A similar statement holds for planes parallel to the other coördinate planes. Hence the locus represented by an equation in three variables, $f(x, y, z) = 0$, is a surface, isolated points or lines, or no real locus.

123. Intersection of surfaces. Curves. Two surfaces will, in general, intersect in a curve. The equations of two surfaces, therefore, considered simultaneously represent the curve of intersection of the two surfaces. From the equations of two surfaces,

$$f_1(x, y, z) = 0 \quad \text{and} \quad f_2(x, y, z) = 0, \tag{3}$$

we obtain by eliminating one of the variables, say z, one equation in two variables,

$$\phi(x, y) = 0. \tag{4}$$

Equation (4) represents a cylindrical surface with elements parallel to the z-axis and is satisfied by all the points whose coördinates satisfy equations (3) simultaneously. Equation (4) represents, therefore, a cylindrical surface through the curve of intersection of the surfaces represented by equations (3). This surface intersects the xy-plane in a curve whose equation is $\phi(x, y) = 0.$

This curve is the projection upon the xy-plane of the curve of intersection of the surfaces represented by equations (3). Similarly, the elimination of y and of x, respectively, from equations (3) will give the cylindrical surfaces which project the curve of intersection of the surfaces upon the xz- and yz-planes.

In general, the curve of intersection of two surfaces is not a plane curve. A curve which does not lie in a plane is called a **skew** curve.

EXAMPLE. Find the equations of the projections upon the coördinate planes of the curve of intersection of the ellipsoid $x^2 + 2\,y^2 + 9\,z^2 = 36$ and the plane $y = 2\,x$.

Eliminating x, y, and z in turn, we obtain

$$y^2 + 4\,z^2 = 16,$$
$$x^2 + z^2 = 4,$$
and
$$y = 2\,x$$

as the equations of the projections of the curve of intersection of the two surfaces upon the yz-, the xz-, and the xy-planes, respectively.

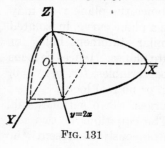

FIG. 131

EXERCISES

Find the projections on the coördinate planes of the curves of intersection of the surfaces in each of the following and make a sketch in each case:

1. $x^2 + y^2 = 25$ and $x + z = 5$.

2. $x^2 + y^2 + z^2 = 36$ and (a) $\sqrt{3}\, y = x$; (b) $y + z = 6$.

3. $y^2 = 9\, x$ and $x + z = 4$.

4. $2\, y^2 = 18 - 3\, x$ and $2\, z = x$.

5. $x^2 + y^2 = 1$ and $z = x^2$.

6. $x^2 + y^2 = 4\, x$ and $x^2 + y^2 = 4\, z$.

7. $x^2 + y^2 + z^2 = 16$ and (a) $x + 2\, z = 4$; (b) $x^2 = 6\, y$.

8. The cone $4(x^2 + y^2) = (z - 4)^2$ and the plane

    (a) $z = 2$.   (c) $2\, x + z = 2$.   (e) $x + z = 4$.

    (b) $x + z = 2$.   (d) $4\, x + z = 6$.   (f) $4\, x + z = 4$.

9. Find the point whose z-coördinate is a maximum on the curve of intersection of the plane $x - y = 4$ and the paraboloid $y^2 + z^2 = 2\, x$.

10. Determine k so that the curve of intersection of the plane $y = kx$ and the ellipsoid $5\, x^2 + 20\, y^2 + 8\, z^2 = 320$ shall be a circle.

124. Sketching of volumes. EXAMPLE. Sketch the volume in the first octant bounded by the surfaces $y^2 + z^2 + 2\, x = 16$, $x + y = 4$, and the coördinate planes.

The surface $y^2 + z^2 + 2\, x = 16$ is a paraboloid of revolution whose axis lies in the x-axis and whose traces in the xy-, yz-, and xz-planes are the parabola $y^2 + 2\, x = 16$, the circle $y^2 + z^2 = 16$, and the parabola $z^2 + 2\, x = 16$,

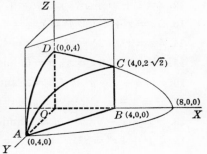

FIG. 132

respectively. The surface $x + y = 4$ is a plane parallel to the z-axis whose trace in the xy-plane is the line $x + y = 4$. The intersection (in the first octant) of the paraboloid and the plane is the curve AC (Fig. 132). The volume requested to be shown is $OABCD$ outlined in the figure.

EXERCISES

Sketch the volume inclosed by the given surfaces. Unless otherwise stated, only the volume in the first octant is to be considered.

1. Inside the cylinder $x^2 + y^2 = 36$ and under the plane $x + y + z = 10$.

2. $y^2 + z^2 = 16$, $x + y = 6$, and the coördinate planes.

3. All the volume above the xy-plane, inside the cylinder $y^2 = 12 - 3x$, and under the plane $2z = x$.

4. $x^2 + y^2 = 4z$, $2y = x$, $x = 4$, $y = 0$, and $z = 0$.

5. $x^2 = 4y$, $y^2 = 4x$, $z = 0$, and $z = 4$.

6. $x^2 + y^2 + z^2 = 18$, $x^2 + y^2 = 3z$, and the coördinate planes.

7. $y^2 = 4x$, $2z = x$, $x = 4$, $y = 0$, and $z = 0$.

8. $x^2 + y^2 = 16$, $4(x^2 + y^2) = z^2$, and the coördinate planes.

9. All the volume inside the paraboloid $x^2 + y^2 + 2z = 16$ and above the plane $2z = 7$.

10. $y^2 + z^2 = 25$, $x^2 + z^2 = 25$, and the coördinate planes.

11. $x^2 + 4y^2 = 16$, $2z = 4 - y^2$, and the coördinate planes.

12. $z = 1 + x^2 + y^2$, $x^2 + y^2 = 1$, $y = x$, $y = 0$, and $z = 0$.

13. $2z = x + 2y$, $2y^2 = x$, $x = 2$, $y = 0$, and $z = 0$.

14. $4z = x^2 + 2y^2$, $y^2 = x$, $x = 4$, $y = 0$, and $z = 0$.

15. $y + z = 6$, $6z = x^2$, $x = 0$, and $y = 0$.

16. $x = 4 - z - y^2$, $y + z = 2$, and the coördinate planes.

17. $z^2 = 4 - x - y$, $x^2 = 9y$, $y = 0$, and $z = 0$.

18. $z^2 = 8(x + y)$, $x + y = 2$, and the coördinate planes.

19. $4y^2 + 4z^2 = x^2$, $x = 4y$, $x = 8$, and $z = 0$.

20. $x^2 + y^2 + z^2 = 20$, $2y = x$, $x = 4$, $z = 2$, $y = 0$, and $z = 0$.

21. $x^2 + y^2 + 2z = 16$, $y^2 + z^2 = 16$, and the coördinate planes.

22. $x^2 + y^2 = 4$, $x^2 + y^2 - z^2 = 1$, and the coördinate planes.

23. $x^2 + y^2 + z^2 = 16$, $x^2 + y^2 = 4x$, $y = 0$, and $z = 0$.

24. In Exercise 23 find the projections on the coördinate planes of the curve of intersection of the sphere and the cylinder.

25. A right circular cylinder with altitude equal to the diameter of the base is cut by a plane which cuts one base in a diameter and is tangent to the other base. Picture the smaller of the two parts into which the cylinder is divided. Select axes and write the equations of the surfaces which bound the part pictured.

125. Spherical coördinates. Another method of locating a point in space is by giving its distance and direction from a fixed point. In Fig. 133 let O be the fixed point and draw OX and OZ making $\angle XOZ = 90°$.

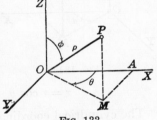

Let θ be the angle between the plane POZ and the plane XOZ and let ϕ be the angle between the lines OP and OZ. The point P is determined by ρ, θ, and ϕ.

If OX and OZ are chosen for the x- and z-axes, respectively, and OY is drawn perpendicular to OX and OZ, relations between

FIG. 133

the spherical and rectangular coördinates of P are easily found. Draw PM perpendicular to the plane XOY and join O and M. Then $\angle MOP = 90° - \phi$, and $OM = OP \cos \angle MOP$, or $OM = \rho \cos (90° - \phi) = \rho \sin \phi$. Hence the rectangular coördinates are

$$x = OA = OM \cos \theta = \rho \sin \phi \cos \theta,$$
$$y = AM = OM \sin \theta = \rho \sin \phi \sin \theta,$$
$$z = MP = \rho \cos \phi.$$

The spherical coördinates can be expressed in terms of the rectangular coördinates by solving the foregoing equations for ρ, ϕ, and θ. Squaring and adding, we have

$$x^2 + y^2 + z^2 = \rho^2, \quad \text{or} \quad \rho = \pm \sqrt{x^2 + y^2 + z^2}.$$

Then from the third of the foregoing equations we obtain

$$\phi = \text{arc cos} \frac{z}{\sqrt{x^2 + y^2 + z^2}},$$

and from the first and second equations we obtain

$$\theta = \text{arc tan} \frac{y}{x}.$$

126. Cylindrical coördinates. Cylindrical coördinates are a combination of polar and rectangular coördinates. Thus in

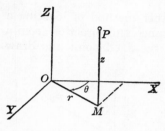

FIG. 134

Fig. 134 the cylindrical coördinates of P are (r, θ, z), where r and θ are the polar coördinates of M, the projection of P upon the xy-plane, and where z is the distance MP.

The rectangular coördinates (x, y, z) of P are related to the cylindrical coördinates (r, θ, z) of P by the equations

$$x = r \cos \theta, \quad y = r \sin \theta, \quad z = z.$$

The cylindrical coördinates (r, θ, z) of P are related to the spherical coördinates (ρ, θ, ϕ) of P by the equations

$$r = \rho \sin \phi, \quad \theta = \theta, \quad z = \rho \cos \phi.$$

EXERCISES

1. Write the rectangular and the cylindrical coördinates of the points whose spherical coördinates are

$$(a) \left(8, \frac{\pi}{4}, \frac{\pi}{3}\right); \qquad (b) \left(2, 0, \frac{\pi}{4}\right); \qquad (c) \left(3, \frac{\pi}{2}, \frac{\pi}{2}\right).$$

2. Write the rectangular and the spherical coördinates of the points whose cylindrical coördinates are

$$(a) \left(6, \frac{\pi}{6}, 8\right); \qquad (b) \left(6, \frac{\pi}{2}, 0\right); \qquad (c) \ (0, \theta, 8).$$

3. Write the spherical and the cylindrical coördinates of the points whose rectangular coördinates are

(a) $(6, 3, 0)$;   (b) $(0, 4, 2)$;   (c) $(4\sqrt{3}, 4, 8)$.

4. Transform the following equations into equations in cylindrical and spherical coördinates:

(a) $x^2 + y^2 = 5z$;   (b) $xz = ay$;   (c) $x^2 + y^2 = 2ax$.

5. Transform the following equations into equations in rectangular coördinates:

(a) $\rho = a$; (b) $r = a$; (c) $z = a \pm r$; (d) $z^2 = a^2 - r^2$.

6. Discuss the equations

(a) $\rho = 8 \cos \phi$.   (c) $r = a \cos \theta$.
(b) $\rho \sin \phi = a$.   (d) $r^2 + a^2z^2 = b^2$.

7. A circular cylinder of diameter 6 inches intersects a sphere of radius 6 inches so that an element of the cylinder coincides with a diameter of the sphere. Choose axes and write the equations of the bounding surfaces of the common volume in (a) rectangular coördinates; (b) spherical coördinates; (c) cylindrical coördinates.

MISCELLANEOUS EXERCISES

1. What surfaces are represented by the following equations?

(a) $x^2 + z^2 = a^2$.   (f) $x^2 + y^2 = z^2$.
(b) $x^2 = 2py$.   (g) $x^2 + 2y^2 + 3z^2 = 4$.
(c) $y = mx + b$.   (h) $xy = z^2$.
(d) $y^2 - z^2 = 0$.   (i) $x + y = z^2$.
(e) $xyz = 0$.   (j) $x^2 + y^2 = z$.

2. Find the equation of the right circular cylinder whose axis is the line $x = 3$, $y = 4$ and whose radius is 5.

3. Find the equation of the sphere which passes through $(0, 0, 0)$, $(1, 3, 2)$, $(1, 2, -3)$, and $(5, 3, 6)$.

4. Show that the plane $5x - y - 4z + 31 = 0$ is tangent to the sphere $x^2 + y^2 + z^2 - 8x - 2y - 4z = 21$, and write the equation of the parallel tangent plane.

5. Find the points where the line $x - 2y - 2z + 6 = 0$, $x + 2z - 2 = 0$ intersects the cone $4x^2 + 4z^2 - y^2 = 0$.

6. Find the equation of the surface of revolution generated by revolving the hyperbola $xy = a^2$, $z = 0$, about one of its asymptotes.

7. The arc of the parabola $x^{\frac{1}{2}} + y^{\frac{1}{2}} = a^{\frac{1}{2}}$ from $(a, 0)$ to $(0, a)$ in the xy-plane is revolved about the x-axis. Find the equation of the surface thus generated.

8. The four-cusped hypocycloid $x^{\frac{2}{3}} + y^{\frac{2}{3}} = a^{\frac{2}{3}}$, $z = 0$, is revolved about the x-axis. Find the equation of the surface thus generated.

9. The line $x + z = 2$, $y = 0$, is revolved about the line $z = 2$ in the xz-plane. Find the equation of the surface thus generated.

10. Find the equation of the surface of revolution generated by revolving the arc of the parabola $y^2 = 4\,px$, $z = 0$, terminated by the ends of the latus rectum about the latus rectum.

11. Discuss the surface $x^{\frac{2}{3}} + y^{\frac{2}{3}} + z^{\frac{2}{3}} = a^{\frac{2}{3}}$.

12. Show that in general the parametric equations $x = f_1(t)$, $y = f_2(t)$, $z = f_3(t)$ represent a skew curve.

13. Discuss the curve $x = t$, $y = t^2$, $z = t^3$.

14. Discuss the curve $x = a \cos t$, $y = a \sin t$, $z = kt$. (This curve is called a **helix**.)

15. Discuss the curve $x = t \cos t$, $y = t \sin t$, $z = t$. (This curve is called a **conical helix**.)

ANSWERS

Pages 5–7

1. a. 6.   **b.** 9.   **c.** -7.   **d.** -2.   **e.** -7.   **f.** 12.

2. 64.   **5. a.** 28.   **6.** 120.

3. 10.   **b.** 45.   **7.** $(3, 13)$, $(3, -11)$; 36.

4. 36; $(6, 2)$.   **c.** 45.   **8.** $(3, 3\sqrt{3})$;

                d. 66. $(3, -3\sqrt{3})$.

10. Quadrants I and III. Quadrants II and IV.

11. a. Lie on a line parallel to y-axis.   **b.** Lie on a line parallel to x-axis.

12. a. Lie on the y-axis.   **b.** Lie on the x-axis.

13. a. Lie on the line bisecting quadrants I and III.

     b. Lie on the line bisecting quadrants II and IV.

19. a. Lie on the line parallel to y-axis and three units to the right of it.

     b. Lie on the line parallel to x-axis and two units below it.

     c. Lie on the line bisecting quadrants I and III.

     d. Lie on the line bisecting quadrants II and IV.

Pages 8–9

1. a. 10.   **3.** $4\sqrt{13}$.   **14.** $(0, 3)$; $(0, 11)$.

   b. 13.   **4.** 48.   **15.** $(0, 1)$.

   c. 19.   **11.** 9; -7.   **16.** $(3 + 3\sqrt{3}, 3 - 3\sqrt{3})$;

   d. $4\sqrt{5}$.   **12. a.** $(\frac{5}{2}, 0)$. $(3 - 3\sqrt{3}, 3 + 3\sqrt{3})$;

   e. $2\sqrt{3}$.   **b.** $(0, -5)$.   **17.** $(-1, 2)$; $(7, -2)$.

   f. $\sqrt{2}\,|\,a - b\,|$.   **13.** $(6, 6)$.   **18.** $(\frac{5}{2}, -3)$.

      19. $(\frac{7}{5}, \frac{24}{5})$; $(\frac{7}{5}, -\frac{24}{5})$; $(-\frac{7}{5}, \frac{24}{5})$; $(-\frac{7}{5}, -\frac{24}{5})$.

      20. $x + y = 7$.

      21. $x^2 + y^2 - 6x - 8y = 0$.

      22. $y^2 = 8x - 16$.

Pages 11–12

2. a. $(2, 5)$.   **b.** $(2, 0)$.   **c.** $(\frac{5}{2}, \frac{3}{2})$.   **d.** $\left(\dfrac{a + b}{2}, \dfrac{c + d}{2}\right)$.

3. $(-8, 5)$.

4. $(-3, \frac{5}{4})$; $(2, \frac{1}{2})$; $(7, -\frac{1}{4})$.   **8. a.** $(1, 5)$.

5. $3\sqrt{13}$; $3\sqrt{10}$; 9.   **b.** $(-35, -19)$.

6. 60.   **c.** $(40, 31)$.

      9. $(1, -\frac{4}{3})$; $(17, 0)$.

10. $\left(1 + 4\sqrt{5},\ 3 + 2\sqrt{5}\right)$.

11. $(7.2,\ 4.8)$.

12. $(4,\ 3)$.

14. $(4,\ 0)$.

15. $(-3,\ 4)$; $(1,\ -8)$; $(9,\ 0)$.

16. $(-3,\ 3)$; $(1,\ 9)$; $(7,\ -1)$.

17. $(-2,\ 1)$; $(10,\ -3)$.

18. $(7,\ 1)$; $(1,\ -7)$.

Pages 15–17

1. a. 1.

b. $\sqrt{3}$.

c. Not defined.

d. -1.

2. a. Positive.

b. Negative.

4. a. 1.

b. $-\frac{3}{5}$

c. 0.

d. Not defined.

7. a. 0; $-\frac{1}{2}$; $-\frac{1}{4}$.

b. Not defined; 2; 4.

c Not defined; $-\frac{1}{6}$; $-\frac{1}{3}$.

10. 11.

11. -6; 1.

12. 60°.

13. 14°.

14. 53° 08′.

15. 45°.

16. a. 18° 26′; 45°; 116° 34′   **b.** 71° 34′; 56° 19′; 52° 07′.

18. $\frac{1}{5}$; -5.   **19.** 2; $-\frac{1}{2}$.   **20.** $-2 - \sqrt{3}$; $-2 + \sqrt{3}$; 1.   **22.** $x + y = 5$.

Pages 18–19

1. a. 9.

b. 31.

c. 37.

2. 40.

3. 48.

6. a. 27.

b. 45.

c. $\left|\dfrac{a^2 - b^2}{2}\right|$.

7. a. 99.

b. 66.

8. 7; -3.

9. $3\sqrt{10}$.

11. 9.

12. $x - 3y + 5 = 0$.

13. $x - 3y + 15 = 0$; $x - 3y = 5$.

Page 24

2. a. $(-3,\ 0)$; $(0,\ 3)$.   **b.** $(-4,\ 0)$; $(0,\ -3)$.   **c.** $(0,\ 0)$.   **d.** $(0,\ 4)$.

4. a. 1 (d); 2 (c); 3, second line.   **b.** 2 (d); 3, third line.

5. (b); (c).

6. $2x - y + 4 = 0$.

7. $2x + y = 9$.

8. $2x - 3y + 1 = 0$.

9. $2x + 5y + 4 = 0$.

10. $y = 5$; $y = -5$.

11 $x = 3$; $x = -3$.

12. a. $x = y$.

b. $x + y = 0$.

13. a. The y-axis.

b. The x-axis.

14. $\frac{13}{2}$.

15. 15.

16. $2x - y = 4$.

Pages 27–28

1. a. $3x - 4y = 18$.

b. $2x + y = 3$.

c. $x - 2y = 7$.

d. $2x - 5y = 0$.

e. $2x + 3y = 15$.

f. $y = 7$.

2. a. $y + 2 = 0$.

b. $x - y = 6$.

c. $x = 4$.

d. $x + y = 2$.

3. a. $3x - 5y = 11$.

b. $x - 2y = 0$.

c. $x + 6y = 6$.

d. $3x + 4y = 10$.

e. $y = 4$.

f. $x = 3$.

4. $x + y = 5$; $2x + y = 3$; $3x - 2y = 15$.
5. $y = 3$; $x = 1$; $2x - y + 1 = 0$.
6. $y = 0$; $y = 4$; $y = 2x$; $y = 2x - 16$; $2x - 5y = 0$; $2x + 3y = 16$.
7. $3x + 2y = 18$; $x + 4y + 14 = 0$; $y = x + 4$.
8. $x = 0$; $y = x$; $x + y = 10$.
9. $y = 0$; $y = \sqrt{3}\,x$; $\sqrt{3}\,x + y = a\sqrt{3}$.
10. $3x - 5y = 0$.
11. $2x - y = 8$; $x + 2y = 4$.
12. $x + 4y = 16$; $4x + y = 19$.

13. 20.

14. $(4, 1)$.

15. $(3, -1)$.

16. 10.

17. $2\sqrt{5}$; $2\sqrt{13}$.

18. $(5, -2)$.

19. $(6, -5)$.

20. $10\sqrt{5}$.

Pages 31–32

1. **a.** $y = -\frac{3}{4}x + 3$; $m = -\frac{3}{4}$; $b = 3$.
   b. $y = 5x - 10$; $m = 5$; $b = -10$.
   c. $y = -\frac{3}{2}x - 1$; $m = -\frac{3}{2}$; $b = -1$.
   d. $y = \frac{1}{3}x$; $m = \frac{1}{3}$; $b = 0$.

2. **a.** $\dfrac{x}{4} + \dfrac{y}{3} = 1$.

   b. $\dfrac{x}{2} + \dfrac{y}{-10} = 1$.

   c. $\dfrac{x}{-\frac{2}{3}} + \dfrac{y}{-1} = 1$.

   d. Because the intercepts are zero.

8. $2x - 7y = 13$; $7x + 2y = 19$.
9. $3x - y = 2$.
10. $(6, 5)$.
11. $2x + 3y + 25 = 0$
12. $5\sqrt{2}$.
13. $45°$; $18° \, 26'$; $116° \, 34'$.
15. $5x + y = 0$; $x - 5y = 0$.

Pages 36–38

1. **a.** $\dfrac{\sqrt{2}\,x}{2} + \dfrac{\sqrt{2}\,y}{2} - 2 = 0$.

   b. $-\dfrac{x}{2} + \dfrac{\sqrt{3}\,y}{2} - 3 = 0$.

   c. $-x - 5 = 0$.

   d. $-\dfrac{\sqrt{2}\,x}{2} - \dfrac{\sqrt{2}\,y}{2} - 1 = 0$.

   e. $\dfrac{\sqrt{3}\,x}{2} + \dfrac{y}{2} = 0$.

   f. $y - 10 = 0$.

2. **a.** $\dfrac{3x}{5} + \dfrac{4y}{5} - 2 = 0$; $\omega = 53° \, 08'$; $p = 2$.

   b. $-\dfrac{5x}{13} + \dfrac{12y}{13} - 3 = 0$; $\omega = 112° \, 37'$; $p = 3$.

   c. $-\dfrac{\sqrt{2}\,x}{2} - \dfrac{\sqrt{2}\,y}{2} - 4\sqrt{2} = 0$; $\omega = \dfrac{5\pi}{4}$; $p = 4\sqrt{2}$.

   d. $-\dfrac{\sqrt{3}\,x}{2} + \dfrac{y}{2} = 0$; $\omega = \dfrac{5\pi}{6}$; $p = 0$.

3. $\frac{11}{5}$.

4. $4x + 2y - 15 = 0$.

6. a. 2.

  b. -1.

  c. -4.

  d. 0.

7. a. 2.

  b. $-\frac{2}{5}$.

8. 5.

9. 8; 8; $4\sqrt{5}$.

11. a. $\sqrt{5}$.

  b. $3\sqrt{10}$.

12. 20.

13. a. $4x + 2y = 25$.

  b. $x - 3y + 5 = 0$.

14. $12x + 5y = 0$; $12x + 5y = 78$.

15. $x + 3y = 14$; $x + 3y + 6 = 0$.

16. $(3, 6)$; $(-1, -2)$.

18. $4x - 4y + 9 = 0$; $8x + 8y = 15$.

19. $x - 8y + 10 = 0$; $9x - 2y + 10 = 0$; $10x + 11y = 4$.

20. $\frac{\sqrt{5}}{2}$.

Pages 40–41

1. a. Parallel to y-axis.

  b. Same y-intercept, 3.

  c. Same y-intercept, 4.

  d. Through same point, $(3, 2)$.

  e. The x-intercept equals y-intercept.

  f. Same y-intercept, 1.

  g. Common perpendicular has inclination angle $\frac{\pi}{3}$.

  h. At same distance, 5, from origin.

2. a. $y = k$; $y = 2$.

  b. $y = \frac{5}{2}x + b$; $y = \frac{5}{2}x - \frac{11}{2}$.

  c. $y = mx$; $y = \frac{2}{3}x$.

  d. $\frac{x}{a} + \frac{y}{10-a} = 1$; $\frac{x}{6} + \frac{y}{4} = 1$, $\frac{x}{5} + \frac{y}{5} = 1$.

3. a. 6.

  b. 2.

  c. 1; $-\frac{2}{3}$.

  d. 3; -4.

4. a. 3; -1.

  b. 1.

  c. Impossible.

5. $x + 5y = 10$.

6. $\frac{x}{4} + \frac{y}{2} = 1$; $x - y = 1$; $2y = x$.

7. $x + y + 1 = 0$; $\frac{2x}{3} + \frac{3y}{2} = 1$.

9. a. $x + 2y = 10$; $8x + y = 20$.

  b. $2x + y = 8$.

  c. Impossible.

10. a. $y = \frac{1}{2}x + 5$.

  b. $\frac{x}{-10} + \frac{y}{5} = 1$.

  c. $-\frac{x}{\sqrt{5}} + \frac{2y}{\sqrt{5}} - 2\sqrt{5} = 0$.

Each part may be written in the form $x - 2y + 10 = 0$.

11. a. $-\frac{x}{5} + \frac{3y}{5} = 1$.

  b. Impossible.

Pages 42–43

1. a. $y = 2x$.
   b. $2x + y = 8$.
   c. $x = 2$; $3x - 4y + 10 = 0$.

2. a. $y = 4$.
   b. $x = -1$.

    3. a. $x = 3y$; $x - y = 4$; $x + y = 8$.
      b. $x + 2y = 10$; $2x + 3y = 18$.
    4. $2x - 3y = 0$; $x - y = 1$; $x + 3y = 9$.
    5. $5x - y = 3$; $x + 5y = 11$.
    6. $3x + y = 10$.
    7. $3x + 2y = 18$; $6x + y = 18$.
    8. a. $3x + 4y = 10$; $x = 2$.
      b. $2x + y = 5$.
      c. Impossible.
   10. Valid only if P lies on first of given lines.

Pages 43–45. Miscellaneous Exercises

2. $\dfrac{7\sqrt{5}}{5}$.
  3. $(6, 1)$.
  4. $(5, 3)$.
  5. $(1, 0)$.
  6. $(5, 2)$.

7. $x + y = a$; $y = (2 + \sqrt{3})(x - a)$; $y = (2 - \sqrt{3})x + a$.
8. $\sqrt{10}$.
  9. 6.
  10. 6.
  11. -4.

12. $x + 2y + 6 = 0$, $3x + y = 17$; $x + y = 1$, $x - 3y = 9$.
13. $(4, 2)$; $(0, -3)$; $(-8, -6)$; $(-4, -1)$.
15. $3x + y = 15$; $x - 3y + 15 = 0$.
16. $4x - y + 4 = 0$; $x + 4y = 16$; $4x - y = 30$; $x + 4y + 18 = 0$.
17. $(-2, -1)$, $(10, 3)$, $(8, 9)$, $(-4, 5)$; $(\frac{11}{2}, \frac{13}{2})$, $(\frac{13}{2}, \frac{7}{2})$, $(-\frac{1}{2}, \frac{9}{2})$, $(\frac{1}{2}, \frac{3}{2})$.
18. $x = 3$; $4x + 3y = 15$.
19. $3x + 4y = 0$; $x + 4y + 8 = 0$; $x + y = 1$.
20. $x - y + 5 = 0$; $7x - y = 7$.
  21. $5x - 2y + 1 = 0$.
  22. 220 ft.

Page 53

23. $y = 2 \pm \sqrt{x + 1}$; $y = 2$.
24. $x = 3 \pm \sqrt{y + 4}$; $x = 3$.
25. $y = \pm \sqrt{x(8 - x)}$.
26. The graph of the new equation is symmetric to the graph of the first equation with respect to the y-axis.

Pages 59–60

2. $f(x) > 0$ for $x > \frac{5}{2}$; $f(x) = 0$ for $x = \frac{5}{2}$; $f(x) < 0$ for $x < \frac{5}{2}$.
3. The Fahrenheit readings are 23°, 32°, 68°, and 89.6°, respectively; the centigrade readings are $-24\frac{4}{9}$°, $-17\frac{7}{9}$°, $-9\frac{4}{9}$°, and 0°, respectively.

4. $v > 0$ for $t < 5$; $v = 0$ for $t = 5$; $v < 0$ for $t > 5$.

6. $(-b \pm \sqrt{b^2 - 4\,ac})/2\,a.$

7. $f(x) > 0$ for $-1 < x < 5$; $f(x) = 0$ for $x = 5$ or -1; $f(x) < 0$ for $x > 5$ or $x < -1$; $f(x)$ is greatest for $x = 2$.

8. Smallest value of $f(x)$ is 1.

10. $V = x^3$; $S = 6\,x^2$; $D = x\sqrt{3}$.

13. 100 ft.

14. $A = 20\,x - \dfrac{x^2}{2}$; 200 sq. rd.

15. $A = x\sqrt{36 - x^2}$; $x = 4^+$ in.

16. $V = 4\,x^3 - 48\,x^2 + 144\,x$; $x = 2$ in.

Page 63

1. The coördinate axes.

Pages 66–67

1. $(2, 2)$; $(-4, 8)$.

2. $(4, 2)$; $(-2, -4)$.

3. $(1, 3)$; $(1, 3)$.

4. $(3, 0)$; $(\frac{9}{5}, \frac{12}{5})$.

5. No intersection.

6. $(-1, 2)$; $(-1, -2)$; $(\frac{3}{2}, 3)$; $(\frac{3}{2}, -3)$.

7. $(1, 2)$.

8. $(2, 4)$; $(2, -4)$; $(-4, 2)$; $(-4, -2)$.

9. $(-1, \sqrt{3})$; $(-1, \sqrt{3})$; $(-1, -\sqrt{3})$; $(-1, -\sqrt{3})$.

10. $(-1, 1)$; $(-1, 1)$; $(\frac{1}{2}, 4)$.

11. $(2, 4)$; $(-2, -4)$; $(4, 2)$; $(-4, -2)$.

12. $(3, \frac{3}{2})$; $(3, \frac{3}{2})$; $(0, 3)$.

13. $(0, 0)$; $(4, 2)$.

14. $(1, 1)$; $(1, 1)$; $(-3, -1)$.

15. $(\sqrt{3}, 2)$; $(\sqrt{3}, -2)$; $(-\sqrt{3}, 2)$; $(-\sqrt{3}, -2)$.

16. $(2, -1)$; $(5, 5)$; $(5, 5)$.

17. $(1, \sqrt{2})$; $(1, -\sqrt{2})$; $(-1, \sqrt{2})$; $(-1, -\sqrt{2})$.

18. $(3, 0)$; $(3, 0)$; $(1, 2)$.

19. $(2, 2)$; $(2, 2)$; $(-1 - \sqrt{3}, -1 + \sqrt{3})$; $(-1 + \sqrt{3}, -1 - \sqrt{3})$.

20. $(-1, 3\sqrt{7})$; $(-1, -3\sqrt{7})$; $(0, 8)$; $(0, 8)$; $(0, -8)$; $(0, -8)$.

21. $(0, 0)$; $(0, 0)$; $(\frac{1}{2}, \frac{1}{8})$.

22. $(0, 0)$; $(0, 0)$; $(3, 3)$; $(-3, -3)$.

23. $(1, -1)$.

24. $(-2, 0)$; $(1, 3)$; $(3, 5)$.

25. $(1, 1)$; $(4, 8)$; $(\frac{4}{9}, -\frac{8}{27})$.

26. $(1, 2)$; $(1, 2)$; $(1, 2)$.

27. $(2, 1)$; $(-2, 1)$.

28. $(0, 4)$; $(1, \frac{3}{2})$; $(1, \frac{3}{2})$.

29. $(-1, -2)$; $(2, 1)$; $(2, 1)$.

30. $(2, 1)$; $(2, -1)$; $(1, 0)$; $(1, 0)$.

31. $y = -x + 1$; $y = \dfrac{x}{2} + 1$.

32. $2\,x + y + 10 = 0$; $2\,x + y = 10$.

33. 1.

34. $m = -\frac{1}{4}\,b^2$.

Pages 70–71

1. a. $x^2 + y^2 = 25$.
   b. $x^2 + y^2 - 2x - 4y = 11$.
2. $4x - 3y = 16$.
3. $x^2 + y^2 - 4x - 3y = 0$.
5. $x^2 + y^2 = 36$.
6. $x^2 - y^2 = 0$.
8. $x^2(x^2 + y^2) = y^2$.
9. a. $y^2 = 6x - 9$.
   b. $y^2 - 8y + 4x = 0$.

10. a. $x^2 = 6y - 9$.
    b. $x^2 - 2x + 2y - 2 = 0$.
11. $3x^2 + 4y^2 = 48$.
12. $3x^2 - y^2 = 48$.
13. $xy = 2$.
14. $xy - 3x + 2y = 0$.
15. $y = 0$; $xy = x^2 - 1$.
16. a. $x = 0$; $2y = x^2 - 1$.
    b. $2x^2y = x^2 - 1$.

17. $2xy = k$, where k is the constant area.
18. $x^2 + y^2 = a^2$, if M is the origin.

Pages 74–75

1. a. $y'^2 = 4x'$.
   b. $x'y' = 2$.
   c. $2y' = x'^2$
   d. $x'^2 + y'^2 = 25$.
2. a. $y' = x'^3$
   b. $y'^2 = x'^3$
   c. $x'y' = 5$.
   d. $y'x'^2 = 4$.
   e. $x'^2 + y'^2 = 36$.
3. a. $x'^2 + y'^2 = 16$.
   b. $x'^2 + 4y'^2 = 16$.
   c. $4x'^2 - 9y'^2 = 36$.

4. $x'^2 + 4y' = 4$; no.
5. $y'^2 = 2x'$.
6. $\left(-\dfrac{b}{2a}, \dfrac{4ac - b^2}{4a} \right)$.
7. $x'^2 = 2y'$.
8. $Ax' + By' = 0$.
9. $x' + 2y' = 0$; $3x' - 7y' = 0$.
11. $4x'^2 + 25y'^2 = 100$.
12. $x'^2 - 4x' - 2y' + 6 = 0$; $x''^2 = 2y''$.
13. $3x^2 - 2xy + 3y^2 = 8$;
    $x'^2 + 2y'^2 = 4$.
14. $2x'y' = a^2$.

Pages 76–77. Miscellaneous Exercises

8. $S = 2\pi \left(r^2 + \dfrac{16}{r} \right)$; $r = 2$ in.

9. a. $y = x^2 - 3$.
   b. $y^2 = \dfrac{2x}{3}$.
   c. $y = x^3$.
   d. $y^2 = -2x^3$.
   e. $xy = -6$.
   f. $y(x - 2) = 2x$.
12. a. $5\sqrt{2}$; 7.
    b. 35.
13. $45°$.
14. $xy^2 - 2x^2y - y^2 + 2xy = 0$.

17. $A + C = 0$.
18. $\left(\sqrt{1 \pm \sqrt{b}}, b \right)$; $\left(\sqrt{1 \pm \sqrt{b}}, b \right)$.
    a. No intersections.
    b. Two points of tangency, $(\pm 1, 0)$.
    c. Four distinct points of intersection.
    d. $(\pm \sqrt{2}, 1)$, and tangent at $(0, 1)$.
    e. $\left(\pm \sqrt{1 + \sqrt{b}}, b \right)$.
19. $(1, \frac{9}{4})$; $(3, \frac{25}{4})$.
20. $(1, 0)$; $(1, 0)$; $(3, 2)$.
22. $m = \pm 2$.
23. $x - 2y = 2$; $x + 4y = 8$.

Pages 79–81

1. a. $x^2 + y^2 = 36$.
   b. $x^2 + y^2 = 40$.
   c. $x^2 + y^2 - 4x - 12y = 0$.

d. $x^2 + y^2 + 2x - 6y = 27$.
e. $x^2 + y^2 - 2rx = 0$.
f. $x^2 + y^2 - 2ry = 0$.

2. a. $(x-3)^2 + (y-1)^2 = 16$; $(3, 1)$; 4.
   b. $(x+2)^2 + (y-\frac{5}{2})^2 = \frac{25}{4}$; $(-2, \frac{5}{2})$; $\frac{5}{2}$.
   c. $(x-4)^2 + (y-4)^2 = 32$; $(4, 4)$; $4\sqrt{2}$.
   d. $(x-5)^2 + y^2 = 36$; $(5, 0)$; 6.
   e. $(x-1)^2 + (y+\frac{2}{3})^2 = \frac{16}{9}$; $(1, -\frac{2}{3})$; $\frac{4}{3}$.
   f. $x^2 + (y+\frac{7}{2})^2 = 9$; $(0, -\frac{7}{2})$; 3.

4. $x^2 + y^2 - 10x - 6y + 25 = 0$; $x^2 + y^2 - 10x - 6y + 9 = 0$.

5. a. $x^2 + y^2 - 6x - 12y + 9 = 0$.
   b. $x^2 + y^2 + 2x + 4y + 4 = 0$.

6. $x^2 + y^2 - 10x + 8y = 0$.

7. $x^2 + y^2 - 2x - 14y + 40 = 0$.   **8.** 12.

10. $(0, 0)$; $(\frac{8}{5}, \frac{16}{5})$.   **11.** $x - 2y + 8 = 0$.   **12.** $(1, 4)$.   **13.** $3x - 5y = 9$.

14. a. $x^2 + y^2 + ax + by = 0$.
   b. $x^2 + y^2 + ax + c = 0$.
   c. $x^2 + y^2 + by + c = 0$.
   d. $x^2 + y^2 + ax + ay + c = 0$.

15. a. $x^2 + y^2 = r^2$.
   b. $x^2 + y^2 + ax = 0$.
   c. $x^2 + y^2 + by = 0$.
   d. $x^2 + y^2 + ax + ay = 0$.
   e. $x^2 + y^2 - 2hx = 36 - h^2$.

16. If the equation is in the form (1) or (2), the difference is in the constant term only.

17. $x^2 + y^2 + 5x - 6y = 28$.

Pages 83–84

1. $a = -1$; $b = -3$; $c = -10$.

2. a. $x^2 + y^2 + 4x - 4y = 42$.
   b. $x^2 + y^2 - 4x - 6y = 12$.
   c. $2x^2 + 2y^2 - 3x - 7y = 14$.
   d. $x^2 + y^2 - 7x - 9y = 0$.

3. a. $x^2 + y^2 - 5x - y = 6$.
   b. $x^2 + y^2 - 2x = 124$.

5. $x^2 + y^2 - 8x - 4y = 12$.

6. $x^2 + y^2 - 8x - 10y + 16 = 0$.

7. $x^2 + y^2 + 2x - 6y = 30$.

8. $x^2 + y^2 - 8x - 14y + 25 = 0$.

9. $x^2 + y^2 - 10x - 10y + 25 = 0$; $x^2 + y^2 - 26x - 26y + 169 = 0$.

10. $x^2 + y^2 - 12x - 18y + 17 = 0$; $x^2 + y^2 + 4x + 14y = 47$.

11. $x^2 + y^2 - 4x + 2 = 0$; $x^2 + y^2 - 12x + 34 = 0$.

12. $x^2 + y^2 - 4x - 4y + 4 = 0$; $x^2 + y^2 + 12x - 12y + 36 = 0$.

13. $x^2 + y^2 + 6x - 10y + 9 = 0$; $x^2 + y^2 - 14x - 20y + 49 = 0$.

14. a. $x^2 + y^2 - 8x - 2y + 7 = 0$; $x^2 + y^2 - 3x - 7y + 12 = 0$.
   b. $x^2 + y^2 - 36x + 2y + 75 = 0$.
   c. $x^2 + y^2 - 11x - 23y + 100 = 0$; $x^2 + y^2 - 19x + y + 28 = 0$.

15. $x^2 + y^2 - 4x - 16y + 43 = 0$; $5x^2 + 5y^2 - 12x - 24y + 31 = 0$.

16. $2x^2 + 2y^2 - 4x - 20y = 29$.

Page 87

1. $2x^2 + 2y^2 - 3x - 14y = 0.$
2. $x^2 + y^2 - 9x + 5y + 14 = 0.$
3. $x^2 + y^2 - 2x + 2y = 16.$
4. a. $x^2 + y^2 + 9x = 4.$
   b. $x^2 + y^2 - 9x - 9y + 5 = 0.$
5. 1. $7x + 2y = 30.$
   2. $13x - 9y = 31.$
   3. $x + y = 0.$
   4. $2x + y = 1.$

6. 10.
7. 4.
9. a. Between the circles.
   b. Common tangent.
   c. Intersects both circles.
   d. Common tangent.
   e. Outside of both circles.
   f. No radical axis in finite plane.
12. $(1, -\frac{5}{2}).$

Pages 88–89. Miscellaneous Exercises

2. $3x^2 + 3y^2 - 2a\sqrt{3}\,y = 3a^2$
5. $x^2 + y^2 - 18x + 12y + 3 = 0.$
3. $(1, 7).$
4. $4\sqrt{5}.$
6. $(7, 1); (-1, 5).$
7. $x^2 + y^2 - 10x - 8y + 31 = 0;\ x^2 + y^2 - 6x + 4y + 3 = 0.$
8. $x^2 + y^2 - 6x = 1;\ x^2 + y^2 - 10x - 8y + 31 = 0.$
9. $x^2 + y^2 = 50;\ x^2 + y^2 = 18.$

10. $(6, -3).$
11. $(\frac{7}{2}, 4).$
12. $(4, 0); (-2, 2).$
15. $3x - y = \pm 20.$

16. $3x - y = 10;\ x - 3y + 10 = 0.$
17. $0;\ \dfrac{2h}{h^2 - 1}.$

24. a. $x^2 + y^2 - 4x - 2y = 0$, circle.
    b. $x^2 + y^2 - 4x - 2y + 5 = 0$, point circle.
    c. $x^2 + y^2 - 4x - 2y + 10 = 0$, imaginary locus.
26. Arc of the circle, $x^2 + y^2 - ax - ay = 0$, where the fixed points are $(0, 0)$ and $(a, 0)$.
27. If the axes are the two perpendicular lines, the equation of the locus is $x^2 + y^2 = 25.$

Pages 92–94

1. a. $(1, 0);\ 4;\ x + 1 = 0.$
   b. $(-\frac{3}{2}, 0);\ 6;\ 2x - 3 = 0.$
   c. $(0, 4);\ 16;\ y + 4 = 0.$
   d. $(0, -\frac{1}{2});\ 2;\ 2y - 1 = 0.$
2. a. $3y^2 = x;\ x^2 = 9y.$
   b. $5y^2 = 9x;\ 3x^2 + 25y = 0.$
   c. $5y^2 + 8x = 0;\ x^2 = 25y.$
   d. $9y^2 + 8x = 0;\ 8x^2 + 3y = 0.$
4. $\theta = 2$ arc tan 2 for all parabolas.
5. $y^2 - 2px + p^2 = 0.$
8. $4x^2 + 4y^2 - 4px = 3p^2.$
9. $x^2 + y^2 - 10x = 0.$

10. $4p.$
11. $(0, 0); (4, 6).$
12. 25.
13. a. $y^2 + 8x = 16.$
    b. $y^2 = 8x + 16.$
    c. $x^2 - 2x - 8y + 9 = 0.$
14. $4\sqrt{2}.$
15. $y^2 = 4x - 8;\ y^2 + 16x = 112.$
16. 9 ft.
17. $\frac{9}{4}$ in.
18. 16 ft.
19. $y = kx^2;\ \frac{9}{2}.$

Pages 96–98

1.

	Vertex	Focus	Latus rectum	Directrix	Axis
a.	$(3, 1)$;	$(5, 1)$;	8;	$x = 1$;	$y = 1$.
b.	$(\frac{3}{2}, -3)$;	$(0, -3)$;	6;	$x = 3$;	$y + 3 = 0$.
c.	$(2, -6)$;	$(2, -\frac{11}{2})$;	2;	$2y + 13 = 0$;	$x = 2$.
d.	$(\frac{5}{2}, \frac{5}{2})$;	$(\frac{5}{2}, \frac{15}{8})$;	$\frac{5}{2}$;	$8y = 25$;	$2x = 5$.
e.	$(2, 0)$;	$(\frac{8}{3}, 0)$;	$\frac{8}{3}$;	$3x = 4$;	$y = 0$.
f.	$(0, 3)$;	$(0, \frac{14}{5})$;	$\frac{4}{5}$;	$5y = 16$;	$x = 0$.

2. a. $y^2 - 6y - 12x + 21 = 0$.

b. $x^2 + 4x + 4y = 4$.

c. $x^2 - 6x - 2y + 10 = 0$.

d. $y^2 + 12x = 24$.

e. $y^2 - 2y - 10x = 24$.

3. $2x - y + 4 = 0$; $2x + y = 0$.

4. a. $y^2 - 2y - 3x + 7 = 0$.

b. $x^2 - 4x + 3y + 1 = 0$.

5. (7) $y^2 + ax + by + c = 0$.

(8) $x^2 + a'x + b'y + c' = 0$.

6. c. x-intercepts: $\dfrac{-b \pm \sqrt{b^2 - 4ac}}{2a}$. Real and distinct if $b^2 - 4ac > 0$; real and equal if $b^2 - 4ac = 0$; imaginary if $b^2 - 4ac < 0$.

7.

	x-intercepts	y-intercepts	Axis	Vertex
a.	1, 5;	5;	$x = 3$;	$(3, -4)$.
b.	$-1, 3$;	3;	$x = 1$;	$(1, 4)$.
c.	$\frac{3}{2}, \frac{3}{2}$;	9;	$2x = 3$;	$(\frac{3}{2}, 0)$.
d.	imaginary;	1;	$2x = 1$;	$(\frac{1}{2}, \frac{1}{2})$.
e.	7;	$\frac{1}{2}, \frac{7}{2}$;	$y = 2$;	$(-9, 2)$.
f.	0;	0, 5;	$2y = 5$;	$(\frac{25}{8}, \frac{5}{2})$.

8. $a = 1, b = -4, c = -5$; $(2, -9)$.

9. $a = 2$; $b = -1$; $c = -3$.

10. a. $2x^2 - 3x - y - 1 = 0$.

b. $2y^2 - y + 9x - 19 = 0$.

11. a. $(2, 2)$; $(-1, -4)$.

b. $(0, 4)$; $(6, 6)$.

12. $10\sqrt{2}$.

13. Focus $(3, 1)$; directrix $x = 1$.

14. $x^2 + y^2 + 2xy - 4x + 4y = 4$. The equation contains the xy-term and both of the x^2- and y^2-terms.

Pages 100–102

1.

	Semiaxes	Vertices	Foci	Eccentricity
a.	5, 3;	$(\pm 5, 0)$;	$(\pm 4, 0)$;	$\frac{4}{5}$.
b.	6, 4;	$(0, \pm 6)$;	$(0, \pm 2\sqrt{5})$;	$\dfrac{\sqrt{5}}{3}$.
c.	10, 5;	$(\pm 10, 0)$;	$(\pm 5\sqrt{3}, 0)$;	$\dfrac{\sqrt{3}}{2}$.
d.	$5\sqrt{2}, 5$;	$(0, \pm 5\sqrt{2})$;	$(0, \pm 5)$;	$\dfrac{1}{\sqrt{2}}$.
e.	$\sqrt{3}, 1$;	$(\pm \sqrt{3}, 0)$;	$(\pm \sqrt{2}, 0)$;	$\dfrac{\sqrt{6}}{3}$.

f. $4\sqrt{5}, 4$; $(0, \pm 4\sqrt{5})$; $(0, \pm 8)$; $\dfrac{2\sqrt{5}}{5}.$

g. $5, 2\sqrt{6}$; $(\pm 5, 0)$; $(\pm 1, 0)$; $\frac{1}{5}.$

h. $10\sqrt{2}, 2$; $(\pm 10\sqrt{2}, 0)$; $(\pm 14, 0)$; $\dfrac{7\sqrt{2}}{19}.$

2. $4 x^2 + 3 y^2 = 300.$

3. a. $3 x^2 + 4 y^2 = 48.$
  b. $34 x^2 + 25 y^2 = 850.$
  c. $3 x^2 + y^2 = 81.$
  d. $x^2 + 2 y^2 = 6.$

5. $5 y^2 = x.$

6. a. $x^2 + 3 y^2 = 28.$
  b. $4 x^2 + y^2 = 52.$

7. $9 x^2 + 25 y^2 = 225.$

8. $x^2 + 4 y^2 = 36.$

9. If the perpendicular lines are the axes, the loci are the ellipses
   $x^2 + 4 y^2 = 64$ and $4 x^2 + y^2 = 64.$

10. a. 3 ft.   **b.** 6 ft.

11. 5 ft. 6.6 in.; 4 ft. 4.4 in.

12. a. $(1, 4)$; $(2, -2)$.
  b. $(4, 0)$; $(4, 0)$; $\left(\dfrac{4}{3}, \dfrac{4\sqrt{2}}{3}\right)$; $\left(\dfrac{4}{3}, -\dfrac{4\sqrt{2}}{3}\right)$.
  c. $(3, 5)$; $(3, -5)$; $(-4, 2)$; $(-4, -2)$.
  d. $(2, 5)$; $(2, -5)$; $(-2, 5)$; $(-2, -5)$.

13. a. $3 x^2 + 4 y^2 = 12.$ **b.** $3 x^2 + 4 y^2 = 12.$

Pages 104–105

1.

	Center	Semiaxes	Vertices	Foci
a.	$(3, 2)$;	$6, 3$;	$(9, 2), (-3, 2)$;	$(3 \pm 3\sqrt{3}, 2).$
b.	$(-2, 4)$;	$6\sqrt{2}, 6$;	$(-2, 4 \pm 6\sqrt{2})$;	$(-2, 10), (-2, -2).$
c.	$(-1, -3)$;	$5, 3$;	$(4, -3), (-6, -3)$;	$(3, -3), (-5, -3).$
d.	$(6, -4)$;	$6, 4$;	$(12, -4), (0, -4)$;	$(6 \pm 2\sqrt{5}, -4).$
e.	$(3, 5)$;	$2\sqrt{10}, 2\sqrt{6}$;	$(3, 5 \pm 2\sqrt{10})$;	$(3, 1), (3, 9).$
f.	$(4, 0)$;	$3, 1$;	$(7, 0), (1, 0)$;	$(4 \pm 2\sqrt{2}, 0).$

2. a. $9(x - 4)^2 + 25(y - 2)^2 = 225.$
  b. $9 x^2 + 8 y^2 + 18 x - 48 y - 207 = 0.$
  c. $x^2 + 2 y^2 - 8 x + 4 y = 0.$
  d. $5 x^2 + 2 y^2 - 40 x - 12 y + 18 = 0.$

3. $x^2 + y^2 - 6 y = 0$; $x^2 + y^2 - 6 y + 4 = 0.$

4. $5 y^2 = 4 x.$

5. a. $(4, 4)$; $(-7, \frac{1}{3})$.
  b. $(-1, 0)$; $(-1, 0)$; $(\frac{1}{2}, \sqrt{3})$; $(\frac{1}{2}, -\sqrt{3})$.

6. $x^2 + ay^2 + bx + cy + d = 0.$

7. $x^2 + 4 y^2 - 4 x - 8 y - 92 = 0.$

8. a. Point ellipse, $(0, 0)$.   **b.** Point ellipse, $(1, 2)$.   **c.** No real locus.

9. $3 x^2 + 3 y^2 - 2 xy - 2 x - 2 y = 1.$ The equation contains the xy-term.

Pages 109–110

1.
	Semiaxes	Vertices	Foci	Eccentricity	Asymptotes
a.	4, 3;	$(\pm 4, 0)$;	$(\pm 5, 0)$;	$\frac{5}{4}$;	$3\,x \pm 4\,y = 0$.
b.	3, 2;	$(\pm 3, 0)$;	$(\pm \sqrt{13}, 0)$;	$\frac{\sqrt{13}}{3}$;	$2\,x \pm 3\,y = 0$.
c.	$3\sqrt{3}$, 3;	$(0, \pm 3\sqrt{3})$;	$(0, \pm 6)$;	$\frac{2\sqrt{3}}{3}$;	$\sqrt{3}\,x \pm y = 0$.
d.	3, 6;	$(0, \pm 3)$;	$(0, \pm 3\sqrt{5})$;	$\sqrt{5}$;	$x \pm 2\,y = 0$.
e.	$2\sqrt{15}, 2\sqrt{10}$;	$(\pm 2\sqrt{15}, 0)$;	$(\pm 10, 0)$;	$\frac{\sqrt{15}}{3}$;	$\sqrt{2}\,x \pm \sqrt{3}\,y = 0$.
f.	$3\sqrt{5}$, 2;	$(0, \pm 3\sqrt{5})$;	$(0, \pm 7)$;	$\frac{7\sqrt{5}}{15}$;	$3\sqrt{5}\,x \pm 2\,y = 0$.
g.	4, 4;	$(\pm 4, 0)$;	$(\pm 4\sqrt{2}, 0)$;	$\sqrt{2}$;	$x \pm y = 0$.
h.	4, 4;	$(0, \pm 4)$;	$(0, \pm 4\sqrt{2})$;	$\sqrt{2}$;	$x \pm y = 0$.

2. $x^2 - 8\,y^2 + 32 = 0$.

3. **a.** $5\,x^2 - 4\,y^2 = 80$.
   b. $9\,x^2 - 40\,y^2 + 360 = 0$.
   c. $x^2 - 4\,y^2 = 16$.
   d. $4\,y^2 - x^2 = 72$.

5. $x^2 + 12\,y^2 - 16\,x = 0$.

6. **a.** $x^2 - 3\,y^2 = 6$.
   b. $5\,x^2 - y^2 + 20 = 0$.

7. $3\,x^2 - y^2 = 12$.

8. $16\,x^2 - 9\,y^2 = 576$.

9. $3\,x^2 - y^2 = 12$.

11. Vertices $(4, 4)$, $(-4, -4)$; axes $8\sqrt{2}$, $8\sqrt{2}$;
    foci $(4\sqrt{2}, 4\sqrt{2})$, $(-4\sqrt{2}, -4\sqrt{2})$.

12. $xy = k$; $\frac{3}{2}$.

13. **a.** $4\,y^2 - x^2 = 16$.
    b. $9\,x^2 - 4\,y^2 = 108$.
    c. $y^2 - x^2 = 25$.
    d. $xy = -9$.

15. **a.** $k = \frac{1}{40}$, $l = \frac{1}{10}$; ellipse.
    b. $k = \frac{2}{5}$, $l = -\frac{3}{5}$; hyperbola.
    c. $k = \frac{1}{25}$, $l = \frac{7}{75}$; ellipse.
    d. $k = -\frac{5}{16}$, $l = \frac{1}{4}$; hyperbola.

16. **a.** $3\,x^2 - y^2 = 12$.
    b. $3\,x^2 - y^2 = 12$.

17. Foci $(\pm 4, 0)$; $e = 2$.

Pages 112–113

1.
	Center	Semiaxes	Vertices
a.	$(2, 3)$;	$3\sqrt{3}$, 3;	$(2 \pm 3\sqrt{3}, 3)$;
b.	$(-2, 3)$;	3, 2;	$(-2, 6)$, $(-2, 0)$;
c.	$(2, -3)$;	1, $\sqrt{3}$;	$(3, -3)$, $(1, -3)$;
d.	$(0, 5)$;	4, 3;	$(0, 9)$, $(0, 1)$;
e.	$(1, 0)$;	2, 4;	$(-1, 0)$, $(3, 0)$;
f.	$(-2, -1)$;	$\sqrt{2}$, $\sqrt{2}$;	$(-2 \pm \sqrt{2}, -1)$;

Foci	Asymptotes
a. $(-4, 3)$, $(8, 3)$;	$3(y - 3) = \pm \sqrt{3}(x - 2)$.
b. $(-2, 3 \pm \sqrt{13})$;	$3(x + 2) = \pm 2(y - 3)$.
c. $(4, -3)$, $(0, -3)$;	$(y + 3) = \pm \sqrt{3}(x - 2)$.
d. $(0, 0)$, $(0, 10)$;	$3(y - 5) = \pm 4 x$.
e. $(1 \pm 2\sqrt{5}, 0)$;	$y = \pm 2(x - 1)$.
f. $(-4, -1)$, $(0, -1)$;	$(y + 1) = \pm (x + 2)$.

2. a. $9(x - 5)^2 - 16(y - 2)^2 = 144$.

  b. $x^2 - 3 y^2 - 2 x + 13 = 0$.

  c. $x^2 - 8 y^2 - 8 x + 48 y - 88 = 0$.

  d. $8 x^2 - y^2 - 16 x + 6 y + 7 = 0$.

3. $x^2 + 4 y^2 - 12 x = 0$.

4. $2 x^2 = 9 y + 9$.

5. $x^2 + ay^2 + bx + cy + d = 0$.

6. a. $a = -5, b = 6, c = -20, d = -7$; hyberbola.

  b. $a = 2, b = -2, c = 8, d = -90$; ellipse.

10. a. $(5, 2)$; $(-10, -8)$.

  b. $(6, 4)$; $(6, -4)$; $(-6, 4)$; $(-6, -4)$.

  c. $(1, 6)$; $(3, 2)$; $(-2, -3)$.

  d. $(1, -4)$; $(5, 4)$.

  e. $(0, 1)$; $(8, 1)$; $(0, -5)$; $(8, -5)$.

11. $3 x^2 + 3 y^2 + 8 xy - 28 x - 28 y + 49 = 0$. The equation contains the xy-term.

12. $7 x'^2 - y'^2 - 28\sqrt{2} x' + 49 = 0$.

Page 116

1. $x'^2 + 4 y'^2 = 4$. Ellipse.

2. $y'^2 = x'$. Parabola.

3. $x'^2 - 3 y'^2 = 27$. Hyperbola.

4. $x'^2 + y' = 4$. Parabola.

5. $x'^2 + 2 y'^2 - x' = 0$. Ellipse.

6. $x'^2 + 3 y'^2 - 18\sqrt{2} x' - 6\sqrt{2} y' + 132 = 0$. Ellipse.

7. $(\sqrt{3} + 1)x'^2 - (\sqrt{3} - 1)y'^2 = 18$. Hyperbola.

8. $x'^2 - 2 y' + 4 = 0$. Parabola.

Pages 118–119

3. a. Parabola.

  b. Ellipse.

  c. Hyperbola.

  d. Ellipse.

  e. Hyperbola.

  f. Parabola.

  g. Hyperbola.

  h. Hyperbola.

  i. Hyperbola.

  j. Two distinct lines.

  4. a. $(\sqrt{3}, \sqrt{3})$; $(\sqrt{3}, \sqrt{3})$; $(-\sqrt{3}, -\sqrt{3})$; $(-\sqrt{3}, -\sqrt{3})$.

  b. $(0, \sqrt{3})$; $(0, -\sqrt{3})$; $(\sqrt{3}, 0)$; $(-\sqrt{3}, 0)$.

5. $ax^2 + xy + by^2 + cx + dy + e = 0$.

6. a. $x^2 - 2 xy + y^2 - 3 x + 5 y = 0$. Parabola.

　b. $4 x^2 - 6 xy + 3 y^2 + 24 x - 24 y + 20 = 0$. Ellipse.

　c. $4 x^2 - 10 xy + 5 y^2 + 20 x - 20 y + 24 = 0$. Hyperbola.

Page 120

1. a. $y^2 - 2 y - 4 x + 5 = 0$. Parabola.

　b. $4 x^2 - 4 xy + y^2 - 8 x - 16 y + 24 = 0$. Parabola.

　c. $8 x^2 + 9 y^2 - 48 x = 0$. Ellipse.

　d. $7 x^2 - 2 xy + 7 y^2 - 24 x - 24 y = 0$. Ellipse.

　e. $4 x^2 - 5 y^2 - 60 y = 0$. Hyperbola.

　f. $x^2 - 4 xy + y^2 + 12 x - 12 y = 0$. Hyperbola.

3. In Exercises 9 (*a*), (*b*) and 10 (*a*), (*b*), parabolas.

In Exercise 11, ellipse.

In Exercises 12 and 13, hyperbolas.

Pages 120–122. Miscellaneous Exercises

1. Ellipse; hyperbola.
　　　　　　　　　　2. $x = a$; $y = b$.

4. a. $27 x^2 - 30 xy + 11 y^2 - 18 x - 30 y - 9 = 0$.

　b. $2\sqrt{3}$.

　c. *x*-intercepts, 1, $- \frac{1}{3}$; *y*-intercepts, 3, $- \frac{3}{11}$.

5. $(0, - 2)$, $(3, \frac{5}{2})$; $(2, 1)$, $(1, - \frac{1}{2})$.

6. $(- 1, - 1)$; $(- 1, - 1)$; $(5 + 2\sqrt{6}, 5 - 2\sqrt{6})$; $(5 - 2\sqrt{6}, 5 + 2\sqrt{6})$.

7. 96.
　　　　　　　　　　9. $x = 1$; $y = 1$.

8. $(2, - 4)$; $(2, 4)$; $(10, 4)$; $(10, - 4)$.　　**13.** $k = \pm \sqrt{a^2m^2 - b^2}$.

15. $b^2x^2 + a^2y^2 = ab^2x$ (if chords are drawn from origin).

22. a. Arc of a parabola.
　　　　　　　　　　c. An ellipse.

　b. One branch of a hyperbola.
　　　　　　　　d. A straight line.

Pages 129–130

12. Amplitude is $\sqrt{k_1{}^2 + k_2{}^2}$; period is $\dfrac{2 \pi}{m}$.

Pages 133–135. Miscellaneous Exercises

12. $x = a \log_e \left(\dfrac{y \pm \sqrt{y^2 - a^2}}{a} \right)$.

13. $y = \dfrac{e^x \pm e^{-x}}{2}$.

14. a. $- .57$

　b. $.57$

　c. $.74$

15. a. $(.6^-, .6^-)$.

　b. $(.4, - .4)$.

　c. $(1, 2)$; $(- 1, \frac{1}{2})$.

　d. $(1.9^-, .9^+)$.

16. a. $(0, 1)$; $(3, - 2)$; $(4, - 3)$.

　b. $(3, 6)$; $(- 3, \frac{3}{2})$; $(- 5, 0)$.

17. Not a higher plane curve. The equation in the form $f(x, y) = 0$ is factorable and represents two ellipses.

18. $(x^2 + y^2 + c^2)^2 - 4 c^2 x^2 = a^4$ (x-axis through fixed points with origin midway between them).

19. $(x^2 + y^2)^2 = 2 a^2(x^2 - y^2)$.

21. If the ends of AB are $(-c, 0)$ and $(c, 0)$ and the constant is $2 a$, the equation of the locus is

a. $\dfrac{x^2}{a^2} + \dfrac{y^2}{a^2 - c^2} = 1.$

b. $\dfrac{x^2}{a^2} - \dfrac{y^2}{c^2 - a^2} = 1.$

c. $(x^2 + y^2 + c^2)^2 - 4(c^2 x^2 + a^2) = 0.$

d. $x^2 + y^2 + c^2 \pm \dfrac{2 c(4 a^2 + 1)x}{4 a^2 - 1} = 0.$

Pages 139–140

3. a. $x^2 + y^2 - 8 x + 4 y + 11 = 0$, circle.
    b. $x^2 + 4 y^2 - 2 x - 24 y + 21 = 0$, ellipse.
    c. $x^2 - 4 y + 4 = 0$, parabola.
    d. $y = e^x + 1$, exponential curve.
    e. $x^2 - y^2 = 4$, hyperbola.
    f. $2 xy - x - y = 0$, hyperbola.
    g. $x^2 y + y - 2 x = 0$, cubic curve.

8. Center $(0, 0)$; $r = \sqrt{a^2 + b^2}$.

9. Center (c, d); semiaxes a, b.

10. $x = \dfrac{2 p}{m^2}, \; y = \dfrac{2 p}{m}.$

11. a. $x = 3 \cos \pi t, \; y = 3 \sin \pi t.$
    b. $x = -3 \sin \pi t, \; y = 3 \cos \pi t.$
    c. $x = 3 \cos \pi(t + \frac{1}{4}), \; y = 3 \sin \pi(t + \frac{1}{4}).$
    (t is time in seconds).

12. $x = v_0 t, \; y = -\frac{1}{2} g t^2.$

13. 69,282 ft.; 10,000 ft.

14. 1385.6 ft.; or 67,896.4 ft.

15. 121 ft. per second; yes.

Pages 142–143

3. 20π; 20.

4. $x = a(\theta - \sin \theta), \; y = a(\cos \theta - 1).$

5. $x = a(\theta + \sin \theta), \; y = a(\cos \theta - 1).$

Page 145

4. Equation can be put in form $(a^2 - x^2 - y^2)^3 = 27 a^2 x^2 y^2$, which is algebraic.

5. $\left(\dfrac{5}{2}, \pm \dfrac{5\sqrt{3}}{2}\right)$; $(-5, 0)$ (each point a point of tangency).

Pages 145–148. Miscellaneous Exercises

1. a. $y = 2 x^2$.

   b. $x^2 y = 1$.

   c. $x^2 - y^2 = x^2 y^2$.

   d. $y^2 - x^2 = 4 x^2 y^2$.

   e. $xy - x^2 - y = 0$.

   f. $y^2 - 2 y - x + 1 = 0$.

   g. $y = 8 x^4 - 8 x^2 + 1$.

7. $x = a \cot \theta$, $y = a \sin^2 \theta$.

8. $x = \pm a \sin \theta$, $y = a(\tan \theta)(1 \pm \sin \theta)$.

9. $y = \dfrac{a^3}{x^2 + a^2}$.

10. $y^2 = \dfrac{x^2(a + x)}{a - x}$.

13. $x = OA(\cos kt + \cos 2 kt)$,

     $y = OA(\sin kt + \sin 2 kt)$.

14. $x = OQ \cos k_1 t + OQ' \cos k_2 t$,

     $y = OQ \sin k_1 t + OQ' \sin k_2 t$.

15. P: $x = 2 \cos \theta$, $y = 2 \sin \theta$;

     Q: $x = 2(\cos \theta + \sqrt{\cos^2 \theta + 8})$, $y = 0$ (where $\theta = kt$).

16. $x = 2 \cos \theta + \sqrt{\cos^2 \theta + 8}$, $y = \sin \theta$ (where $\theta = kt$).

17. $(x^2 + 5 y^2 - 13)^2 = 16(1 - y^2)(9 - y^2)$, for $x > 0$.

18. $x = b \cos \theta$, $y = (a + b) \sin \theta$.

19. $x = b \cos \theta$, $y = b \sin \theta + a \cos \theta$.

20. $x = t(8 \pi - \sin 4 \pi t)$, $y = 2 - t \cos 4 \pi t$.

Pages 150–151

3. Pole.

4. $(6, 0)$; $\left(6, \dfrac{\pi}{3}\right)$; $\left(6, \dfrac{2 \pi}{3}\right)$; $(6, \pi)$; $\left(6, \dfrac{4 \pi}{3}\right)$; $\left(6, \dfrac{5 \pi}{3}\right)$.

5. $\left(-1, \dfrac{4 \pi}{3}\right)$; $\left(1, -\dfrac{5 \pi}{3}\right)$; $\left(-1, -\dfrac{2 \pi}{3}\right)$.

6. 1. $(2\sqrt{3}, 2)$; $(-2\sqrt{3}, -2)$; $(2\sqrt{3}, -2)$; $(-2\sqrt{3}, 2)$; $(2\sqrt{3}, 2)$;

     $(2\sqrt{3}, -2)$; $(-2\sqrt{3}, 2)$.

  2. $(3\sqrt{2}, 3\sqrt{2})$; $(-1, -\sqrt{3})$; $(0, 5)$; $(0, 5)$; $(-3, 0)$; $(3, 0)$; $(a, 0)$.

7. $\left(2\sqrt{2}, \dfrac{\pi}{4}\right)$; $\left(2\sqrt{2}, \dfrac{3 \pi}{4}\right)$; $\left(2\sqrt{2}, \dfrac{5 \pi}{4}\right)$; $\left(2\sqrt{2}, \dfrac{7 \pi}{4}\right)$; $(2, 0)$; $\left(2, \dfrac{\pi}{2}\right)$;

   $\left(2, \dfrac{2 \pi}{3}\right)$; $\left(2, \dfrac{5 \pi}{3}\right)$.

10. 7.   **11.** 20.   **12. a.** $18\sqrt{3}$.   **b.** $47\sqrt{3}$.   **c.** $9\sqrt{3}$.

Pages 153–154

3. a. $x^2 = 4 y$.

   b. $4 y = x^3$.

   c. $xy = 1$.

   d. $y^2 = 4 x$.

   e. $x^3 = 4 y^2$.

   f. $xy = x + y$.

4. Straight line.

5. $x^2 + y^2 - 4 x - 4 y = 0$; $\left(2\sqrt{2}, \dfrac{\pi}{4}\right)$.

7. a. $y^2 = 4 x + 4$, parabola.

   b. $3 x^2 + 4 y^2 - 6 x - 9 = 0$, ellipse.

   c. $3 x^2 - y^2 + 12 x + 9 = 0$, hyperbola.

8. a. $x^4 + y^4 + 2\,x^2y^2 - 4\,x^2y - 4\,y^3 + 3\,y^2 - x^2 = 0.$
    b. $x^4 + 2\,x^2y^2 + y^4 = x^2 - y^2.$

9. a. $\rho = 8 \cos\theta.$ **10. a.** $\rho = \tan\theta.$
   b. $\rho = -\,8 \sin\theta.$ **b.** $\rho^2 = \tan\theta.$
   c. $\rho = 3.$ **c.** $\rho = \tan^2\theta.$
   d. $\rho^2 = 9 \sec 2\,\theta.$

Pages 156–157

1. $\rho \cos\theta = 5.$ **3. a.** $\rho \cos\theta = \pm\,6.$
2. $\rho \sin\theta = 3.$ **b.** $\rho \sin\theta = \pm\,2.$

5. a. $x = 3.$ **c.** $y = \sqrt{3}\,x.$ **e.** $x + y = 4.$
   b. $y + 1 = 0.$ **d.** $4\,y = 3\,x.$ **f.** $x - \sqrt{3}\,y + 6 = 0.$

6. $\rho \cos(\theta - \omega) = p.$

7. $\theta = 0;\ \rho \cos\theta = 6;\ \theta = \dfrac{\pi}{2};\ \rho \sin\theta = 6;\ \theta = \dfrac{\pi}{4};\ \rho \cos\left(\theta - \dfrac{\pi}{4}\right) = 3\sqrt{2}.$

13. A circle   **15.** $\rho = \dfrac{ep}{1 + e \sin\theta}.$

Page 160

6. a. $y = x \tan \dfrac{a}{\sqrt{x^2 + y^2}}.$ **c.** $(x^2 + y^2)^3 = a^2(x^2 - y^2)^2.$
   b. $(x^2 + y^2)^3 = 4\,a^2x^2y^2.$ **d.** $(x^2 + y^2 - bx)^2 = a^2(x^2 + y^2).$

Pages 161–162

1. $\left(3, \pm\dfrac{\pi}{3}\right).$ **3.** $\left(3, \pm\dfrac{\pi}{3}\right);\ \left(3, \pm\dfrac{2\,\pi}{3}\right).$

2. $\left(6, \dfrac{\pi}{6}\right);\ \left(6, \dfrac{5\,\pi}{6}\right).$ **4.** $\left(\dfrac{3}{2}, \pm\dfrac{\pi}{3}\right);$ and the pole.

5. $\left(1, \dfrac{\pi}{6}\right);\ \left(1, \dfrac{5\,\pi}{6}\right);\ \left(1, \dfrac{7\,\pi}{6}\right);\ \left(1, \dfrac{11\,\pi}{6}\right);$ and four other intersections.

6. $\left(\dfrac{1}{2}, \dfrac{\pi}{6}\right);\ \left(\dfrac{1}{2}, \dfrac{5\,\pi}{6}\right);\ \left(-1, \dfrac{3\,\pi}{2}\right);$ and the pole.

7. $\left(2\sqrt{2}, \dfrac{\pi}{4}\right);$ and the pole.

8. $\left(1, \dfrac{2\,\pi}{3}\right);\ \left(1, \dfrac{4\,\pi}{3}\right);$ and two other intersections.

9. $\left(1, \dfrac{\pi}{2}\right);\ \left(2, \dfrac{\pi}{6}\right);\ \left(2, \dfrac{5\,\pi}{6}\right).$ **11.** $\left(1, \pm\dfrac{\pi}{3}\right).$

10. $\left(1, \dfrac{\pi}{2}\right);\ \left(1, \dfrac{\pi}{2}\right).$ **12.** $\left(2 + \sqrt{2}, \pm\dfrac{\pi}{4}\right);\ \left(2 - \sqrt{2}, \pm\dfrac{3\,\pi}{4}\right).$

13. $(0, 0)$; $\left(\dfrac{3\sqrt{3}}{2}, \dfrac{\pi}{3}\right)$; $\left(-\dfrac{3\sqrt{3}}{2}, -\dfrac{\pi}{3}\right)$.

14. $\left(3\sqrt{2}, \pm\dfrac{\pi}{8}\right)$; $\left(3\sqrt{2}, \pm\dfrac{5\,\pi}{8}\right)$; $\left(3\sqrt{2}, \pm\dfrac{9\,\pi}{8}\right)$; $\left(3\sqrt{2}, \pm\dfrac{13\,\pi}{8}\right)$; and the pole.

15. $\left(\pm\dfrac{\sqrt[4]{8}}{2}, \dfrac{\pi}{8}\right)$; and the pole.

16. $\left(1, \pm\dfrac{2\,\pi}{3}\right)$; and two other intersections.

17. $\left(1, \dfrac{\pi}{4}\right)$; $\left(1, \dfrac{5\,\pi}{4}\right)$; and two other intersections.

18. $\left(\sqrt{2}, \dfrac{\pi}{4}\right)$; $\left(\sqrt{2}, \dfrac{5\,\pi}{4}\right)$.

19. $(a, 1)$; $(-a, -1)$; and an infinite number of other intersections.
20. $(0, 0)$; $(a, 1)$.

Pages 162–164. Miscellaneous Exercises

7. a. $\left(a, \pm\dfrac{\pi}{2}\right)$.

b. $(1, 0)$; $(1, \pi)$; $\left(1+\dfrac{\sqrt{3}}{2}, \dfrac{\pi}{3}\right)$; $\left(1-\dfrac{\sqrt{3}}{2}, -\dfrac{\pi}{3}\right)$; and the pole.

c. $(1, 0)$; $(1, \pi)$; $\left(-1, -\dfrac{\pi}{2}\right)$, the latter a point of tangency.

8. a. $\rho = \csc 4\,\theta$.   b. $\rho = e^{\theta}$.

10. $\rho \cos\theta + a \cos 2\,\theta = 0$.

11. $\rho = 2\,a \sin\theta \tan\theta$; $y^2 = \dfrac{x^3}{2\,a - x}$.

12. $\rho = a \sec\theta \pm b$.

13. $\rho = a$, where $2\,a$ is the constant length.

14. $\rho = a \sin 2\,\theta$, where $2\,a$ is the constant length.

15. $\rho \sin 2\,\theta = a$, a is the constant distance.

16. $\rho^2 = 2\,a^2 \cos 2\,\theta$.

19. $\rho = a\left(3 - 4 \sin^2 \dfrac{\theta}{2}\right)$.

Pages 168–170

1. a. 9.   b. $5\sqrt{2}$.   c. 14.   d. 11.   **2.** 30.

	$\text{Cos }\alpha$	$\text{Cos }\beta$	$\text{Cos }\gamma$
4. a.	$\frac{2}{3}$,	$\frac{2}{3}$,	$\frac{1}{3}$.
b.	$-\frac{8}{9}$,	$\frac{4}{9}$,	$-\frac{1}{9}$.
c.	$\frac{4}{5}$,	$\frac{3}{5}$,	0.
d.	0,	0,	1.

5.   Cos α Cos β Cos γ

a. $\frac{6}{7}$, $\frac{3}{7}$, $-\frac{2}{7}$.

b. $-\frac{7\sqrt{10}}{30}$, $\frac{\sqrt{10}}{6}$, $\frac{2\sqrt{10}}{15}$.

c. $-\frac{3\sqrt{10}}{10}$, $-\frac{\sqrt{10}}{10}$, 0.

d. $-\frac{7\sqrt{3}}{15}$, $-\frac{\sqrt{3}}{3}$, $-\frac{\sqrt{3}}{15}$.

e. $-\frac{\sqrt{2}}{2}$, $-\frac{\sqrt{2}}{2}$, 0.

f. 1, 0, 0.

6. a. $\gamma = 45°, 135°$.   **b.** Impossible.

8. $\alpha = \beta = \gamma = 54° \ 44'$; $\alpha = \beta = \gamma = 125° \ 16'$.

9.   Cos α Cos β Cos γ **10. a.** 3, 2, 1.

a. $\frac{1}{3}$, $\frac{2}{3}$, $\frac{2}{3}$.   **b.** $-3, 1, 1$.

b. $\frac{2}{11}$, $-\frac{6}{11}$, $\frac{9}{11}$.   **c.** $5, -2, 4$.

c. $\frac{\sqrt{5}}{5}$, $\frac{6\sqrt{5}}{25}$, $-\frac{8\sqrt{5}}{25}$,   **d.** $1, -1, 0$.

d. $\frac{\sqrt{2}}{2}$, $\frac{\sqrt{2}}{2}$, 0.

e. $\frac{2}{7}$, $\frac{3}{7}$, $\frac{6}{7}$.

f. 1, 0, 0.

11. $5x + 2y + 4z = 40$, plane.

12. $x^2 + y^2 + z^2 - 6x - 4y - 12z = 0$, sphere.

13. $x^2 + y^2 - 6x - 4y = 0$, circle.   **14.** $(0, 0, 0)$; $(6, 0, 0)$.

Pages 171–172

4. $60°$.   **5.** $36° \ 52'$.   **6.** $64° \ 54'$.

Pages 175–176

1. Intercepts are given in the order x, y, z. Traces are in the order xy-plane, yz-plane, xz-plane.

a. 6, 6, 12; $x + y = 6$, $2y + z = 12$, $2x + z = 12$.

b. $-7, \frac{14}{3}, \frac{7}{3}$; $2x - 3y + 14 = 0$, $3y + 6z = 14$, $x - 3z + 7 = 0$.

c. $\frac{15}{2}, 3, -\frac{15}{4}$; $2x + 5y = 15$, $5y - 4z = 15$, $2x - 4z = 15$.

d. $6, -3, 6$; $x - 2y = 6$, $2y - z + 6 = 0$, $x + z = 6$.

2. a. 4.   **5.** $(2, -1, 6)$.   **9.** $60°$.

b. 2.   **6. a.** $\frac{6}{11}, -\frac{2}{11}, \frac{9}{11}$.   **10.** $54° \ 44'$.

c. $\sqrt{5}$.   **b.** $\frac{11}{15}, \frac{2}{3}, -\frac{2}{15}$.

d. $\sqrt{6}$.   **c.** $\frac{3}{5}, -\frac{4}{5}, 0$.

d. 0, 0, 1.

14. a. 4. **b.** $-\frac{1}{3}$. **c.** 0.

16. $\dfrac{a_2}{a_1} = \dfrac{b_2}{b_1} = \dfrac{c_2}{c_1} = \dfrac{d_2}{d_1} = k$, ($k$ is any constant $\neq 0$). **17.** $\frac{3}{2}$.

Page 178

1. a. $x + 2\,y + 3\,z = 8$.
 b. $x - y - 2\,z + 2 = 0$.
 c. $3\,x + y - 4\,z = 0$.
 d. $x + y - z = 0$.
2. $2\,x - 3\,y = 0$.
3. $5\,y + 3\,z = 15$.
4. $2\,x + z = 13$.

5. $x = 0$; $y = 0$;
   $4\,x + 3\,z = 24$; $2\,y + z = 8$.
7. $3\,x + 6\,y + 2\,z = 49$.
8. $x - 4\,y + 3\,z + 1 = 0$.
9. $(8, 4, 1)$.
10. $x - 3\,y + 2\,z = 11$.
11. $5\,x + y + z = 7$.

12. $4\,x - y + 2\,z = 11$.

Pages 182–183

1. a. $x + 4\,y = 8$; $y - z + 1 = 0$; $x + 4\,z = 12$.
 b. $3\,x + 2\,y = 36$; $y + 3\,z = 9$; $x - 2\,z = 6$.
 c. $x = 2\,y$; $3\,y + z = 12$; $3\,x + 2\,z = 24$.
 d. $x = y$; $2\,y = z$; $2\,x = z$.
 e. $x + y = 5$; $y - 2\,z + 5 = 0$; $x + 2\,z = 10$.
2. a. $(12, -1, 0)$; $(8, 0, 1)$; $(0, 2, 3)$.
 b. $(6, 9, 0)$; $(12, 0, 3)$; $(0, 18, -3)$.
 c. $(8, 4, 0)$; $(0, 0, 12)$.
 d. $(0, 0, 0)$.
 e. $(10, -5, 0)$; $(5, 0, \frac{5}{2})$; $(0, 5, 5)$.

3. a. $\dfrac{x - 6}{8} = \dfrac{y - 2}{4} = \dfrac{z - 4}{1}$.

 b. $\dfrac{x + 1}{6} = \dfrac{y - 3}{-3} = \dfrac{z + 2}{2}$.

 c. $\dfrac{x}{7} = \dfrac{y + 3}{5} = \dfrac{z - 8}{1}$.

 d. $\dfrac{x - 5}{8} = \dfrac{y - 2}{5} = \dfrac{z}{1}$.

 e. $\dfrac{x - 3}{4} = \dfrac{y - 2}{3}$, $z = 0$.

4. $\dfrac{x - 2}{11} = \dfrac{y - 6}{2} = \dfrac{z - 1}{10}$.

5. $x = y = z$.

7. $2\sqrt{6}$.

9. $\dfrac{x - 5}{2} = \dfrac{y - 4}{3} = \dfrac{z - 8}{6}$.

10. $(-2, 1, 0)$.

11. $(3, 5, 3)$.

12. 3.

13. $6\sqrt{3}$.

14. a. $\dfrac{x}{6} = \dfrac{y - \frac{7}{2}}{3} = \dfrac{z + \frac{7}{3}}{2}$.

 b. $\dfrac{x - 11}{2} = \dfrac{y - 9}{2} = \dfrac{z}{1}$.

 c. $\dfrac{x}{1} = \dfrac{y + 10}{2} = \dfrac{z + 2}{2}$.

Pages 183–184. Miscellaneous Exercises

1. $x + 2\,z = 9$.
6. $x + 4\,y + 2\,z = 1$.

2. $(\frac{5}{3}, \frac{5}{3}, \frac{16}{3})$.

5. $30°$

7. $5\,x - 7\,y - 4\,z + 59 = 0$.

8. $\dfrac{x-6}{2} = \dfrac{y-4}{2} = \dfrac{z-1}{1};\ \dfrac{x-6}{34} = \dfrac{y-4}{-38} = \dfrac{z-1}{-1}.$

9. $2\sqrt{6}$.   10. 5.   12. $3x - 5y - 5z + 4 = 0.$ 13. $7x + 7z = 4.$

Page 186

20. $y^2 = 8x - 16.$ 21. $16x^2 + 25y^2 - 96x - 256 = 0.$

Page 188

1. $y^2 + z^2 = 2x.$ 4. $16x^2 + 16z^2 - y^2 = 0.$

2. $x^2 + 4y^2 + 4z^2 = 16.$ 5. $x^2 + y^2 = z^3.$

3. $4x^2 + 4y^2 - z^2 = 16.$

18. $(x - x_1)^2 + (y - y_1)^2 + (z - z_1)^2 = d^2.$ Yes. A spherical surface.

19. $y^2 + z^2 - 2ax + a^2 = 0.$ 22. a. $b^2x^2 + a^2y^2 + a^2z^2 = a^2b^2.$

20. $25x^2 + 25y^2 + 9z^2 = 2025.$ b. $b^2x^2 + a^2y^2 + b^2z^2 = a^2b^2.$

21. $x^2 + y^2 - (z - 4)^2 = 0.$ 23. $(x^2 + y^2 + z^2 - a^2 - b^2)^2 = 4b^2(a^2 - z^2).$

Page 197

In exercises 1–8 the projections are given in the order xy-plane; yz-plane; xz-plane.

1. Circle $x^2 + y^2 = 25$; circle $y^2 + z^2 - 10z = 0$; segment of line $x + z = 5.$

2. a. Segment of line $\sqrt{3}\,y = x$; ellipse $4y^2 + z^2 = 36$; ellipse $4x^2 + 3z^2 = 108.$

    b. Ellipse $x^2 + 2y^2 - 12y = 0$; segment of line $y + z = 6$; ellipse $x^2 + 2z^2 - 12z = 0.$

3. Parabola $y^2 = 9x$; parabola $y^2 = 36 - 9z$; half of line $x + z = 4.$

4. Parabola $2y^2 = 18 - 3x$; parabola $y^2 = 9 - 3z$; half of line $2z = x.$

5. Circle $x^2 + y^2 = 1$; arc of parabola $y^2 + z = 1$; arc of parabola $z = x^2.$

6. Circle $x^2 + y^2 = 4x$; circle $y^2 + z^2 = 4z$; segment of line $x = z.$

7. a. Ellipse $5x^2 + 4y^2 = 8x + 48$; ellipse $y^2 + 5z^2 = 16z$; segment of line $x + 2z = 4.$

    b. Arc of parabola $x^2 = 6y$; arc of circle $y^2 + z^2 + 6y = 16$; fourth degree curve $x^4 + 36x^2 + 36z^2 = 576.$

8. a. Circle $x^2 + y^2 = 1$; segment of line $z = 2$; segment of line $z = 2.$

    b. Ellipse $3x^2 + 4y^2 = 4x + 4$; ellipse $4y^2 + 3z^2 = 8z$; segment of line $x + z = 2.$

    c. Parabola $y^2 = 2x + 1$; parabola $y^2 = 3 - z$; half of line $2x + z = 2.$

    d. Hyperbola $3x^2 - 4x - y^2 + 1 = 0$; hyperbola $16y^2 - 3z^2 + 20z = 28$; the line $4x + z = 6$ except portion for which $\frac{1}{3} < x < 1.$

8. e. Point ellipse $3x^2 + 4y^2 = 0$; point ellipse $3(4-z)^2 + 4y^2 = 0$; the point $(0, 0, 4)$.

f. Two lines $y = \pm x\sqrt{3}$; two lines $4y = \pm \sqrt{3}(4-z)$; the line $4x + z = 4$.

9. $(5, 1, 3)$. **10.** $\pm \frac{1}{2}$.

Pages 198–199

24. $x^2 + y^2 = 4x$; $z^4 = 16(z^2 - y^2)$; arc of curve $z^2 = 16 - 4x$.

25. $x^2 + y^2 = a^2$; $z = 2x$; $z = 0$, origin at center of base, plane cuts base in y-axis, axis of cylinder is z-axis.

Pages 200–201

1. Rectangular coördinates

   a. $(2\sqrt{6}, 2\sqrt{6}, 4)$;

   b. $(\sqrt{2}, 0, \sqrt{2})$;

   c. $(0, 3, 0)$;

Cylindrical coördinates

$\left(4\sqrt{3}, \dfrac{\pi}{4}, 4\right)\cdot$

$(\sqrt{2}, 0, \sqrt{2})$.

$\left(3, \dfrac{\pi}{2}, 0\right)\cdot$

2. Rectangular coördinates

   a. $(3\sqrt{3}, 3, 8)$;

   b. $(0, 6, 0)$;

   c. $(0, 0, 8)$;

Spherical coördinates

$\left(10, \dfrac{\pi}{6}, \arctan \dfrac{3}{4}\right)\cdot$

$\left(6, \dfrac{\pi}{2}, \dfrac{\pi}{2}\right)\cdot$

$(8, \theta, 0)$.

3. Spherical coördinates

   a. $\left(3\sqrt{5}, \arctan \dfrac{1}{2}, \dfrac{\pi}{2}\right)$;

   b. $\left(2\sqrt{5}, \dfrac{\pi}{2}, \arccos \dfrac{\sqrt{5}}{5}\right)$;

   c. $\left(8\sqrt{2}, \dfrac{\pi}{6}, \dfrac{\pi}{4}\right)$;

Cylindrical coördinates

$\left(3\sqrt{5}, \arctan \dfrac{1}{2}, 0\right)\cdot$

$\left(4, \dfrac{\pi}{2}, 2\right)\cdot$

$\left(8, \dfrac{\pi}{6}, 8\right)\cdot$

4. Cylindrical coördinates

   a. $r^2 = 5z$;

   b. $z = a \tan \theta$;

   c. $r = 2a \cos \theta$;

Spherical coördinates

$\rho = 5 \cot \phi \csc \phi$.

$\rho = a \tan \theta \sec \phi$.

$\rho = 2a \cos \theta \csc \phi$.

5. a. $x^2 + y^2 + z^2 = a^2$.

   b. $x^2 + y^2 = a^2$.

   c. $x^2 + y^2 = (a-z)^2$.

   d. $x^2 + y^2 + z^2 = a^2$.

7. a. $x^2 + y^2 + z^2 = 36$; $x^2 + y^2 - 6x = 0$.

   b. $\rho = 6$; $\rho \sin \phi = 6 \cos \theta$.

   c. $r^2 + z^2 = 36$; $r = 6 \cos \theta$.

Pages 201–202. Miscellaneous Exercises

1. **a.** Circular cylindrical surface.
   b. Parabolic cylindrical surface.
   c. Plane.
   d. Two intersecting planes.
   e. The three coördinate planes.
   f. Cone of revolution.
   g. Ellipsoid.
   h. Elliptic cone.
   i. Parabolic cylindrical surface.
   j. Paraboloid of revolution.

2. $(x - 3)^2 + (y - 4)^2 = 25$.

3. $x^2 + y^2 + z^2 - 14\,x = 0$.

4. $5\,x - y - 4\,z = 53$.

5. $(2, 4, 0); \ (0, 2, 1)$.

6. $x^2(y^2 + z^2) = a^4$ (about x-axis).

7. $y^2 + z^2 = \left(a + x - 2\sqrt{ax}\right)^2$ \quad $(0 \leqq x \leqq a, \ -a \leqq y \leqq a)$.

8. $y^2 + z^2 = \left(a^{\frac{2}{3}} - x^{\frac{2}{3}}\right)^3$.

9. $x^2 - y^2 = (z - 2)^2$.

10. $16\,p^2(x - p)^2 + 16\,p^2z^2 - (4\,p^2 - y^2)^2 = 0$ \quad $(y^2 \leqq \mid 2\,p \mid)$.

SIGNS

Positive's

sin + csc +	All +
tan + ctn +	cos + sec +

Negative

cos tan ctn sec	none
sin cos sec csc	sin tan ctn csc

Angle	Sin θ	Cos θ	tan θ
0°	0	1	0
30°	.5	$\sqrt{3}/2$	$1/\sqrt{3}$
45°	$\sqrt{2}/2$	$\sqrt{2}/2$	1
60°	$\sqrt{3}/2$	.5	$\sqrt{3}$
90°	1	0	∞

INDEX

(The numbers refer to the pages.)

FGHIJKLMN   70698765

PRINTED IN THE UNITED STATES OF AMERICA